$$a_2 = a - \frac{f(a_1)}{f'(a_1)}$$

$$y = x^2(a - x^2)$$

ELEMENTARY CALCULUS

by

A. KEITH, M.A., B.Sc.,

Principal Lecturer in Methods in the Glasgow Training Centre

AND

W. J. DONALDSON, M.A., B.Sc., Ed.B., Ph.D.,

Lecturer in Mathematics in the Aberdeen Training Centre

ROBERT GIBSON AND SONS, GLASGOW, LTD.

45 QUEEN STREET   GLASGOW, C.1.

PRINTED IN GREAT BRITAIN BY BELL AND BAIN, LTD., GLASGOW.

PREFACE

The purpose of this book is to provide for beginners an elementary introduction to the Calculus. Part I, which is published separately, is intended for readers who wish merely to have an acquaintance with the most elementary ideas of the subject. Its scope is limited to the application of the Calculus to the simplest of algebraic functions. In Part II, the treatment is extended to include trigonometric, exponential and logarithmic functions, and although no attempt has been made to cover a specific syllabus, it is hoped that adequate treatment is provided for the Scottish Leaving Certificate Additional Papers in Mathematics, for the Higher School Certificate examinations of England and Northern Ireland, for the Higher National Certificate syllabus, and also for first-year University courses in engineering and physics.

There is probably more exposition in this book than is normally expected in a mathematics textbook. This is intentional, for the needs of the private student who lacks the guidance and aid of a teacher have not been forgotten. For the same reason, the book contains an unusually large number of worked examples. These should be regarded as part of the text since they often contain information which does not appear in the text proper.

It may seem that the requirements of the more serious student of Mathematics have been overlooked, for some of the treatment offered and some of the arguments employed are not completely rigorous ; but it is hoped that even potential mathematics specialists will find here a suitable introduction to the more exact and refined treatment of the subject given in such a book as Professor Gibson's *Elementary Treatise on the Calculus.*

The authors acknowledge with gratitude the many valuable suggestions made by Dr. James Robertson when the book was in manuscript form. They also wish to express their thanks to Professor Thomas M. MacRobert and The Glasgow University Court for permission to include exercises taken from Glasgow University examination papers.

A. K.
W. J. D.

GLASGOW,
January, 1952.

" Any normal boy or girl of sixteen could master the Calculus in half the time often devoted to stumbling through Book One of Cæsar's Gallic War. And it does seem to some modern minds that Newton and Leibnitz were more inspiring leaders than Julius Cæsar and his unimaginative lieutenant, Titus Labienus."

E. T. BELL, *The Queen of Sciences.*

CONTENTS

PART II

PART TWO

§ 25. LIMITS.

Although the term " limit " and the phrase " limiting value " have already occurred several times in Part I of this book, we have so far relied on more or less intuitive arguments, and no attempt has been made to define precisely what is meant by a *limit*. In the paragraphs which follow we shall examine in detail a number of particular limits in order to clarify some of these vague, intuitive ideas.

(i) Let us consider the function defined by the equation

$$y = \frac{x^2 - 4}{x - 2}.$$

From this equation it is possible to find the value of y corresponding to any chosen value of x ; all we have to do is to carry out the operational instructions indicated. Thus, when $x = 5$,

$$x^2 = 25 \ ; \quad x^2 - 4 = 21 \ ; \quad x - 2 = 3 \ ;$$

so that, for $x = 5$, y has the value $\frac{21}{3}$, that is, 7.

The last step in this evaluation is clearly a division, namely, $21 \div 3$. Moreover, for any other value of x the corresponding final step is inevitably one of division. Such a step will, however, present no difficulty, provided division by zero is not involved. *Division by zero has no meaning.**

When x has the value 2, y takes the form $\frac{0}{0}$, which is meaningless.

---

* To divide a number a by a second number b is to find that number which when multiplied by b gives a. If b is zero, then we must find a number which when multiplied by zero gives a. There is no such number ; therefore division by zero has no meaning.

Since, however,

$x^2 - 4 = (x + 2)(x - 2)$, for *all* values of x, *including* $x = 2$,

$y = \dfrac{x^2 - 4}{x - 2} = x + 2$ for all values of x for which the division

by $(x - 2)$ is valid.

That is, $y = x + 2$ for all values of x, *except* $x = 2$.
Now, $x + 2$ is a linear function of x ; the equation $y = x + 2$, $(x \neq 2)$, is therefore represented graphically by a straight line *with one point missing*, namely, the point $(2, 4)$. Since it is impossible to draw a straight line which is complete but for one point, no attempt is made to illustrate the situation graphically. Nevertheless the reader will probably find no difficulty in forming a mental picture of the line complete in every respect but for the point $(2, 4)$. From this mental picture, or from other considerations, it is clear that the nearer x approaches the value 2— either from values above or below 2—the nearer does the value of y approach the value 4. In fact, by giving x a value sufficiently near to 2, we can obtain a value of y as near to 4 *as we please*. For example, if we want a value of y within 0·000001 of the value 4, all we need do is choose a value of x within the range $2 \pm 0 \cdot 000001$. This we are permitted to do, for x can have any value except the value 2.

We therefore say that although $y = \dfrac{x^2 - 4}{x - 2}$ has no **value** when $x = 2$, it has a definite **limit**, namely 4, which it approaches as x approaches the value 2. This idea may be expressed more briefly as follows :

$$\text{as } x \longrightarrow 2, \quad \frac{x^2 - 4}{x - 2} \longrightarrow 4 ;$$

or, more concisely still,

$$\underset{x \longrightarrow 2}{L} \frac{x^2 - 4}{x - 2} = 4.$$

This collection of symbols is read " the limit of $\dfrac{x^2-4}{x-2}$ as x tends to 2 is 4."

(ii) Let a circle of radius r be drawn with O as centre (Fig. 40), and let OA, OB be two radii such that angle AOB is acute and contains θ radians.

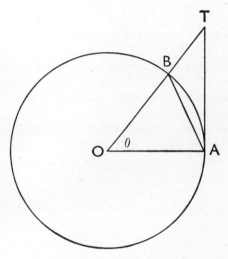

FIG. 40.

Join AB and let the tangent at A meet OB produced in T.

Considering the areas of the triangle OAB, the sector OAB, and the triangle OAT, and using well-known trigonometric formulæ, we see at once that

$$\triangle OAB < \text{area of sector } OAB < \triangle OAT.$$

Therefore $\tfrac{1}{2}OA \cdot OB \sin \theta < \tfrac{1}{2}OA^2 \cdot \theta < \tfrac{1}{2}OA \cdot AT,$

that is, $\tfrac{1}{2}r^2 \sin \theta < \tfrac{1}{2}r^2\theta < \tfrac{1}{2}r^2 \tan \theta, \ \ 0 < \theta < \dfrac{\pi}{2}.$

Thus $\sin \theta < \theta < \tan \theta,$

or $\sin \theta < \theta < \dfrac{\sin \theta}{\cos \theta}.$

159

Dividing by sin θ, which is positive since angle AOB is acute, we have

$$1 < \frac{\theta}{\sin \theta} < \frac{1}{\cos \theta},$$

or, inverting, $\qquad 1 > \frac{\sin \theta}{\theta} > \cos \theta.$

Thus, provided θ is acute, the quotient $\frac{\sin \theta}{\theta}$ lies between $\cos \theta$ and 1. But as θ becomes smaller and smaller numerically, $\cos \theta$ approaches the value 1, and therefore $\frac{\sin \theta}{\theta}$, which is always intermediate in value between $\cos \theta$ and 1, must also approach the value 1. That is,

$$\lim_{\theta \to 0} \frac{\sin \theta}{\theta} = 1.$$

Similarly, since $\qquad \sin \theta < \theta < \tan \theta,$

we have $\qquad \cos \theta < \frac{\theta}{\tan \theta} < 1,$

or, inverting, $\qquad \frac{1}{\cos \theta} > \frac{\tan \theta}{\theta} > 1.$

Therefore, $\qquad \lim_{\theta \to 0} \frac{\tan \theta}{\theta} = 1.$

These results mean, in effect, that when θ is small, sin θ and tan θ are both approximately equal in value to θ, expressed, it will be remembered, in radians. Thus, using five-figure tables we have :

Angle AOB	$\sin \theta$	θ	$\tan \theta$
5°	0·08716	0·08727	0·08749
4°	0·06976	0·06981	0·06993
3°	0·05233	0·05235	0·05241
2°	0·03490	0·03491	0·03492
1°	0·01745	0·01745	0·01746

(iii) Consider the geometric progression

$$\tfrac{1}{2} + \tfrac{1}{4} + \tfrac{1}{8} + \dots.$$

The sum to n terms of a geometric progression whose first term is a and whose common ratio is r is given by the formula

$$S_n = \frac{a(1 - r^n)}{1 - r}.$$

In the above example, $a = \tfrac{1}{2}$ and $r = \tfrac{1}{2}$.

Therefore,
$$S_n = \frac{\dfrac{1}{2}\left(1 - \dfrac{1}{2^n}\right)}{1 - \dfrac{1}{2}} = 1 - \frac{1}{2^n}.$$

In particular, $S_5 = 1 - \dfrac{1}{2^5} = 1 - \dfrac{1}{32} = 0\cdot96875,$

$$S_{10} = 1 - \frac{1}{2^{10}} = 1 - \frac{1}{1024} = 0\cdot99902,$$

$$S_{15} = 1 - \frac{1}{2^{15}} = 1 - \frac{1}{32768} = 0\cdot99997.$$

It is clear that as n increases, S_n remains less than 1 but approaches more and more closely to that number, so that the difference between 1 and S_n can be made as small as we please by taking sufficiently large values of n. It is possible, for example, to choose n so that this difference is less than $\dfrac{1}{1,000,000,000}$. For

$$1 - S_n = \frac{1}{2^n} < \frac{1}{10^9},$$

if $2^n > 10^9$,

that is, if $n \log_{10} 2 > 9$,

that is, if $n > \dfrac{9}{0 \cdot 3010} = 29 \cdot 9 \ldots .$

Accordingly, the sum to 30 (or more) terms differs from 1 by less than the specified amount. In similar fashion, the appropriate number of terms could be found whatever the desired approximation.

Thus we can say that S_n tends to the limit 1 as n increases indefinitely, or as n " tends to infinity." That is,

$$\underset{n \longrightarrow \infty}{L} \left(1 - \frac{1}{2^n} \right) = 1.$$

This result is often expressed as follows :

$$\tfrac{1}{2} + \tfrac{1}{4} + \tfrac{1}{8} + \ldots \text{ to infinity} = \mathbf{1},$$

but such a statement must be interpreted with caution. It does *not* mean that if we start with $\tfrac{1}{2}$, and to it add $\tfrac{1}{4}$, and then $\tfrac{1}{8}$, and then $\tfrac{1}{16}$, and go on like this for ever, each time adding a term which is one-half of the previous term, the aggregate will eventually come to 1. We can find the sum of a finite number of items, but we cannot add up an infinite number of things, for the process has no ending. The exact meaning of a **sum to infinity** must be expressed in terms of some property of the sum of a *finite* number of terms, and that property, in the above case, is that if S_n denotes the sum to n terms, as n increases indefinitely S_n tends to the limit 1.

(iv) In Fig. 41 let AB, BC be adjacent sides of a regular n-sided polygon inscribed in a circle with centre O and radius r.

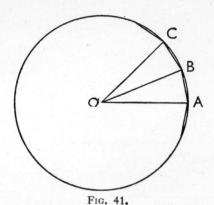

FIG. 41.

Then,   angle $AOB = \dfrac{2\pi}{n}$ radians,

the area of $\triangle OAB = \frac{1}{2}r^2 \sin\left(\dfrac{2\pi}{n}\right)$,

and the area of the inscribed polygon $= I = \frac{1}{2}nr^2 \sin\left(\dfrac{2\pi}{n}\right)$.

If, now, we draw the tangents to the circle at the points A, B, C, ..., we obtain a regular n-sided polygon circumscribing the given circle. (The circumscribed polygon is shown separately in Fig. 42 for the sake of clearness.)

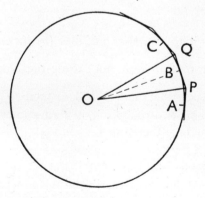

FIG. 42.

163

Then,   angle $POQ = \dfrac{2\pi}{n}$ radians,

the area of $\triangle OPQ = OB \, . \, QB = r \, . \, r \tan\left(\dfrac{\pi}{n}\right)$,

and the area of the circumscribed polygon $= C = nr^2 \tan\left(\dfrac{\pi}{n}\right)$.

But clearly the area (A) of the circle is less than the area (C) of the circumscribed polygon and greater than the area (I) of the inscribed polygon.

That is, $I < A < C$,

or $\tfrac{1}{2}nr^2 \sin\left(\dfrac{2\pi}{n}\right) < A < nr^2 \tan\left(\dfrac{\pi}{n}\right)$,

and these inequalities hold whatever the value of n.

But $I = \tfrac{1}{2}nr^2 \sin\left(\dfrac{2\pi}{n}\right) = \pi r^2 \, . \, \dfrac{\sin\left(\dfrac{2\pi}{n}\right)}{\dfrac{2\pi}{n}}$,

and $C = nr^2 \tan\left(\dfrac{\pi}{n}\right) = \pi r^2 \, . \, \dfrac{\tan\left(\dfrac{\pi}{n}\right)}{\dfrac{\pi}{n}}$.

Therefore, if the number of sides (n) increases indefinitely, $\dfrac{2\pi}{n}$ and $\dfrac{\pi}{n}$ both tend to zero, and, using the limits established in (ii) above, we see that both I and C tend to the value πr^2.

But the area (A) of the circle is always intermediate in value between I and C ; therefore

$$A = \pi r^2,$$

and we may regard the area of the circle as the limit of the area of the inscribed (or circumscribed) polygon as the number of sides increases indefinitely.

The real significance of the word *limit* should now be fairly clear. In each of the examples examined above there are two variables, one of which is a function of the other. Thus,

in (i), y is a function of x ;

in (ii), $\dfrac{\sin \theta}{\theta}$ is a function of θ ;

in (iii), S_n is a function of n ;

and in (iv), I and C are functions of n.

In (i) and (ii), the independent variable is made to assume a value all but equal to a definite number, namely 2 in the case of x, and 0 in the case of θ ; in (iii) and (iv), the independent variable is made to increase beyond all bound. In the former cases, the definite number is called the " limit " of the independent variable, but it should be noted most carefully that it is not a *value* which the independent variable actually takes. In the latter cases, the independent variable is said to have infinity for its limit—which merely means that it becomes greater than any number, no matter how great this number may be.

In each case, as the independent variable approaches more and more closely to its limit, the function at the same time becomes more and more nearly equal to another definite number, which is called its limit. We can always make the independent variable differ so little from its limit that the function differs by as little as we please from its limit, though we can never make the function equal its limit. Thus, we can make the difference between the function and its limit less than 0·001, or less than 0·00001, or less than 0·0000001, and so on ; all we need do is choose appropriate values for the independent variable sufficiently near to its limit.

In two of the illustrations used above—(iii) and (iv)—we have considered infinity as the limit of the independent variable, but so far we have not considered the possibility of a *function* having infinity as its limit. Let us therefore examine the function defined by the equation $y = 1/x$.

Since division by zero is debarred, y has no value when
$x = 0$. However, as x approaches zero through decreasing
positive values, it is clear that y will take increasingly large
positive values. For example,

$$\text{when } x = 0 \cdot 1, \quad y = 10 \ ;$$
$$\text{when } x = 0 \cdot 01, \quad y = 100 \ ;$$
$$\text{when } x = 0 \cdot 001, \ y = 1{,}000 \ ;$$

and so on. The value of y cannot be made so great that it
cannot be made still greater by a further reduction in the
numerical value of x. The situation may be adequately summed
up, therefore, by writing

as $x \longrightarrow 0$ through decreasing positive values, $y \longrightarrow + \infty$.

Similarly

as $x \longrightarrow 0$ through increasing negative values, $y \longrightarrow - \infty$.

We see also that

as $x \longrightarrow + \infty$, $y \longrightarrow 0$ through positive values ;

and   as $x \longrightarrow - \infty$, $y \longrightarrow 0$ through negative values.

These four limits are depicted graphically in Fig. 43, which
represents the curve $y = \dfrac{1}{x}$.

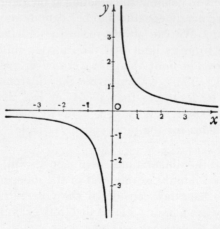

Fig. 43.

It is clear from the graph that each branch of the curve extends to infinity in two directions, and as it does so it approaches more and more closely to two straight lines—the coordinate axes. The curve is said to have these two lines as **asymptotes.** Further examples of asymptotes are given in **§** 28.

This brings us to the end of the section on limits. For the reader who wants a formal definition, the following may be sufficient :

A function $f(x)$ is said to tend to the limit L as x tends to l if the difference between $f(x)$ and L can be made as small as we please by taking x sufficiently close to l.

But the more discriminating reader will object that the phrases " as small as we please " and " sufficiently close " are not entirely clear.   In that case, we must substitute the more precise—but rather more difficult—definition first given by Cauchy about 1820 :

A function $f(x)$ is said to tend to the limit L as x tends to l if corresponding to every positive number ε, however small, there can be found a positive number δ, depending on ε, such that*

$$|f(x) - L| < \varepsilon$$
for all values of x $(x \neq l)$ in the range
$$|x - l| < \delta.$$

The latter definition is not easy ; it embodies in a few words the result of centuries of persistent effort to put the concept of a " limit " on a satisfactory mathematical basis.   But although this concept cannot be adequately expressed any more simply, that does not mean that in problems involving limits this test must be applied rigorously on every occasion.   The reader will

---

* By $|f(x) - L|$, which is read " the **modulus** of $f(x) - L$," is meant the *numerical* value of $f(x) - L$.   Thus, if in any investigation the value of a variable x must be numerically less than 1, we may write either $-1 < x < 1$, or, more concisely, $|x| < 1$.

find that in the exercises which follow, the general ideas which he has acquired about limits in studying the examples quoted earlier in this section will be sufficient, just as at an earlier stage in his studies he probably solved many questions on loci before he was able to give a precise definition of a " locus."

Examples

1. Find the limit of the function $\dfrac{x^3 + a^3}{x + a}$ as x tends to the value $- a$.

When $x = - a$, the function assumes the meaningless form $\dfrac{0}{0}$.

But $\dfrac{x^3 + a^3}{x + a} = \dfrac{(x + a)(x^2 - ax + a^2)}{x + a} = x^2 - ax + a^2,$

provided $x \neq - a$.

As $x \longrightarrow - a$, $\dfrac{x^3 + a^3}{x + a} \longrightarrow a^2 + a^2 + a^2 = 3a^2.$

Therefore, $\underset{x \longrightarrow - a}{L} \ \dfrac{x^3 + a^3}{x + a} = 3a^2.$

2. Find the limit of the function $\dfrac{\sec 3x}{\sec x}$ as x tends to $\dfrac{\pi}{2}$.

When $x = \dfrac{\pi}{2}$, the function assumes the unintelligible form $\dfrac{\infty}{\infty}$.

Limits in which the independent variable tends to some value which is not zero or infinity are often more easily dealt with by changing the independent variable.

Let $x = \dfrac{\pi}{2} - y$, so that as $x \longrightarrow \dfrac{\pi}{2}$, $y \longrightarrow 0$.

We have $\dfrac{\sec 3x}{\sec x} = \dfrac{\cos x}{\cos 3x} = \dfrac{\sin y}{- \sin 3y} = - \dfrac{1}{3} \left(\dfrac{\sin y}{y} \right) \left(\dfrac{3y}{\sin 3y} \right).$

As $y \longrightarrow 0$, $\dfrac{\sin y}{y} \longrightarrow 1$ and $\dfrac{3y}{\sin 3y} \longrightarrow 1.$

Therefore $$\underset{x \to \frac{\pi}{2}}{L} \frac{\sec 3x}{\sec x} = -\frac{1}{3}.$$

3. Find the limit of the function $\dfrac{x^2 + 2}{2x^2 + 3}$ as x tends to infinity.

We have $\dfrac{x^2 + 2}{2x^2 + 3} = \dfrac{1 + \dfrac{2}{x^2}}{2 + \dfrac{3}{x^2}}$, dividing both numerator and

denominator by x^2.

When $x \to \infty$, $\dfrac{1}{x^2} \to 0$; therefore

$$\underset{x \to \infty}{L} \frac{x^2 + 2}{2x^2 + 3} = \frac{1}{2}.$$

(In Example **2** we have tacitly assumed that the limit of the product of a number of functions is equal to the product of the limits of the functions. In Example **3** we likewise assume that the limit of the quotient of two functions is equal to the quotient of the limits of the functions. These two results can easily be proved, the latter holding provided that the limit of the divisor is not zero.)

4. Find the limit of the function $\dfrac{1 - \sqrt{(1 - x)}}{x}$ as x tends to zero.

Multiplying both numerator and denominator of the given function by $1 + \sqrt{(1 - x)}$, we have

$$\frac{1 - \sqrt{(1 - x)}}{x} = \frac{1 - (1 - x)}{x\{1 + \sqrt{(1 - x)}\}} = \frac{1}{1 + \sqrt{(1 - x)}},$$

provided $x \neq 0$.

When $x \to 0$, $1 + \sqrt{(1 - x)} \to 2$; therefore

$$\underset{x \to 0}{L} \frac{1 - \sqrt{(1 - x)}}{x} = \frac{1}{2}.$$

5. Prove that, for all rational values of n,

$$L_{x \to a} \frac{x^n - a^n}{x - a} = na^{n-1}.$$

(The only justification for interpolating such a lengthy exercise at this point is that this result is required in the next section (page 178)).

Rational numbers include all integers, positive or negative, and all fractions of the type $\frac{p}{q}$, where p and q are integers, positive or negative.

Case 1.—Let n be a positive integer. Then,

$$x^n - a^n = (x - a)(x^{n-1} + ax^{n-2} + \ldots + a^{n-2}x + a^{n-1}),$$

and if $x \neq a$, we have

$$\frac{x^n - a^n}{x - a} = x^{n-1} + ax^{n-2} + \ldots + a^{n-2}x + a^{n-1},$$

$$\to a^{n-1} + a^{n-1} + \ldots \text{ to } n \text{ terms, as } x \to a.$$

Therefore,

$$L_{x \to a} \frac{x^n - a^n}{x - a} = na^{n-1}, \text{ for } n \text{ a positive integer.}$$

Case 2.—Let n be a positive fraction $\frac{p}{q}$, where p and q are positive integers.

Now let $x = y^q$ and let $a = b^q$, so that when $x \to a$, $y \to b$. We have

$$\frac{x^n - a^n}{x - a} = \frac{x^{\frac{p}{q}} - a^{\frac{p}{q}}}{x - a} = \frac{y^p - b^p}{y^q - b^q} = \frac{\dfrac{y^p - b^p}{y - b}}{\dfrac{y^q - b^q}{y - b}}, \text{ provided } y \neq b.$$

170

Therefore, $\displaystyle \lim_{x \to a} \frac{x^n - a^n}{x - a} = \lim_{y \to b} \frac{\dfrac{y^p - b^p}{y - b}}{\dfrac{y^q - b^q}{y - b}}$

$$= \frac{pb^{p-1}}{qb^{q-1}}, \text{ by case 1 on previous page}$$

$$= \frac{p}{q} \cdot b^{p-q},$$

$$= \frac{p}{q} \cdot a^{\frac{p}{q}-1}, \ (b = a^{\frac{1}{q}}),$$

$$= na^{n-1}.$$

Combining cases 1 and 2, we see that if n is any *positive* rational number

$$\lim_{x \to a} \frac{x^n - a^n}{x - a} = na^{n-1}.$$

Case 3.—Let n be any negative rational number (either integral or fractional). Then $-n$ will be a positive rational number, say m; that is, $n = -m$. We have

$$\frac{x^n - a^n}{x - a} = \frac{x^{-m} - a^{-m}}{x - a} = -\frac{1}{x^m a^m} \cdot \frac{x^m - a^m}{x - a}$$

$$\longrightarrow -\frac{1}{a^{2m}} \cdot ma^{m-1}, \text{ as } x \longrightarrow a$$

(since m is a positive rational number).

Therefore,

$$\lim_{x \to a} \frac{x^n - a^n}{x - a} = -ma^{-m-1} = na^{n-1}, \text{ since } n = -m.$$

Thus, for *all* rational values of n

$$\lim_{x \to a} \frac{x^n - a^n}{x - a} = na^{n-1}.$$

6. Show, using the Binomial Theorem, that

$$\mathcal{L}_{n \to \infty} \left(1 + \frac{1}{n}\right)^n = e,$$

where e is the number defined by the infinite series given on page 102.

As n is to tend to infinity, we may regard $\frac{1}{n}$ as numerically less than unity, and therefore we may expand $\left(1 + \frac{1}{n}\right)^n$ by the Binomial Theorem.*   Thus

$$\left(1 + \frac{1}{n}\right)^n = 1 + \frac{n}{1} \cdot \left(\frac{1}{n}\right) + \frac{n(n-1)}{1 \cdot 2} \cdot \left(\frac{1}{n}\right)^2 +$$
$$\frac{n(n-1)(n-2)}{1 \cdot 2 \cdot 3} \cdot \left(\frac{1}{n}\right)^3 + \dots$$

$$= 1 + \frac{1}{1} + \frac{1}{1 \cdot 2}\left(1 - \frac{1}{n}\right)$$
$$+ \frac{1}{1 \cdot 2 \cdot 3}\left(1 - \frac{1}{n}\right)\left(1 - \frac{2}{n}\right) + \dots.$$

If we now let n tend to infinity, then each of the factors $\left(1 - \frac{1}{n}\right)$, $\left(1 - \frac{2}{n}\right)$, etc., will tend to 1, and, assuming that the limit of an infinite series equals the sum of the limits of each of the terms of the series (a result which, however plausible, requires justification), we have

$$\mathcal{L}_{n \to \infty} \left(1 + \frac{1}{n}\right)^n = 1 + \frac{1}{1} + \frac{1}{1 \cdot 2} + \frac{1}{1 \cdot 2 \cdot 3} + \dots$$

$$= e \text{ (see page 102).}$$

---

* The Binomial Theorem states that

$$(1 + x)^n = 1 + nx + \frac{n(n-1)}{1 \cdot 2}x^2 + \frac{n(n-1)(n-2)}{1 \cdot 2 \cdot 3}x^3 + \dots.$$

When n is a positive integer, the series terminates after $(n + 1)$ terms and the expansion holds for all values of x; if n is not a positive integer, the series does not terminate, and the theorem states that, provided $-1 < x < 1$, its sum to infinity is $(1 + x)^n$. For further information, the reader is referred to McArthur and Keith, *Intermediate Algebra* (Methuen, 1942).

7. Show that the function $\dfrac{x^2 - 4}{x^3 - 3x - 2}$ has no value when $x = 2$, and find its limit as x approaches 2.

8. Find the limits of the following functions as h tends to zero:

   (i) $\dfrac{1}{h}\left(\dfrac{1}{x + h} - \dfrac{1}{x}\right)$;

   (ii) $\dfrac{1}{h}\{\sqrt{(x + h)} - \sqrt{x}\}$;

   (iii) $\dfrac{1}{h}\{\sin(x + h) - \sin x\}$;

   (iv) $\dfrac{1}{h}\{\cos(x + h) - \cos x\}$.

9. Evaluate the following limits:

   (i) $\dfrac{x^2 - 4}{x - 2}$, as $x \to 2$;

   (ii) $\dfrac{x + 1}{x^{\frac{1}{3}} + 1}$, as $x \to -1$;

   (iii) $\dfrac{x^3 - 3x^2 + 4}{x^3 - 2x^2 - 4x + 8}$, as $x \to 2$;

   (iv) $\dfrac{\sqrt{(1 + x^2)} - 1}{x^2}$, as $x \to 0$;

   (v) $\dfrac{x^2}{3 - \sqrt{(9 + x^2)}}$, as $x \to 0$;

   (vi) $\sqrt{(x + 1)} - \sqrt{x}$, as $x \to \infty$;

   (vii) $\dfrac{x + 1}{x - 1}$, as $x \to \infty$;

   (viii) $\dfrac{x + 1}{x^2 + 1}$, as $x \to \infty$;

   (ix) $\dfrac{3x^2 + 2x - 5}{x^2 - 5x + 3}$, as $x \to \infty$;

   (x) $\sqrt{(x^2 + ax + b)} - x$, as $x \to \infty$.

10. Evaluate the following limits:

    (i) $\dfrac{\sin 2x}{x}$, as $x \longrightarrow 0$;

    (ii) $\dfrac{\sin 2x}{\sin 3x}$, as $x \longrightarrow 0$:

    (iii) $\dfrac{\sin^2 x}{x}$, as $x \longrightarrow 0$;

    (iv) $\dfrac{\sin x}{x\,(x-1)}$, as $x \longrightarrow 0$;

    (v) $\dfrac{x \sin x}{1 - \cos x}$, as $x \longrightarrow 0$;

    (vi) $\dfrac{1 - \cos x}{x^2}$, as $x \longrightarrow 0$;

    (vii) $\dfrac{\sin x}{x + \tan x}$, as $x \longrightarrow 0$;

    (viii) $\dfrac{1}{\sin x} - \dfrac{1}{\tan x}$, as $x \longrightarrow 0$;

    (ix) $\tan x - \sec x$, as $x \longrightarrow \dfrac{\pi}{2}$;

    (x) $\dfrac{\cos \frac{1}{2}x}{\pi - x}$, as $x \longrightarrow \pi$.

11. A right circular cone of height h and base-radius r is divided into n slices of equal thickness by planes parallel to the base. If each slice is regarded as a right circular cylinder with the smaller face of the slice as base, show that the sum of the volumes of the cylinders so formed is

$$\frac{1}{6}\pi r^2 h \left(1 - \frac{1}{n}\right)\left(2 - \frac{1}{n}\right),$$

and deduce a formula for the volume of the cone.

12. A hemisphere of radius r is divided into n slices of equal thickness by planes parallel to the circular face, and the slices are regarded as right circular cylinders, exactly as in Example 11. Show that the sum of the volumes of the cylinders so formed is

$$\frac{1}{6}\pi r^3 \left(1 - \frac{1}{n}\right)\left(4 + \frac{1}{n}\right),$$

and deduce a formula for the volume of a sphere of radius r.

13. By the method of Example **11**, show that the volume of a frustum of a right circular cone is $\frac{1}{3}\pi h\,(a^2 + ab + b^2)$, where h is the height of the frustum, and a and b are the radii of the circular ends.

14. The area under the curve $y = x^2$ from $x = 1$ to $x = 2$ is divided by ordinates into n strips of equal width. If each strip is trimmed to the form of a rectangle with the smaller ordinate as height, show that the sum of the areas so formed is

$$\frac{1}{6}\left(7 - \frac{1}{n}\right)\left(2 - \frac{1}{n}\right),$$

and deduce the area under the curve from $x = 1$ to $x = 2$. Verify your result by integration.

15. A right circular cone has a slant height l and a base-radius r. By regarding the curved surface of the cone as the limit of the lateral surface of a pyramid whose vertex is the vertex of the cone and whose base is a regular n-sided polygon inscribed in the base of the cone, show that the area of the curved surface of the cone is $\pi l r$.

16. The slant height of a frustum of a right circular cone is l, and a and b are the radii of the circular ends. Show by the method of the previous example that the area of the curved surface of the frustum is $\pi l\,(a + b)$.

§ 26. STANDARD DERIVATIVES.

In **§ 7**, the idea of a derivative was first introduced from geometrical considerations, and then later interpreted as a rate. It is possible, however, to define a derivative without any reference to either graphs or rates. With each of the simple functions considered in the early sections of this book, the derivative $\dfrac{dy}{dx}$ was found in the end by evaluating the limit of the ratio $\dfrac{\delta y}{\delta x}$ as δx tends to zero ; that is, the derivative of a function is the limit of the ratio

$$\frac{\text{increment of the function}}{\text{increment of the independent variable}}$$

when the denominator tends to zero. Thus, if $y = f(x)$,

$$\frac{dy}{dx} = \mathop{L}_{\delta x \longrightarrow 0} \frac{\delta y}{\delta x} = \mathop{L}_{\delta x \longrightarrow 0} \frac{f(x + \delta x) - f(x)}{\delta x}.$$

This equation may be regarded as the **definition** of the derivative of the function $f(x)$.

Strictly we ought to add that all that has been said above applies only if $f(x)$ is a **continuous** function, or if $f(x)$ is, at least, continuous over the range of values of x under consideration. Without a lengthy interpolation at this stage it is difficult to give a precise definition of " continuity " ; we shall therefore have to content ourselves with the somewhat loose statement that a function is continuous if its graph has no sudden gaps or jumps.

Thus,

    (i) the function x^2 is continuous for all values of x ;

(ii) the function $\dfrac{1}{x}$ is continuous except when $x = 0$ (see Fig. 43) ;

(iii) the function $\tan x$ is continuous except when $x = \pm \dfrac{\pi}{2}$, $\pm \dfrac{3\pi}{2}$, $\pm \dfrac{5\pi}{2}$, etc.,

and so on.

The functions with which we shall deal will all be continuous, except possibly for isolated values of the independent variable, and therefore in order to avoid tedious repetition we shall usually omit the adjective "continuous." It must be understood, however, that continuity is implied even although it is not expressly stated. No confusion should arise because the discontinuities (if any) will be evident from the analytical form of the function.

In Part I of this book, we confined our attention to functions mainly of two simple types. We shall now use the definition given at the beginning of this section to establish the derivatives of other functions to which the rules of differentiation already derived do not extend. Although we shall be concentrating for some time on the mere *technique* of differentiation, the significance of the derivative should not be forgotten. No matter what function $f(x)$ we consider, its derivative gives a measure of the rate at which the function varies with respect to its independent variable for the particular value x. Alternatively, if we think rather of the curve $y = f(x)$, the derivative gives the gradient of the curve at the point whose abscissa is x.

Differentiation of a power

Let $y = x^n$, where n is rational ;

then $\quad \dfrac{dy}{dx} = \displaystyle\lim_{\delta x \to 0} \dfrac{f(x + \delta x) - f(x)}{\delta x}$, where $f(x) = x^n$,

$$= \underset{\delta x \longrightarrow 0}{L} \frac{(x + \delta x)^n - x^n}{(x + \delta x) - x},$$

$$= nx^{n-1} \text{ (see Example 5, page 170)}.$$

That is, $\qquad\qquad \dfrac{d}{dx}(x^n) = nx^{n-1}$.   .   .   .   .   (1)

We have used this result many times in Part I of this book. It was not possible, however, to establish its general truth until the limit referred to above had been derived.

Differentiation of trigonometric functions

(i) Let $y = \sin x$,

then $\qquad \dfrac{dy}{dx} = \underset{\delta x \longrightarrow 0}{L} \dfrac{f(x + \delta x) - f(x)}{\delta x}$, where $f(x) = \sin x$,

$$= \underset{\delta x \longrightarrow 0}{L} \frac{\sin(x + \delta x) - \sin x}{\delta x}.$$

Now, from Trigonometry,

$$\sin A - \sin B = 2 \cos\left(\frac{A + B}{2}\right) \sin\left(\frac{A - B}{2}\right),$$

for all values of A and B ;

therefore $\sin(x + \delta x) - \sin x = 2 \cos\left(x + \dfrac{\delta x}{2}\right) \sin \dfrac{\delta x}{2}$,

and $\qquad \dfrac{\sin(x + \delta x) - \sin x}{\delta x} = \dfrac{\sin \dfrac{\delta x}{2}}{\dfrac{\delta x}{2}} \cdot \cos\left(x + \dfrac{\delta x}{2}\right)$,

so that $\qquad\qquad \dfrac{dy}{dx} = \underset{\delta x \longrightarrow 0}{L} \left(\dfrac{\sin \dfrac{\delta x}{2}}{\dfrac{\delta x}{2}}\right) \cos\left(x + \dfrac{\delta x}{2}\right).$

As δx tends to zero, the first factor of the right-hand side tends to 1 (see page 160), and the second to cos x.

Therefore $$\frac{d}{dx}(\sin x) = \cos x \quad . \qquad . \qquad . \qquad . \quad (2)$$

(ii) Let $y = \cos x$,

then $$\frac{dy}{dx} = \underset{\delta x \to 0}{L} \frac{\cos(x + \delta x) - \cos x}{\delta x}.$$

Now, from Trigonometry,

$$\cos A - \cos B = -2 \sin\left(\frac{A - B}{2}\right) \sin\left(\frac{A + B}{2}\right),$$

for all values of A and B;

therefore $\cos(x + \delta x) - \cos x = -2 \sin\dfrac{\delta x}{2} \sin\left(x + \dfrac{\delta x}{2}\right),$

and $$\frac{dy}{dx} = \underset{\delta x \to 0}{L} \; -\frac{\sin\dfrac{\delta x}{2}}{\dfrac{\delta x}{2}} \cdot \sin\left(x + \frac{\delta x}{2}\right) = -\sin x,$$

that is, $$\frac{d}{dx}(\cos x) = -\sin x \quad . \qquad . \qquad . \quad (3)$$

(iii) Let $y = \tan x$,

then $\dfrac{dy}{dx} = \underset{\delta x \to 0}{L} \dfrac{\tan(x + \delta x) - \tan x}{\delta x},$

$$= \underset{\delta x \to 0}{L} \frac{\sin(x + \delta x)\cos x - \cos(x + \delta x)\sin x}{\delta x \cdot \cos x \cdot \cos(x + \delta x)},$$

$$= \mathop{L}_{\delta x \to 0} \frac{\sin \delta x}{\delta x} \cdot \frac{1}{\cos x \cos (x + \delta x)},$$

$$= \frac{1}{\cos^2 x} = \sec^2 x.$$

Therefore $\qquad \dfrac{d}{dx} (\tan x) = \sec^2 x \qquad . \qquad . \qquad . \qquad (4)$

This last result shows incidentally that the gradient of the curve $y = \tan x$ is always positive.

Differentiation of inverse functions

The equation $2x - y + 3 = 0$ defines a relationship which exists between two variables x and y. If we re-write the equation in the equivalent form $y = 2x + 3$, the relation assumes a form which gives y as a function of x. But we could equally well write $x = \frac{1}{2}(y - 3)$, giving x as a function of y. More generally, the equation $y = f(x)$ which defines y as a function of x can often be re-arranged in a form $x = \Phi(y)$ which defines x as a function of y. The two functions $f(x)$ and $\Phi(x)$ which are related in this way are said to be **inverse** functions. Thus,

x^2 and $\pm \sqrt{x}$ are inverse functions ;

$\sin x$ and $\sin^{-1} x$ are inverse functions ;

$\tan x$ and $\tan^{-1} x$ are inverse functions ;

$\log_a x$ and a^x are inverse functions.

The " inverse " nature of these pairs of functions is possibly more clearly seen when we reflect that

$$(\pm \sqrt{x})^2 = x, \qquad \sin (\sin^{-1} x) = x,$$

$$\tan (\tan^{-1} x) = x, \qquad \log_a (a^x) = x.$$

Let $f(x)$ and $\Phi(x)$ be inverse functions. Then if $y = f(x)$, it follows, from the meaning of inverse functions, that $x = \Phi(y)$, and the respective derivatives of the two functions $f(x)$ and

$\Phi(y)$ may be denoted $\dfrac{dy}{dx}$ and $\dfrac{dx}{dy}$. From the forms of these symbols one might expect $\dfrac{dy}{dx}$ and $\dfrac{dx}{dy}$ to be reciprocals of each other ; in fact this is true, but the result is not an obvious one for it will be recalled that $\dfrac{dy}{dx}$ and $\dfrac{dx}{dy}$ are not ratios. However, the result is easily established as follows.

If δx and δy are corresponding increments in x and y, then, assuming that $f(x)$ is continuous, as δx tends to zero so also does δy. When x increases by an amount δx, y increases by δy, and vice-versa. Since, from elementary Algebra,

$$\frac{\delta y}{\delta x} \cdot \frac{\delta x}{\delta y} = 1,$$

then
$$\lim_{\delta x \to 0} \frac{\delta y}{\delta x} \times \lim_{\delta y \to 0} \frac{\delta x}{\delta y} = 1,$$

that is,
$$\frac{dy}{dx} \cdot \frac{dx}{dy} = 1.$$

Therefore
$$\frac{dx}{dy} = \frac{1}{\dfrac{dy}{dx}}, \text{ and } \frac{dy}{dx} = \frac{1}{\dfrac{dx}{dy}}.$$

Expressed in this form the result is of great value in establishing the derivatives of inverse functions.

(i) Let $y = \sin^{-1} x$;

then
$$x = \sin y, \text{ and } \frac{dx}{dy} = \cos y.$$

Therefore $\dfrac{dy}{dx} = \dfrac{1}{\dfrac{dx}{dy}} = \dfrac{1}{\cos y} = \pm \dfrac{1}{\sqrt{(1 - \sin^2 y)}} = \pm \dfrac{1}{\sqrt{(1 - x^2)}}.$

The ambiguity in sign is due to the fact that $\sin^{-1} x$ is not necessarily an acute angle—not even if y is positive. Since

181

$\sin y = x$, $\cos y$ must always have the numerical value $\sqrt{(1 - x^2)}$, but may turn out to be either positive or negative (Fig. 44).

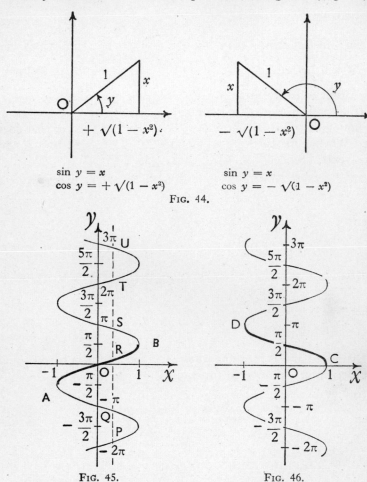

$$\sin y = x$$
$$\cos y = + \sqrt{(1 - x^2)}$$

$$\sin y = x$$
$$\cos y = - \sqrt{(1 - x^2)}$$

FIG. 44.

FIG. 45.   FIG. 46.

The graph of $y = \sin^{-1} x$ (Fig. 45) makes the reason for the ambiguity even clearer. For any given value of x, necessarily between -1 and $+1$, there is an infinite number of values of y, but only two different values of $\dfrac{dy}{dx}$; at the points P, R, T, etc., the gradients are all equal and positive, at Q, S, U, etc., the gradients are all equal and negative, and have the same numerical value as those at P, R, T, etc.

To remove the ambiguity it is convenient, for our purpose, to define $\sin^{-1} x$ to be that angle between $-\dfrac{\pi}{2}$ and $\dfrac{\pi}{2}$ whose sine is x, that is, the function whose graph is the arc AB in Fig. 45. The gradient of this function is positive for all values of x, and hence if $\sin^{-1} x$ is restricted to the range $-\dfrac{\pi}{2}$ to $\dfrac{\pi}{2}$, we have

$$\frac{d}{dx}(\sin^{-1} x) = + \frac{1}{\sqrt{(1 - x^2)}} \qquad . \qquad . \quad (5)$$

(ii) Let $y = \cos^{-1} x$.

We will define $\cos^{-1} x$ to be that angle between* 0 and π whose cosine is x, that is, the function whose graph is the arc CD in Fig. 46.

Since $y = \cos^{-1} x$, $x = \cos y$,

and $\qquad\qquad\qquad \dfrac{dx}{dy} = -\sin y.$

Therefore $\qquad\qquad \dfrac{dy}{dx} = \dfrac{1}{\dfrac{dx}{dy}} = -\dfrac{1}{\sin y} = \mp \dfrac{1}{\sqrt{(1 - x^2)}}.$

But, for the range $0 < y < \pi$, the gradient of the curve is negative for all values of x. Therefore if $\cos^{-1} x$ is restricted to lie between 0 and π, we have

$$\frac{d}{dx}(\cos^{-1} x) = -\frac{1}{\sqrt{(1 - x^2)}} \qquad . \qquad . \quad (6)$$

---

* The reader should reflect for himself why the range is $-\dfrac{\pi}{2}$ to $\dfrac{\pi}{2}$ in the case of $\sin^{-1} x$, and 0 to π in the case of $\cos^{-1} x$.

(iii) Let $y = \tan^{-1} x$ (Fig. 47).

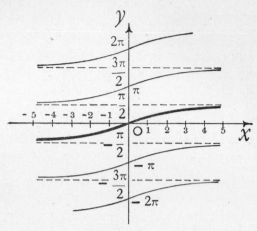

FIG. 47.

Since $y = \tan^{-1} x$, $x = \tan y$,

and
$$\frac{dx}{dy} = \sec^2 y.$$

Therefore
$$\frac{dy}{dx} = \frac{1}{\dfrac{dx}{dy}} = \frac{1}{\sec^2 y} = \frac{1}{1 + \tan^2 y} = \frac{1}{1 + x^2}.$$

That is,
$$\frac{d}{dx}(\tan^{-1}x) = \frac{1}{1 + x^2} \quad . \quad . \quad . \quad (7)$$

There is no ambiguity of sign in this case, for although there is an infinite number of values of y corresponding to each value of x, the values of $\dfrac{dy}{dx}$ for any particular value of x are all equal. Nevertheless, we find it convenient to regard $\tan^{-1} x$ as that angle between $-\dfrac{\pi}{2}$ and $\dfrac{\pi}{2}$ whose tangent is x, that is, the function whose graph consists of that branch in Fig. 47 which lies between $y = -\dfrac{\pi}{2}$ and $y = \dfrac{\pi}{2}$.

Differentiation of the exponential function

If y is a function of x, its derivative $\dfrac{dy}{dx}$ is usually some quite different function of x. But there is a particular function—and one of some importance—whose derivative is identical with the function itself ; that is, for this function

$$\frac{dy}{dx} = y.$$

It is found that this unusual function may be represented by the infinite series

$$y = 1 + x + \frac{x^2}{1 \cdot 2} + \frac{x^3}{1 \cdot 2 \cdot 3} + \frac{x^4}{1 \cdot 2 \cdot 3 \cdot 4} + \cdots$$

$$+ \frac{x^n}{1 \cdot 2 \cdot 3 \cdots n} + \cdots,$$

or, using the factorial notation,*

$$y = 1 + x + \frac{x^2}{2!} + \frac{x^3}{3!} + \frac{x^4}{4!} + \cdots + \frac{x^n}{n!} + \cdots.$$

Assuming that $\dfrac{dy}{dx}$ may be found by differentiating each term of the series separately, we have

$$\frac{dy}{dx} = 0 + 1 + \frac{2x}{2!} + \frac{3x^2}{3!} + \frac{4x^3}{4!} + \cdots + \frac{nx^{n-1}}{n!} + \cdots,$$

$$= 1 + x + \frac{x^2}{2!} + \frac{x^3}{3!} + \cdots + \frac{x^{n-1}}{(n-1)!} + \cdots,$$

---

* In the factorial notation, the product $n(n-1)(n-2)\cdots 3 \cdot 2 \cdot 1$ is denoted by $n!$ or $\lfloor n$, provided n is a positive integer.

showing that $$\frac{dy}{dx} = y.$$

In order to find the value to which this infinite series converges, let us consider the function

$$\left(1 + \frac{1}{n}\right)^{nx}.$$

It has already been indicated (see Example **6,** page 172) that as n tends to infinity, the function $\left(1 + \frac{1}{n}\right)^{n}$ tends to the value e. Hence

$$\underset{n \longrightarrow \infty}{L} \left(1 + \frac{1}{n}\right)^{nx} = e^{x}.$$

Also, by the Binomial Theorem,

$$\left(1 + \frac{1}{n}\right)^{nx} = 1 + \frac{nx}{1} \cdot \left(\frac{1}{n}\right) + \frac{nx\,(nx - 1)}{1 \cdot 2} \cdot \left(\frac{1}{n}\right)^{2}$$

$$+ \frac{nx\,(nx - 1)(nx - 2)}{1 \cdot 2 \cdot 3} \cdot \left(\frac{1}{n}\right)^{3} + \dots$$

$$= 1 + \frac{x}{1} + \frac{x\left(x - \frac{1}{n}\right)}{1 \cdot 2} + \frac{x\left(x - \frac{1}{n}\right)\left(x - \frac{2}{n}\right)}{1 \cdot 2 \cdot 3} + \dots.$$

But, as n tends to infinity, each of the factors $x - \frac{1}{n}, x - \frac{2}{n}$, etc., tends to x, hence we may write

$$e^{x} = 1 + \frac{x}{1} + \frac{x^{2}}{2!} + \frac{x^{3}}{3!} + \dots.$$

It can be shown* that this expansion is true for all values of x. Any function in which the independent variable occurs

---

* This section contains several (possibly annoying) assumptions. To discuss this function adequately, a knowledge of the theory of infinite series is necessary. Readers who wish further information on the subject are referred to McArthur and Keith, *Intermediate Algebra* (Methuen), Chapter XVII, and to G. Gibson, *Elementary Treatise on the Calculus* (Macmillan), Chapter V.

as an index, or *exponent*, is called an " exponential " function ; e^x is one such function, and being a function of particular importance, having applications in almost every branch of mathematics, it is generally known as **the exponential function.** Its most characteristic feature is that its rate of change is equal to the function itself, that is,

$$\frac{d}{dx}(e^x) = e^x. \qquad . \qquad . \qquad . \qquad . \qquad (8)$$

Differentiation of the logarithmic function

Let $y = \log_e x$, then $x = e^y$,

and $\qquad\qquad \dfrac{dx}{dy} = e^y.$

Therefore $\qquad \dfrac{dy}{dx} = \dfrac{1}{\dfrac{dx}{dy}} = \dfrac{1}{e^y} = \dfrac{1}{x}$

That is, $\qquad \dfrac{d}{dx}(\log_e x) = \dfrac{1}{x} \qquad . \qquad . \qquad . \qquad (9)$

In numerical calculations logarithms are taken to the base 10— *common* logarithms ; this is because our system of number notation is a decimal system. In theoretical work, however, logarithms are always taken to the base e—*natural*, or *Napierian*, logarithms. In the pages which follow, we shall therefore use the symbol $\log x$ to denote $\log_e x$, the base being omitted.

Fig. 48 shows on the same diagram the graphs of the functions e^x and $\log x$. Clearly, since they are inverse functions, if the point (a, b) lies on one curve, the point (b, a) must lie on the other ; the one graph may therefore be found from the other* by interchanging corresponding values of x and y, or by constructing its reflection in the line $y = x$.

* These statements hold for *all* pairs of inverse functions.

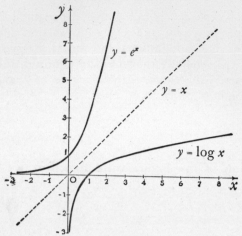

FIG. 48.

The results numbered (1) - (9) may be regarded as standard derivatives, and should be committed to memory. For convenience they are listed below.

Function	Derivative
x^n	nx^{n-1}
$\sin x$	$\cos x$
$\cos x$	$-\sin x$
$\tan x$	$\sec^2 x$
$\sin^{-1} x$	$\dfrac{1}{\sqrt{(1-x^2)}}$
$\cos^{-1} x$	$-\dfrac{1}{\sqrt{(1-x^2)}}$
$\tan^{-1} x$	$\dfrac{1}{1+x^2}$
e^x	e^x
$\log x$	$\dfrac{1}{x}$

188

§27. GENERAL RULES OF DIFFERENTIATION.

It often happens that we have to deal with functions which consist of a combination of simpler functions of the types considered in the last section. We must now investigate how such combinations of functions may be differentiated.

Differentiation of a sum of functions

Let
$$y = u + v,$$
where u and v are functions of x.

When x receives the increment δx, let the corresponding increments of y, u, v, be δy, δu, δv.

Then
$$y + \delta y = (u + \delta u) + (v + \delta v),$$
so that
$$\delta y = \delta u + \delta v,$$
and
$$\frac{\delta y}{\delta x} = \frac{\delta u}{\delta x} + \frac{\delta v}{\delta x}.$$

Let $\delta x \longrightarrow 0$; then
$$\frac{\delta y}{\delta x} \longrightarrow \frac{dy}{dx}, \quad \frac{\delta u}{\delta x} \longrightarrow \frac{du}{dx}, \quad \frac{\delta v}{\delta x} \longrightarrow \frac{dv}{dx}.$$

Therefore,
$$\frac{dy}{dx} = \frac{du}{dx} + \frac{dv}{dx}.$$

In particular, if $y = u + C$, where C is a constant, then
$$\frac{dy}{dx} = \frac{du}{dx} + \frac{dC}{dx} = \frac{du}{dx}, \text{ since } \frac{dC}{dx} = 0.$$

Thus, two functions which differ only by a constant have the same derivative.

The result established on page 189 may be extended to include more than two functions ; thus,

if $y = u + v + w,$ $\dfrac{dy}{dx} = \dfrac{du}{dx} + \dfrac{dv}{dx} + \dfrac{dw}{dx}$;

and if $y = u + v - w,$ $\dfrac{dy}{dx} = \dfrac{du}{dx} + \dfrac{dv}{dx} - \dfrac{dw}{dx}.$

For example, if $y = \sin x + \cos x - \tan x,$

$$\frac{dy}{dx} = \cos x - \sin x - \sec^2 x.$$

The result does not necessarily hold if the number of functions is infinite—as in the case of an infinite series—though the observant reader may recall that we differentiated such an infinite series on page 185. In that particular case, the procedure can be justified, though the argument is beyond the scope of this book.

Differentiation of a product of functions

Let $y = uv,$
where u and v are functions of x.

When x receives the increment δx, let the corresponding increments of $y,$ $u,$ $v,$ be $\delta y,$ $\delta u,$ $\delta v.$

Then $y + \delta y = (u + \delta u)(v + \delta v),$

so that $\delta y = v\, \delta u + u\, \delta v + \delta u . \delta v,$

and $\dfrac{\delta y}{\delta x} = v\,\dfrac{\delta u}{\delta x} + u\,\dfrac{\delta v}{\delta x} + \delta u . \dfrac{\delta v}{\delta x}.$

Let $\delta x \longrightarrow 0$; then

$\dfrac{\delta y}{\delta x} \longrightarrow \dfrac{dy}{dx},$ $\dfrac{\delta u}{\delta x} \longrightarrow \dfrac{du}{dx},$ $\dfrac{\delta v}{\delta x} \longrightarrow \dfrac{dv}{dx},$ and $\delta u \longrightarrow 0.$

Therefore, $\mathbf{\dfrac{dy}{dx} = v\,\dfrac{du}{dx} + u\,\dfrac{dv}{dx}.}$

For example, if $y = x^2 \log x,$

$$\frac{dy}{dx} = 2x \log x + x^2 . \frac{1}{x} = x\,(1 + 2 \log x).$$

The result may be extended to include a product of three or more functions ; thus, if $y = uvw$, where u, v, w are functions of x,

$$\frac{dy}{dx} = vw \frac{du}{dx} + uw \frac{dv}{dx} + uv \frac{dw}{dx},$$

or, dividing by uvw,

$$\frac{1}{y} \frac{dy}{dx} = \frac{1}{u} \frac{du}{dx} + \frac{1}{v} \frac{dv}{dx} + \frac{1}{w} \frac{dw}{dx}.$$

This last form of the " product rule " is often referred to as the *logarithmic differentiation* of a product. The reason for this title will be given later (see Example **5**, page 201).

A particular case of the product rule for two functions occurs when v is a constant, say C ; that is, $y = Cu$, where u is a function of x. Then

$$\frac{dy}{dx} = u \frac{dC}{dx} + C \frac{du}{dx} = C \frac{du}{dx}, \quad \text{since } \frac{dC}{dx} = 0.$$

That is, a constant factor remains as a factor in the derivative ; for example, $\dfrac{d}{dx} (3 \sin x) = 3 \dfrac{d}{dx} (\sin x) = 3 \cos x.$

Differentiation of a quotient of two functions

Let
$$y = \frac{u}{v},$$

where u and v are functions of x.

When x receives the increment δx, let the corresponding increments in y, u, v be δy, δu, δv.

Then
$$y + \delta y = \frac{u + \delta u}{v + \delta v},$$

so that
$$\delta y = \frac{u + \delta u}{v + \delta v} - \frac{u}{v} = \frac{v \, \delta u - u \, \delta v}{v \, (v + \delta v)},$$

and
$$\frac{\delta y}{\delta x} = \frac{1}{v \, (v + \delta v)} \left(v \frac{\delta u}{\delta x} - u \frac{\delta v}{\delta x} \right).$$

Let $\delta x \longrightarrow 0$; then

$$\frac{\delta y}{\delta x} \longrightarrow \frac{dy}{dx}, \quad \frac{\delta u}{\delta x} \longrightarrow \frac{du}{dx}, \quad \frac{\delta v}{\delta x} \longrightarrow \frac{dv}{dx}, \quad \text{and } \delta v \longrightarrow 0.$$

Therefore,
$$\frac{dy}{dx} = \frac{v \dfrac{du}{dx} - u \dfrac{dv}{dx}}{v^2},$$

provided, of course, v is not zero for the particular value of x considered.

For example, if $y = \tan x = \dfrac{\sin x}{\cos x}$,

$$\frac{dy}{dx} = \frac{\cos x \,(\cos x) - \sin x \,(- \sin x)}{\cos^2 x}$$

$$= \frac{\cos^2 x + \sin^2 x}{\cos^2 x} = \sec^2 x.$$

The " quotient rule " may also be expressed in another form. We have

$$\frac{dy}{dx} = \frac{v \dfrac{du}{dx} - u \dfrac{dv}{dx}}{v^2},$$

so that
$$v^2 \frac{dy}{dx} = v \frac{du}{dx} - u \frac{dv}{dx},$$

and
$$\frac{v}{u} \frac{dy}{dx} = \frac{1}{u} \frac{du}{dx} - \frac{1}{v} \frac{dv}{dx},$$

that is,
$$\frac{1}{y} \frac{dy}{dx} = \frac{1}{u} \frac{du}{dx} - \frac{1}{v} \frac{dv}{dx}.$$

This is also an example of " logarithmic differentiation " (see page 201).

A particular case of the quotient rule occurs when $u = 1$; that is, $y = \dfrac{1}{v}$. The formula then becomes :

$$\frac{dy}{dx} = \frac{v \dfrac{d}{dx}(1) - 1 \cdot \dfrac{dv}{dx}}{v^2} = -\frac{1}{v^2}\frac{dv}{dx}.$$

For example, if $y = \cot x = \dfrac{1}{\tan x}$,

$$\frac{dy}{dx} = -\frac{1}{\tan^2 x} \cdot \sec^2 x = -\operatorname{cosec}^2 x.$$

Differentiation of a function of a function

Let y be a function $f(u)$ of u, where u is a function $F(x)$ of x ; then y is a function of a function of x (see page 51).

When x receives the increment δx, let the corresponding increment of u be δu ; when u receives the increment δu, let the corresponding increment of y be δy.

Hence, δy is the increment of y which corresponds to the increment δx of x.

When δx tends to zero, so also do δu and δy.

Now, by elementary algebra,

$$\frac{\delta y}{\delta x} = \frac{\delta y}{\delta u} \cdot \frac{\delta u}{\delta x}.$$

Let $\delta x \longrightarrow 0$; then $\delta u \longrightarrow 0$ also, and

$$\frac{\delta y}{\delta x} \longrightarrow \frac{dy}{dx}, \quad \frac{\delta y}{\delta u} \longrightarrow \frac{dy}{du}, \quad \frac{\delta u}{\delta x} \longrightarrow \frac{du}{dx}.$$

Therefore,
$$\mathbf{\frac{dy}{dx} = \frac{dy}{du} \cdot \frac{du}{dx}.}$$

The result may clearly be extended. Thus, if

$$y = f(u), \quad u = F(v), \quad v = \Phi(x),$$

then
$$\frac{dy}{dx} = \frac{dy}{du} \cdot \frac{du}{dv} \cdot \frac{dv}{dx},$$

and so on.

For example, if $y = \sqrt{(3x^2 - 4x + 5)}$,

then $y = \sqrt{u}$, where $u = 3x^2 - 4x + 5$.

Therefore $\dfrac{dy}{dx} = \dfrac{dy}{du} \cdot \dfrac{du}{dx} = \dfrac{1}{2\sqrt{u}} \cdot (6x - 4)$,

$$= \dfrac{3x - 2}{\sqrt{(3x^2 - 4x + 5)}}.$$

With practice, the reader will soon be able to write down at sight such a derivative, without explicitly introducing the symbol u. Thus,

if $y = \sin(3x + 4)$, $\dfrac{dy}{dx} = 3\cos(3x + 4)$;

if $y = e^{-4t}$, $\dfrac{dy}{dx} = -4e^{-4t}$;

if $y = \log(a + bx)$, $\dfrac{dy}{dx} = \dfrac{b}{a + bx}$;

if $y = (3x^2 - x + 6)^5$, $\dfrac{dy}{dx} = 5(6x - 1)(3x^2 - x + 6)^4$;

if $y = \dfrac{1}{\sqrt{(ax^2 + bx + c)}}$, $\dfrac{dy}{dx} = -\tfrac{1}{2} \cdot \dfrac{2ax + b}{(ax^2 + bx + c)^{\frac{3}{2}}}$;

and so on.

A knowledge of the foregoing rules of differentiation enables us to find the derivative of *any* algebraic function. The reader may be alarmed at the formidable list of exercises which appears at the end of this section. Nevertheless he would do well to work conscientiously through this list. No facility in the Calculus will be acquired until the technique of differentiation has been mastered.

Differentiation of an implicit function

Equations such as

$$x^2 + xy + y^2 - 1 = 0 \qquad . \qquad . \qquad . \quad (1)$$

or $$2xy + 3\tan y - 4 = 0 \qquad . \qquad . \qquad . \quad (2)$$

may be regarded as defining y as a function of x, for if x is given any value, the resulting equation in y may be solved—algebraically in the case of (1), graphically in the case of (2)—and the corresponding value or values of y ascertained. A function defined in this way is said to be defined **implicitly** ; in contradistinction, a function defined by an equation in the form $y = f(x)$ is said to be defined **explicitly.**

To find the derivative of an implicit function we may adopt one of two different procedures.

(i) We may (if possible) solve the equation for y and so find the corresponding explicit functional form. Thus, if $x^2 + xy + y^2 - 1 = 0$,

we have $\qquad y^2 + xy + (x^2 - 1) = 0,$

so that $\qquad y = \dfrac{-x \pm \sqrt{(4 - 3x^2)}}{2}.$

Differentiating, we have

$$\frac{dy}{dx} = \tfrac{1}{2}\left\{-1 \pm \frac{(-6x)}{2\sqrt{(4 - 3x^2)}}\right\},$$

$$= -\tfrac{1}{2}\left\{1 \pm \frac{3x}{\sqrt{(4 - 3x^2)}}\right\}.$$

Thus, when $x = 1$,

$$y = \tfrac{1}{2}(-1 \pm 1) = 0 \text{ or } -1 ;$$

and $\qquad \dfrac{dy}{dx} = -\tfrac{1}{2}(1 \pm 3) = -2 \text{ or } 1.$

That is, at the point $(1, 0)$, the gradient is -2 ; at the point $(1, -1)$, the gradient is 1.

(ii) It is not always convenient (or even possible—as in the case of equation (2) above) to solve the original equation and so obtain y as an explicit function of x. The following method of finding $\dfrac{dy}{dx}$ is, however, always available.

We have already seen that the equation

$$x^2 + xy + y^2 - 1 = 0$$

defines y as a function of x, say $y = \Phi(x)$. By substitution we therefore have

$$x^2 + x \cdot \Phi(x) + \{\Phi(x)\}^2 - 1 = 0.$$

Let us denote the left-hand side of this identity by $f(x)$.
No change in x can alter $f(x)$ from its constant value, namely 0.

Therefore $\dfrac{d}{dx}\{ f(x) \} = 0.$

It follows that the derivative of the expression $x^2 + xy + y^2 - 1$ with respect to x is zero. Thus, bearing in mind that y is a function of x, we have

$$2x + \left(y + x\frac{dy}{dx}\right) + 2y\frac{dy}{dx} = 0,$$

so that $\dfrac{dy}{dx} = -\dfrac{2x + y}{x + 2y}.$

When $x = 1$, $y + y^2 = 0$, so that $y = 0$ or -1.

At the point $(1, 0)$, $\dfrac{dy}{dx} = -\dfrac{2 + 0}{1 + 0} = -2$;

at the point $(1, -1)$, $\dfrac{dy}{dx} = -\dfrac{2 - 1}{1 - 2} = 1,$

in complete agreement with the results obtained in (i) above.

If we wish to find the stationary points of the curve $x^2 + xy + y^2 - 1 = 0$, we find the values of x and y which make $\dfrac{dy}{dx}$ vanish.

$$\frac{dy}{dx} = 0, \text{ when } y = -2x.$$

At points on the curve where $y = -2x$, we have
$$x^2 - 2x^2 + 4x^2 - 1 = 0,$$
$$3x^2 = 1,$$
$$x = \pm \frac{1}{\sqrt{3}}.$$

Thus, the stationary points of the given curve are $\left(\pm\dfrac{1}{\sqrt{3}}, \mp\dfrac{2}{\sqrt{3}}\right)$. Their exact nature may be found by considering the sign of $\dfrac{dy}{dx}$ to the left and to the right of these points.

Freedom equations

If x and y may have **any** values we please, then the variable point $P(x, y)$ may be regarded as free to wander all over the plane of the coordinate axes. The point is said to have two **degrees of freedom**—x can have any value, and y can have any value.

Suppose, however, that we stipulate that as the point P moves, its abscissa and its ordinate must always be equal. The point has been deprived of one of its freedoms, for although x may still have any value, once this value is fixed so also is the value of y. We say that the point is now " constrained " in its movement ; it is constrained to move along the straight line whose equation is $y = x$, and this equation is therefore known as the **constraint equation** of the locus of the moving point.

In general, if a point is restricted to move on a plane curve (or a line), it has one degree of freedom—the freedom to move on that curve (or line)—and one degree of constraint—the compulsion to remain on the curve (or line). The freedom is therefore a disciplined freedom. The (x, y) equation of the constraining curve (or line) is called the constraint equation of the moving point.

It is sometimes convenient, however, to define the coordinates of a moving point by means of *two* equations, expressing x and y separately in terms of a third variable, say t^* ; for example,

---

* Although the subsidiary variable or **parameter** is often (but not always) denoted by t, the reader must not interpret this as meaning that it represents " time." The symbol t in such a context as this merely denotes a variable to each of whose values there correspond one value of x and one value of y.

197

$$\left.\begin{array}{l} x = t - 2, \\ y = t^2 + 1. \end{array}\right\} \quad \cdot \quad \cdot \quad \cdot \quad \cdot \quad (1)$$

At first it looks as if the point (x, y) has two degrees of freedom, since x may have any value we please by choosing t appropriately, and similarly for y. But eliminating t from the equations (1) we have

$$y = (x + 2)^2 + 1 = x^2 + 4x + 5, \quad \cdot \quad \cdot \quad (2)$$

showing that the two apparent freedoms specified by the equations (1) are in effect reduced to one by the restriction on the point to move on the curve $y = x^2 + 4x + 5$.

As we have already seen, equation (2) is known as the constraint equation of the moving point. For no very obvious reason, the equations (1) are referred to as the **freedom equations** of the locus of the moving point.

Less accurately, the equations

$$x = t - 2, \; y = t^2 + 1$$

are often spoken of as freedom equations *of the curve* whose constraint equation is

$$y = x^2 + 4x + 5.$$

There would be no great value in quoting the freedom equations of a curve if our first step in each case were to derive the corresponding constraint equation. It often happens, however, that the freedom equations of a curve are more easily manipulated than its constraint equation, and therefore we must investigate at this stage how to find the derivative of y with respect to x for a curve defined in this way.

Let x and y be each defined as functions of a parameter t, and let δx, δy be the increments in x, y corresponding to an increment δt in t. Then, by simple algebra,

$$\frac{\delta y}{\delta x} = \frac{\delta y}{\delta t} \div \frac{\delta x}{\delta t}.$$

Let $\delta t \longrightarrow 0$; then $\delta x \longrightarrow 0$, and

$$\frac{\delta y}{\delta x} \longrightarrow \frac{dy}{dx}, \quad \frac{\delta y}{\delta t} \longrightarrow \frac{dy}{dt}, \quad \frac{\delta x}{\delta t} \longrightarrow \frac{dx}{dt}.$$

Therefore, $$\frac{dy}{dx} = \frac{dy}{dt} \div \frac{dx}{dt},$$

provided, of course, $\frac{dx}{dt}$ is not zero for the particular value of t considered.

For conciseness, derivatives with respect to t are often denoted by the " point " notation of Newton (page 132). This last result may therefore be expressed as follows—

$$\frac{dy}{dx} = \frac{\dot{y}}{\dot{x}}.$$

By way of illustration, let us find $\frac{dy}{dx}$ for the curve discussed above. Its freedom equations are

$$x = t - 2, \; y = t^2 + 1.$$

We therefore have $\qquad \dot{x} = 1, \; \dot{y} = 2t,$

so that $$\frac{dy}{dx} = \frac{\dot{y}}{\dot{x}} = 2t. \qquad . \qquad . \qquad . \qquad . \qquad (3)$$

We have already seen that the corresponding constraint equation of this curve is

$$y = x^2 + 4x + 5,$$

and therefore, $$\frac{dy}{dx} = 2x + 4. \qquad . \qquad . \qquad . \qquad . \qquad (4)$$

How can we reconcile the apparently different results (3) and (4)? The first gives an expression for $\frac{dy}{dx}$ in terms of the parameter t; the second gives the equivalent expression for $\frac{dy}{dx}$ in terms of the independent variable x. The equivalence may be seen by writing $t - 2$ for x in (4).

Any information which can be derived from (4) may also be deduced from (3). For example, from (4), the curve has clearly only one stationary point, namely when $x = -2$; from (3), the curve has (just as obviously) only one stationary point, namely when $t = 0$, that is, when $x = -2$, since $x = t - 2$.

Examples.

1. Differentiate $x \log \sin x$.

Let $y = x \log \sin x$; then

$$\frac{dy}{dx} = \log \sin x + x \, \frac{d}{dx} \, (\log \sin x),$$

$$= \log \sin x + x \cdot \frac{1}{\sin x} \cdot \cos x,$$

$$= \log \sin x + x \cot x.$$

2. Differentiate $\dfrac{\sqrt{(a^2 - x^2)}}{x}$.

Let $y = \dfrac{\sqrt{(a^2 - x^2)}}{x}$; then

$$\frac{dy}{dx} = \frac{x \dfrac{d}{dx} \{ \sqrt{(a^2 - x^2)} \} - \sqrt{(a^2 - x^2)} \cdot 1}{x^2},$$

$$= \frac{x \cdot \dfrac{(-2x)}{2\sqrt{(a^2 - x^2)}} - \sqrt{(a^2 - x^2)}}{x^2},$$

$$= \frac{-x^2 - (a^2 - x^2)}{x^2 \sqrt{(a^2 - x^2)}} = \frac{-a^2}{x^2 \sqrt{(a^2 - x^2)}}.$$

3. Find the derivatives of $\sin^{-1} \dfrac{x}{a}$, $\cos^{-1} \dfrac{x}{a}$, $\tan^{-1} \dfrac{x}{a}$.

(a) $\dfrac{d}{dx} \left(\sin^{-1} \dfrac{x}{a} \right) = \dfrac{1}{a} \cdot \dfrac{1}{\sqrt{\left(1 - \dfrac{x^2}{a^2} \right)}} = \dfrac{1}{\sqrt{(a^2 - x^2)}}.$

(b) $\dfrac{d}{dx} \left(\cos^{-1} \dfrac{x}{a} \right) = \dfrac{1}{a} \cdot \dfrac{-1}{\sqrt{\left(1 - \dfrac{x^2}{a^2} \right)}} = \dfrac{-1}{\sqrt{(a^2 - x^2)}}.$

(c) $\dfrac{d}{dx} \left(\tan^{-1} \dfrac{x}{a} \right) = \dfrac{1}{a} \cdot \dfrac{1}{1 + \dfrac{x^2}{a^2}} = \dfrac{a}{a^2 + x^2}.$

These three results are often regarded as standard derivatives to be committed to memory.

4. Differentiate $\log \{ x + \sqrt{(x^2 \pm a^2)} \}$.

Let $y = \log \{ x + \sqrt{(x^2 \pm a^2)} \}$; then

$$\frac{dy}{dx} = \frac{1}{x + \sqrt{(x^2 \pm a^2)}} \left(1 + \frac{x}{\sqrt{(x^2 \pm a^2)}} \right),$$

$$= \frac{1}{\sqrt{(x^2 \pm a^2)}}.$$

5. Differentiate $\sqrt{\dfrac{(1 + x)(2 - x)}{(1 - x)(2 + x)}}$.

If, as in this case, the function to be differentiated consists of a fairly involved product, it is usually easier to begin by taking the logarithm of the function. Thus, denoting the given function by y, we have

$$\log y = \tfrac{1}{2} [\log (1 + x) + \log (2 - x) - \log (1 - x) - \log (2 + x)],$$

and, differentiating,

$$\frac{1}{y} \cdot \frac{dy}{dx} = \tfrac{1}{2} \left[\frac{1}{1 + x} - \frac{1}{2 - x} + \frac{1}{1 - x} - \frac{1}{2 + x} \right],$$

$$= \tfrac{1}{2} \left[\frac{2}{(1 + x)(1 - x)} - \frac{4}{(2 - x)(2 + x)} \right],$$

$$= \frac{2 + x^2}{(1 + x)(1 - x)(2 - x)(2 + x)}.$$

Therefore,

$$\frac{dy}{dx} = \sqrt{\left\{ \frac{(1 + x)(2 - x)}{(1 - x)(2 + x)} \right\}} \cdot \frac{2 + x^2}{(1 + x)(1 - x)(2 - x)(2 + x)},$$

$$= \frac{2 + x^2}{(1 + x)^{\frac{1}{2}} (1 - x)^{\frac{3}{2}} (2 - x)^{\frac{1}{2}} (2 + x)^{\frac{3}{2}}}.$$

This method of procedure is, for obvious reasons, referred to as **logarithmic differentiation.**

More generally, if we wish to differentiate

$$y = uvw,$$

where u, v, w are functions of x, and if we take logarithms before differentiating, we have

$$\log y = \log u + \log v + \log w.$$

Now differentiating, we have

$$\frac{1}{y} \cdot \frac{dy}{dx} = \frac{1}{u} \cdot \frac{du}{dx} + \frac{1}{v} \cdot \frac{dv}{dx} + \frac{1}{w} \cdot \frac{dw}{dx},$$

a form of the " product rule " which has already been established (see page 191).

Similarly, if $\qquad y = \dfrac{u}{v}$,

taking logarithms, we have
$$\log y = \log u - \log v,$$
and differentiating, we obtain
$$\frac{1}{y} \cdot \frac{dy}{dx} = \frac{1}{u} \cdot \frac{du}{dx} - \frac{1}{v} \cdot \frac{dv}{dx},$$
a form of the " quotient rule " which has already been established (see page 192).

6. Differentiate $(x + 2)^{x+1}$.

When the independent variable occurs as an index, or part of an index, logarithmic differentiation should be employed.

Thus, if $y = (x + 2)^{x+1}$, taking logarithms we have
$$\log y = (x + 1) \log (x + 2).$$

Therefore, $\dfrac{1}{y} \cdot \dfrac{dy}{dx} = \log (x + 2) + \dfrac{x + 1}{x + 2}$,

and $\qquad \dfrac{dy}{dx} = (x + 2)^{x+1} \left\{ \log (x + 2) + \dfrac{x + 1}{x + 2} \right\}$,

$$= (x + 2)^x \left\{ (x + 2) \log (x + 2) + (x + 1) \right\} .$$

7. Find the second derivative of $e^{-2x} \cos 3x$.

Let $y = e^{-2x} \cos 3x$; then
$$\frac{dy}{dx} = - 2e^{-2x} \cos 3x - 3e^{-2x} \sin 3x ,$$

and $\dfrac{d^2y}{dx^2} = (4e^{-2x} \cos 3x + 6e^{-2x} \sin 3x)$

$$- (- 6e^{-2x} \sin 3x + 9e^{-2x} \cos 3x),$$

$$= e^{-2x} (12 \sin 3x - 5 \cos 3x).$$

8. Find an expression for the nth derivative of $\sin ax$.

Let $y = \sin ax$; then

$$\frac{dy}{dx} = a \cos ax ; \qquad \frac{d^2y}{dx^2} = - a^2 \sin ax ;$$

$$\frac{d^3y}{dx^3} = - a^3 \cos ax ; \frac{d^4y}{dx^4} = a^4 \sin ax ;$$

and so on.

These derivatives may, however, be arranged as follows:

$$\frac{dy}{dx} = a \sin \left(ax + \frac{\pi}{2} \right) ; \quad \frac{d^2y}{dx^2} = a^2 \sin (ax + \pi) ;$$

$$\frac{d^3y}{dx^3} = a^3 \sin \left(ax + \frac{3\pi}{2} \right) ; \quad \text{and so on.}$$

These forms of the first three derivatives show that

$$\frac{d^ny}{dx^n} = a^n \sin \left(ax + \frac{n\pi}{2} \right).$$

9. If $y = Cx + \frac{1}{C}$, where C is an arbitrary constant, verify that

$$x \left(\frac{dy}{dx} \right)^2 - y \frac{dy}{dx} + 1 = 0.$$

We have $\qquad\qquad y = Cx + \frac{1}{C},$

and therefore $\qquad \frac{dy}{dx} = C.$

Eliminating C between these two equations, we have

$$y = x \frac{dy}{dx} + \frac{1}{\dfrac{dy}{dx}} \, ,$$

or $\qquad\quad x \left(\frac{dy}{dx} \right)^2 - y \frac{dy}{dx} + 1 = 0.$

A relation of this kind, involving x, y, and one or more of the derivatives of y, is known as a **differential equation**. The **order** of the differential equation is that of the highest derivative which occurs in it ; the **degree** of the differential equation is that of the highest derivative when the equation has been cleared of fractions and so expressed that the powers of all the derivatives are positive integers. Thus, the above differential equation is of the first order and of the second degree. On the other hand, the differential equation

$$x \frac{d^2y}{dx^2} - 3 \frac{dy}{dx} + 5x^2y = \log x$$

is of the second order and of the first degree.

203

If a given equation involving x and y contains an arbitrary constant C, then by differentiation we can obtain an equation involving x, y, $\dfrac{dy}{dx}$, and C. It is now possible to eliminate the arbitrary constant C between these two equations and a differential equation of the first order is obtained. Similarly, if the given equation contains two arbitrary constants, C_1 and C_2, we can differentiate twice, and from the three equations, C_1 and C_2 may be eliminated, giving a differential equation of the second order, and so on. The original equation in each case is called the **complete primitive** of the resulting differential equation.

The complete primitive contains one or more arbitrary constants, and therefore represents geometrically a system of related curves (or lines). The corresponding differential equation does not contain any of the arbitrary constants and therefore must represent geometrically some property which all the members of the system have in common.

This process by which we obtain a differential equation from its complete primitive has no great value in itself. The converse problem—that of passing from the differential equation to the complete primitive, or the **general solution,** as it is generally called under these circumstances—is of immeasurably greater importance, and § **33** is devoted to this problem. Nevertheless the formation of differential equations does throw some light on the methods to be adopted in " solving " differential equations.

Examples (continued)

10. From the complete primitive $xy = Ae^x + Be^{-x}$, where A and B are arbitrary, prove that

$$x \frac{d^2y}{dx^2} + 2 \frac{dy}{dx} - xy = 0.$$

Since $\qquad xy = Ae^x + Be^{-x}$

we have, by differentiation,

$$y + x \frac{dy}{dx} = Ae^x - Be^{-x}.$$

Differentiating again, we have

$$2\frac{dy}{dx} + x\frac{d^2y}{dx^2} = Ae^x + Be^{-x}.$$

The elimination of A and B presents no difficulty in this case, since the right-hand side of this last equation clearly equals xy. The required result follows immediately.

11. If $y = (m + nx) e^{-x}$, where m and n are arbitrary, derive the corresponding differential equation.

We have $\qquad \dfrac{dy}{dx} = ne^{-x} - (m + nx) e^{-x},$

$$= ne^{-x} - y,$$

so that m is eliminated at once.

Differentiating once more, we have

$$\frac{d^2y}{dx^2} = -ne^{-x} - \frac{dy}{dx},$$

and clearly n may be eliminated by adding the last two equations.

Thus, $\qquad \dfrac{d^2y}{dx^2} + \dfrac{dy}{dx} = -\dfrac{dy}{dx} - y,$

hence $\qquad \dfrac{d^2y}{dx^2} + 2\dfrac{dy}{dx} + y = 0,$

which is the required differential equation.

[An alternative mode of procedure with this example would be to multiply both sides of the equation by e^x before differentiating.]

12. Write down the derivatives of the following functions of x:

(i) $(2x - 5)^4$,
(ii) $(3 - 5x)^3$,
(iii) $\sqrt{(3 - x)}$,
(iv) $\sqrt{(3 - 4x^2)}$,
(v) $(2x^2 - 3)^4$,
(vi) $\sqrt{(x^2 - x - 1)}$,
(vii) $\sin 3x$,
(viii) $\cos 2x$,
(ix) $\tan \frac{1}{2}x$,
(x) $\sin (2x - 1)$,
(xi) $\cos (3 - 4x)$,
(xii) $\tan \left(\dfrac{x - 2}{3}\right)$,
(xiii) $\log (1 + 2x)$,
(xiv) $\log (3x^2 - 1)$,
(xv) e^{3x},
(xvi) e^{-2x},
(xvii) $e^{-\frac{1}{2}x^2}$,
(xviii) $\cos^2 3x$,
(xix) $\sin^3 2x$,
(xx) $\tan^2 (ax + b)$,

205

R. Wilson V̄
R.B.A.I.

(xxi) log (sin x),
(xxii) $e^{\sin x}$,
(xxiii) $\sin^{-1}(1-x)$,
(xxiv) $\tan^{-1}(1+x)$,
(xxv) log $(1+\cos x)$,
(xxvi) sin (sin x),
(xxvii) $e^{-\sqrt{x}}$,
(xxviii) log $(1+e^x)$,
(xxix) log (log x),
(xxx) $\sin^{-1}(\cos x)$.

13. Differentiate the following products :

(i) $(3x-7)(4x+1)$,
(ii) $x^2(1-x)^3$,
(iii) $(x^2+1)(3x+5)^2$,
(iv) $(x+3)\sqrt{(x+1)}$,
(v) $(2-x)\sqrt{(3+4x)}$,
(vi) $(1+x^{\frac{1}{2}})^{\frac{1}{3}}(1+x^{\frac{1}{3}})^{\frac{1}{2}}$,
(vii) $(x+1)(x-2)(x+3)$,
(viii) $\sin^3 x \cos 2x$,
(ix) sin mx cos nx,
(x) $\cos 3x \sin^3 x$,
(xi) $\cos^3 2x \sin^2 3x$,
(xii) $\left(\sin\dfrac{x}{3}\right)^3 \left(\cos\dfrac{x}{2}\right)^2$,
(xiii) $(x^2+1)\tan 2x$,
(xiv) $e^x \cos x$,
(xv) $e^{ax} \cos bx$,
(xvi) $x^2 e^{3x}$,
(xvii) xe^{-x^2},
(xviii) $e^{-x}(\sin x + \cos x)$,
(xix) $x^n \log x$,
(xx) $\sqrt{x}\cdot\sin^{-1} x$.

14. Differentiate the following quotients :

(i) $\dfrac{x^2+x-1}{x-1}$,
(ii) $\dfrac{(x-1)(2-x)}{x-3}$,
(iii) $\dfrac{x^2(x+3)}{x+1}$,
(iv) $\dfrac{x^2+1}{(x+1)^2}$,
(v) $\dfrac{3x+2}{\sqrt{(2x+1)}}$,
(vi) $\dfrac{5-4x}{\sqrt{(3-2x)}}$,
(vii) $\dfrac{6x+5}{\sqrt{(3x-2)}}$,
(viii) $\dfrac{x(x+2)}{(x+1)^2}$,
(ix) $\dfrac{x(x-4)}{(x-2)^2}$,
(x) $\dfrac{2x-1}{x^2(x-1)^2}$,
(xi) $\dfrac{\sqrt{(x^2+4)}}{2x^2-1}$,
(xii) $\sqrt{\left(\dfrac{1-x}{1+x}\right)}$,
(xiii) $\dfrac{1-2x}{\sqrt{(2x^2-2x-3)}}$,
(xiv) $\dfrac{1}{x^3}(4x-x^2)^{\frac{3}{2}}$,
(xv) $\dfrac{1-2x}{\sqrt{(3-x+x^2)}}$,
(xvi) $\dfrac{(2ax-x^2)^{\frac{3}{2}}}{x^3}$,

(xvii) $\sqrt{\left(\dfrac{x^2 + 2x - 3}{x^2 - 4x - 5}\right)}$,

(xviii) $\dfrac{x}{\cos x}$,

(xix) $\dfrac{1 + \sin x}{1 - \sin x}$,

(xx) $\dfrac{\sin x}{1 + \tan x}$.

15. Differentiate the following functions of functions of x:

(i) $\tan^3 4x$,

(ii) $\sqrt{(\tan 2x)}$,

(iii) $e^{-\sin^2 x}$,

(iv) $\dfrac{e^x - 1}{e^x + 1}$,

(v) $\log\left(\dfrac{1 - x}{1 + x}\right)$,

(vi) $\sqrt{(3 \sin^2 x + 4 \cos^2 x)}$,

(vii) $\dfrac{e^x}{\sin x + \cos x}$,

(viii) $\sin^{-1}\left(\dfrac{1}{x}\right)$,

(ix) $(x + 1) \cos^{-1}\left(\dfrac{x - 1}{x}\right)$,

(x) $\sqrt{x} \cdot \sin^{-1}\sqrt{x}$, ?

(xi) $\sin^{-1}\left(\dfrac{x^3 - 1}{x^3 + 1}\right)$,

(xii) $\sqrt{\left\{\sin\left(x^2 + \dfrac{2}{x}\right)\right\}}$,

(xiii) $\sec^{-1}(2x - 3)$,

(xiv) $\log\dfrac{\cos x}{2 - \sin x}$,

(xv) $\tan^{-1}\left(\dfrac{2x - 3}{3x + 2}\right)$,

(xvi) $\tan^{-1}\left(\dfrac{\cos 2x + 2 \cos x}{\sin 2x + 2 \sin x}\right)$,

(xvii) $\left\{x + \sqrt{(1 - x^2)}\right\} e^{\sin^{-1}x}$,

(xviii) $\dfrac{1}{x}\sqrt{(x^2 - a^2)} - \log\left\{x + \sqrt{(x^2 - a^2)}\right\}$,

(xix) $(x - 1) \sin^{-1}(x - 1) + \sqrt{(2x - x^2)}$,

(xx) $\dfrac{2x}{\sqrt{(x - x^2)}} + \sin^{-1}(1 - 2x)$.

16. Find by logarithmic differentiation the derivatives of the following functions of x:

(i) 2^{x+1},

(ii) $(x^2 + 1)^{x^2}$,

(iii) $\dfrac{x^{\frac{1}{2}}(3 - x)^{\frac{1}{5}}}{(2x + 1)^{\frac{2}{3}}}$,

(iv) $(\sin x)^x$,

(v) $e^{\cos 2x \sin^2 x}$,

(vi) $\dfrac{(2x + 1)^{\frac{1}{2}}(4x + 5)^{\frac{1}{4}}}{(4x - 3)^{\frac{1}{4}}}$,

(vii) $\dfrac{x^{\frac{3}{2}}(2-x)^2(1+x)}{(5+2x)^3}$,   (viii) e^{e^x} .

17. Find $\dfrac{dy}{dx}$ for the implicit functions of x defined by the following equations:

    (i) $x^{\frac{2}{3}}+y^{\frac{2}{3}}=a^{\frac{2}{3}}$,

    (ii) $x^2-xy+4y^2=15$,

    (iii) $6x^2+4xy-3y^2=2$,

    (iv) $2x^2+2xy+y^2-3x+1=0$,

    (v) $ax^2+2hxy+by^2=1$,

    (vi) $ax^2+2hxy+by^2+2gx+2fy+c=0$,

    (vii) $x^3-3x^2y+xy^2=18$,

    (viii) $x-y=\log(x+y)$,

    (ix) $x\log y=\cos 2x+\sin 2y$,

    (x) $x^2=2y^2\log y$.

18. Find the nth derivatives of the following functions of x:

    (i) x^n,   (ii) x^{2n},   (iii) $\dfrac{1}{x}$,

    (iv) e^x,   (v) e^{-x},   (vi) e^{-3x},

    (vii) $\cos^2 x$,   (viii) $x^2\log x$.

19. Express $\dfrac{5x+1}{3-5x-2x^2}$ in partial fractions, and hence find its nth derivative.

20. If $y=e^x\sin x$, show that $\dfrac{dy}{dx}=\sqrt{2}\,e^x\sin\left(x+\dfrac{\pi}{4}\right)$, and hence find the value of $\dfrac{d^n y}{dx^n}$.

21. By eliminating the arbitrary constants A and B, find the differential equations of which the following equations are the complete primitives:

    (i) $y=A\cos nx+B\sin nx$,

    (ii) $y=e^{-2x}(A\cos 3x+B\sin 3x)$,

    (iii) $y=(A+Bx)e^{-nx}$,

(iv) $y = \dfrac{Ax}{x+B}$,

(v) $y = \dfrac{A+Bx}{\sqrt{x}}$,

(vi) $y = e^{-x} A \cos (2x+B) + 5x^2$,

(vii) $y = e^{-x} (A \log x + B)$,

(viii) $y = \log \left(A + \dfrac{B}{x} \right)$,

(ix) $y = Ax + B \sqrt{(x^2+1)}$,

(x) $y = x \left\{ A + B \log x + \tfrac{1}{2} (\log x)^2 \right\}$,

(xi) $xy = (A + Bx) e^x$,

(xii) $x \log y = A \cos 2x + B \sin 2x$.

22. If $y = x \sqrt{(1-x)}$, prove that $\dfrac{dy}{dx} = \dfrac{y}{x} - \dfrac{x^2}{2y}$.

23. If $y = x \sqrt{(1-x^2)}$, prove that $(1-x^2) \dfrac{d^2y}{dx^2} = x \dfrac{dy}{dx} - 4y$.

24. If $y = \left\{ 1 + (1+x)^{\frac{1}{2}} \right\}^{\frac{1}{3}}$, find the value of $\dfrac{dy}{dx}$. Solve the equation for x in terms of y, and hence find the value of $\dfrac{dx}{dy}$. Verify that $\dfrac{dy}{dx} \cdot \dfrac{dx}{dy} = 1$.

25. Show that the sum of the intercepts on the coordinate axes of the tangent to the curve $\sqrt{x} + \sqrt{y} = \sqrt{a}$ at any point (h, k) on it is a constant.

26. Find the equation of the tangent at the point $P\,(1, 1)$ on the curve $3\,(y+1)^2 = (x+2)\,(x+1)^2$. If this tangent meets the curve again in Q, find the coordinates of Q, and show that the tangent at P is the normal at Q.

27. Verify that the point $P\,(0, 4)$ lies on each of the curves

$$ y = \frac{19x + 8}{2x^2 + 5x + 2}, \quad y = \frac{4\,(4x^2 + 3x - 4)}{5x - 4}, $$

and that the tangents to the curves at P are at right angles.

8

28. Find the gradient at any point of the curve
$$y \sqrt{(12 - x)} = \sqrt[3]{(2 - x)},$$
and deduce the equation of the tangent at the point where
$x = -6$. State the values of x at which the tangent is (i) parallel
to the x-axis, (ii) parallel to the y-axis.

29. Find from first principles the gradient at any point of the curve
$y = \dfrac{ax}{x + a}$. Find the gradients of the curves
$$y = \frac{x}{\sqrt{(1 - 2x)}}, \quad y = \frac{2x(1 - x)}{2 - x},$$
and verify that all three curves touch at the origin.

30. If $y = 3x^3 + 8x + 24 \sin x - 24x \cos x - 8 \sin x \cos x$, show
that $\dfrac{dy}{dx}$ is a perfect square, and deduce that y is positive for all
positive values of x.

31. If $y = \cos \theta + \theta \sin \theta - \frac{1}{2} \sin^2 \theta$, find the value of $\dfrac{dy}{d\theta}$, and
hence show that y increases from 1 to $\dfrac{\pi - 1}{2}$ as θ increases from
0 to $\dfrac{\pi}{2}$.

32. Prove that the function $x - \frac{1}{2}x^2 + \frac{1}{3}x^3 - \log(1 + x)$ is
positive for all positive values of x. What is its sign in the
range $-1 < x < 0$?

33. Find the points on the curve $x^2 - 2xy + 5y^2 = 4$ at which the
tangent is (i) parallel to the x-axis, (ii) parallel to the y-axis.

34. Show that the curves
$$(x - y)^2 = x + y, \quad 3(x^2 + y^2) + 2xy = 3,$$
intersect orthogonally at the points $(0, 1)$, $(1, 0)$.

35. If PQ is an arc of a circle subtending an angle 2θ radians at the
centre O, and if PT, QT are the tangents at P, Q, show that the
area PQT enclosed by the arc and the tangents bears to the area
of the sector OPQ the ratio $(\tan \theta - \theta) : \theta$. If θ is increasing
at the rate of $0 \cdot 2$ radians per second, find, for the instant when
$\theta = \dfrac{\pi}{6}$, the rate at which the above ratio is increasing.

36. For the following curves, defined by freedom equations, find $\frac{dy}{dx}$ and $\frac{d^2y}{dx^2}$ in terms of the parameter :

(i) $x = 6t^2,\quad y = 4t^3 - 3t$;

(ii) $x = t + \dfrac{1}{t},\quad y = t - \dfrac{1}{t}$;

(iii) $x = e^t \cos 2t,\quad y = e^t \sin 2t$;

(iv) $x = a\,(\theta - \sin \theta),\quad y = a\,(1 - \cos \theta)$;

(v) $x = 2 \cos \theta - \cos 2\theta,\quad y = 2 \sin \theta - \sin 2\theta$;

(vi) $x = \dfrac{4at}{(1 + t^2)^2},\quad y = \dfrac{4at^2}{(1 + t^2)^2}.$

37. Prove that the equation of the tangent to the curve
$$x = a\,(\sin^3 t + \cos^3 t),\qquad y = a\,(\sin^3 t - \cos^3 t)$$
at the point $t = \tan^{-1}\frac{4}{3}$ has the equation $y = 7x - \dfrac{24}{5}\,a.$

38. For the curve
$$x = a\,(1 + \sin \theta),\qquad y = a\,(\theta + \sin \theta \cos \theta),$$
find $\frac{dy}{dx}$ and $\frac{d^2y}{dx^2}$ in terms of θ. Verify that the constraint equation of the curve is

$$ay = (x - a)\,\sqrt{(2ax - x^2)} + a^2 \sin^{-1}\left(\frac{x - a}{a}\right).$$

Find $\frac{d^2y}{dx^2}$ by direct differentiation, and verify that your result agrees with that previously found.

39. A particle moves in the xy-plane according to the freedom equations
$$x = a \cos^3 \omega t,\quad y = a \sin^3 \omega t,$$
where t denotes time. If v and f denote respectively its speed and its acceleration at time t, show that
$$f^2 = 3\omega^2\,(3a^2\omega^2 - v^2).$$

40. Use logarithmic differentiation to prove that if
$$x^a y^b = (x + y)^{a+b}$$
then $\dfrac{dy}{dx} = \dfrac{y}{x}$, provided that $ay \neq bx.$

§ 28. ROUGH GRAPHS.

In **§ 13** we discussed the use of the derivative in helping to determine the rough outline of a curve whose equation is known, but our limited knowledge of differentiation at the time compelled us to confine our attention to simple polynomials in x. It will be recalled that the method involves an examination of the sign of the derivative $\dfrac{dy}{dx}$. The range of values of x for which $\dfrac{dy}{dx}$ is positive (or negative) gives the range for which y is an increasing (or decreasing) function, and the values (if any) of x for which $\dfrac{dy}{dx} = 0$ give the abscissæ of the stationary points of the curve.

Now that we can differentiate many more types of functions, we are in a position to apply this knowledge to sketching the graphs of these functions, but certain results of a general nature must first be established.

Concavity and convexity

We have already found that in order to decide the nature of a particular stationary point—whether a maximum or minimum turning point or a point of inflexion with a horizontal tangent—two procedures are available. We can either examine the sign of the derivative to the left and to the right of the stationary point (**§ 13**) or we can make use of the second derivative (**§ 18**). Using this latter procedure we found that if $\dfrac{d^2y}{dx^2}$ is negative, the stationary point is a maximum turning point ; if $\dfrac{d^2y}{dx^2}$ is positive, the stationary point is a minimum turning point ; at a " horizontal " point of inflexion, $\frac{d^2y}{dx^2} = 0$, **but this condition though necessary is not sufficient.** In other words, although at a stationary point $\frac{d^2y}{dx^2}$ may be zero, that does not guarantee that the point in question is a point of inflexion (though this will generally be so). It may, in fact, be a maximum or minimum turning point. When $\frac{d^2y}{dx^2} = 0$, the only reliable test is provided by examining the sign of $\frac{dy}{dx}$ to the left and to the right of the stationary point. For example, if $y = x^4$, then

$$\frac{dy}{dx} = 4x^3, \text{ and } \frac{d^2y}{dx^2} = 12x^2.$$

At the origin, $\frac{dy}{dx} = 0$, and $\frac{d^2y}{dx^2} = 0$.

But, since $\frac{dy}{dx} = 4x^3$, it is clear that to the left of the origin—when x is negative—the gradient of the curve is negative, and to the right of the origin the gradient is positive. Despite the fact that $\frac{d^2y}{dx^2} = 0$ when $x = 0$, the origin is therefore a minimum turning point (as is indeed obvious from the equation $y = x^4$ which shows that y is positive for all values of x except the value zero).

The references above to the sign of the second derivative $\frac{d^2y}{dx^2}$ are but particular instances of a more general truth, which we shall now investigate.

If at a point $P(x, y)$ on a curve $y = f(x)$, $\frac{d^2y}{dx^2}$ is negative, that is, $\frac{d}{dx}\left(\frac{dy}{dx}\right)$ is negative, then it follows from the meaning of a derivative that $\dfrac{dy}{dx}$ is a decreasing function of x at P. There are three possibilities, indicated in Fig. 49.

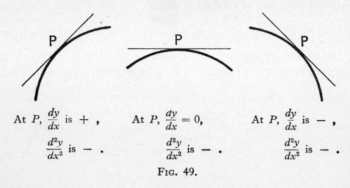

At P, $\dfrac{dy}{dx}$ is $+$,   At P, $\dfrac{dy}{dx} = 0$,   At P, $\dfrac{dy}{dx}$ is $-$,

$\dfrac{d^2y}{dx^2}$ is $-$. $\dfrac{d^2y}{dx^2}$ is $-$. $\dfrac{d^2y}{dx^2}$ is $-$.

Fig. 49.

The common feature of each of these arcs is that in the immediate neighbourhood of P the curve lies wholly below the tangent at P. Each curve is therefore said to be **concave downwards** (or **convex upwards**) at P.

If, at P, $\dfrac{d^2y}{dx^2}$ is positive, then $\dfrac{dy}{dx}$ is an increasing function of x, and once more there are three possibilities (Fig. 50).

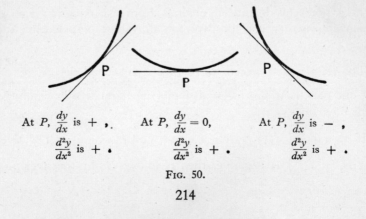

At P, $\dfrac{dy}{dx}$ is $+$,.   At P, $\dfrac{dy}{dx} = 0$,   At P, $\dfrac{dy}{dx}$ is $-$,

$\dfrac{d^2y}{dx^2}$ is $+$. $\dfrac{d^2y}{dx^2}$ is $+$. $\dfrac{d^2y}{dx^2}$ is $+$.

Fig. 50.

This time, in the immediate neighbourhood of P each curve lies wholly above the tangent at P and is said to be **concave upwards** at P.

If, at P, $\dfrac{d^2y}{dx^2} = 0$, then $\dfrac{dy}{dx}$ has a stationary value at P. There are several possibilities this time of which the most common are shown in Fig. 51.

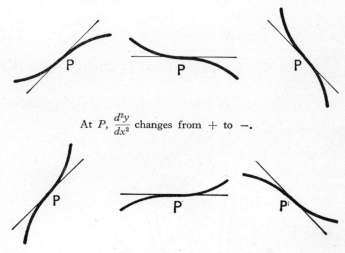

At P, $\dfrac{d^2y}{dx^2}$ changes from $+$ to $-$.

At P, $\dfrac{d^2y}{dx^2}$ changes from $-$ to $+$.

FIG. 51.

In each of these cases, P is a point of inflexion, but, as has been suggested above, there are other possibilities.

Clearly, from what has already been said about concavity, $\dfrac{d^2y}{dx^2}$ *must* be zero at a point of inflexion,* for the curve changes from concave upwards (or downwards) to concave downwards (or upwards) ; but the **converse is not true.** If, at P, $\dfrac{d^2y}{dx^2} = 0$,

---

* The reader should observe that we are now considering points of inflexion with oblique tangents as well as those with horizontal tangents.

it does *not* follow that P is a point of inflexion, though this will usually be so. It will be a point of inflexion only if, in addition, the concavity of the curve changes at P from upwards to downwards, or vice versa, that is, if $\dfrac{d^2y}{dx^2}$ changes sign at P.

By way of illustration, let us consider the curve $y = x^4 + 4x$.

We have $\qquad \dfrac{dy}{dx} = 4x^3 + 4$, and $\dfrac{d^2y}{dx^2} = 12x^2$.

Thus, $\qquad \dfrac{d^2y}{dx^2} = 0$ when $x = 0$.

But $\dfrac{d^2y}{dx^2}$ is positive to the left and to the right of the origin, that is, $\dfrac{d^2y}{dx^2}$ does *not* change sign when $x = 0$, and therefore the origin is *not* a point of inflexion.

Fig. 52 shows on the same diagram the graphs
$$y = x^4, \ y = 4x, \text{ and } y = x^4 + 4x.$$

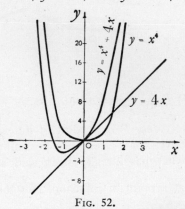

FIG. 52.

It will be seen that for small values of x, that is, near the origin, the curve $y = x^4 + 4x$ approximates to the line $y = 4x$; for large values of x, the curve $y = x^4 + 4x$ approximates to the curve $y = x^4$.

Examples

1. Sketch the curve whose equation is $y = x^4 - 2x^3 + 1$.

Differentiating, we have

$$\frac{dy}{dx} = 4x^3 - 6x^2 = 2x^2\,(2x - 3)\;;$$

and $$\frac{d^2y}{dx^2} = 12x^2 - 12x = 12x\,(x - 1).$$

For stationary points, $\dfrac{dy}{dx} = 0$, that is, $x = 0$ or $x = \frac{3}{2}$.

For *possible* points of inflexion, $\dfrac{d^2y}{dx^2} = 0$, that is, $x = 0$ or 1.

A table showing the essential variations in the signs and values of $\dfrac{dy}{dx}$, $\dfrac{d^2y}{dx^2}$, and y may now be constructed.

x	$-\infty$	$\to$	0	$\to$	1	$\to$	$\frac{3}{2}$	$\to$	$+\infty$
$\dfrac{dy}{dx}$		$-$	0	$-$	-2	$-$	0	$+$	
$\dfrac{d^2y}{dx^2}$		$+$	0	$-$	0	$+$	$+$	$+$	
y	$+\infty$	$\searrow$	1	$\searrow$	0	$\searrow$	$-\dfrac{11}{16}$	$\nearrow$	$+\infty$

An examination of the sign of $\dfrac{dy}{dx}$ shows that the point $(0, 1)$ is a point of inflexion with a horizontal tangent, the point $(1, 0)$ is a point of inflexion with an inflexional tangent of gradient -2, and the point $(\frac{3}{2}, -\frac{11}{16})$ is a minimum turning point.

The sign of $\dfrac{d^2y}{dx^2}$ confirms these conclusions, for to the left of the point $(0, 1)$ the curve is concave upwards, between the points $(0, 1)$ and $(1, 0)$ the curve is concave downwards, and to the right of the point $(1, 0)$ the curve is concave upwards.

A sketch of the curve appears in Fig. 53.

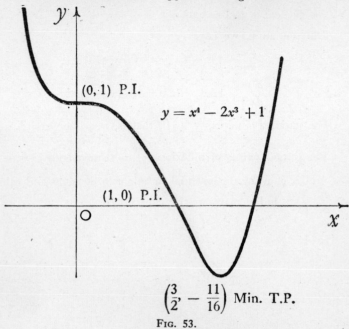

$(0, 1)$ P.I.

$y = x^4 - 2x^3 + 1$

$(1, 0)$ P.I.

$\left(\dfrac{3}{2}, -\dfrac{11}{16}\right)$ Min. T.P.

FIG. 53.

2. Sketch the curve whose equation is $y = \dfrac{2x}{3 + x^2}$.

This curve is symmetrical about the origin, for if the point (a, b) lies on it, so also does the point $(-a, -b)$.

Differentiating, we have

$$\frac{dy}{dx} = \frac{(3 + x^2)\, 2 - 2x \,.\, 2x}{(3 + x^2)^2} = \frac{2\,(3 - x^2)}{(3 + x^2)^2};$$

and $$\frac{d^2y}{dx^2} = 2 \,.\, \frac{(3 + x^2)^2\,(- 2x) - (3 - x^2)\,(3 + x^2)\,.\, 4x}{(3 + x^2)^4}$$

$$= 2 \,.\, \frac{(- 2x)\,(3 + x^2 + 6 - 2x^2)}{(3 + x^2)^3}$$

$$= \frac{- 4x\,(3 - x)\,(3 + x)}{(3 + x^2)^3}.$$

218

Thus, $\dfrac{dy}{dx} = 0$, when $x = \pm \sqrt{3}$;

and $\dfrac{d^2y}{dx^2} = 0$, when $x = 0$, or ± 3.

We can therefore compile the following table of signs :

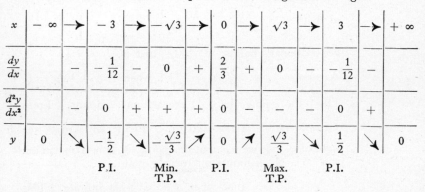

x	$-\infty$	→	-3	→	$-\sqrt{3}$	→	0	→	$\sqrt{3}$	→	3	→	$+\infty$
$\dfrac{dy}{dx}$		$-$	$-\dfrac{1}{12}$	$-$	0	$+$	$\dfrac{2}{3}$	$+$	0	$-$	$-\dfrac{1}{12}$	$-$	
$\dfrac{d^2y}{dx^2}$		$-$	0	$+$	$+$	$+$	0	$-$	$-$	$-$	0	$+$	
y	0	↘	$-\dfrac{1}{2}$	↘	$-\dfrac{\sqrt{3}}{3}$	↗	0	↗	$\dfrac{\sqrt{3}}{3}$	↘	$\dfrac{1}{2}$	↘	0
			P.I.		Min. T.P.		P.I.		Max. T.P.		P.I.		

Fig. 54 shows a sketch of the curve.

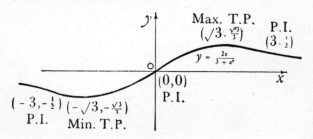

FIG. 54.

3. Sketch the curve whose freedom equations are
$$x = 6t^2, \ y = 4t^3 - 3t.$$

(i) Since x cannot be negative, no part of the curve lies to the left of the y-axis.

(ii) Since x involves only an even power of t, and y involves odd powers only, the curve is symmetrical about the x-axis.

(iii) The curve cuts the x-axis where $y = 0$, that is, where $t = 0$ or $t^2 = \frac{3}{4}$; that is, at the points $(0, 0)$, $\frac{9}{2}, 0)$.

(iv) Differentiating, we have $\dot{x} = 12t$, and $\dot{y} = 12t^2 - 3$,

so that $$\frac{dy}{dx} = \frac{\dot{y}}{\dot{x}} = \frac{4t^2 - 1}{4t}.$$

For stationary points, $\frac{dy}{dx} = 0$; that is, $t = \pm \frac{1}{2}$.

When $t = \frac{1}{2}$, $x = \frac{3}{2}$, $y = -1$; when $t = -\frac{1}{2}$, $x = \frac{3}{2}$, $y = 1$.
Thus, the points $(\frac{3}{2}, \pm 1)$ are stationary points. From a consideration of the sign of $\frac{dy}{dx}$ to the left and to the right of $x = \frac{3}{2}$, we see that the point $(\frac{3}{2}, 1)$ is a maximum and $(\frac{3}{2}, -1)$ a minimum turning point.

We also see that when $t = 0$, $\frac{dy}{dx}$ is infinite. This means that when $t = 0$, that is, at the origin, the tangent is perpendicular to the x-axis.

(v) Differentiating once more,* we have
$$\frac{d^2y}{dx^2} = \frac{d}{dx}\left(\frac{4t^2 - 1}{4t}\right) = \frac{d}{dt}\left(\frac{4t^2 - 1}{4t}\right)\frac{dt}{dx}$$
$$= \left(1 + \frac{1}{4t^2}\right)\frac{1}{12t},$$
$$= \frac{4t^2 + 1}{48t^3}.$$

Since $\frac{d^2y}{dx^2}$ cannot vanish for real values of t, the curve has no points of inflexion.

---

* The reader should observe carefully that to find $\frac{d^2v}{dx^2}$ we must differentiate $\frac{dy}{dx}$ with respect to x, and **not with respect to t.**

A sketch of the curve is given in **Fig. 55.**

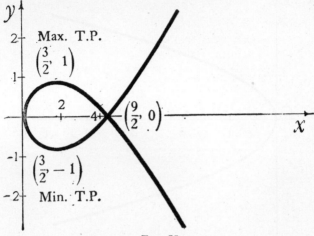

FIG. 55.

Multiple-valued functions

Almost all the functions which we have graphed so far (see also § 13) have been **single-valued** functions, that is, functions such that to each value of the independent variable there corresponds one and only one value of the function. It is possible, however, to have functions such that to each value of the independent variable there correspond two (or more) values of the function. For example, if $y^2 = x$, then $y = \pm \sqrt{x}$, and to each value of x there correspond two values of y. We therefore say that if $y^2 = x$, y is a **two-valued** function of x. Since, however, $\sqrt{x}$ is imaginary if x is negative, this two-valued function of x is defined only for $x \geqslant 0$.

A two-valued function may be regarded as consisting of **two** single-valued functions ; thus, in the above example, the two single-valued functions are $y = + \sqrt{x}$, and $y = - \sqrt{x}$. Since the curve $y = x^2$ is a parabola symmetrical about the y-axis, we see, by interchanging x and y, that the curve $x = y^2$ (or $y^2 = x$) is a parabola symmetrical about the x-axis (Fig. 56).

221

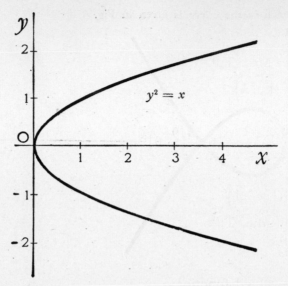

FIG. 56.

A little thought will show that the upper half of the curve represents the equation $y = + \sqrt{x}$, and the lower half the equation $y = - \sqrt{x}$.

This is a perfectly general result. If the graph of a two-valued function is drawn, it will be found that different parts of the graph (though not necessarily the upper and lower halves) represent the corresponding two single-valued functions. Let us take another illustration. The equation

$$2x^2 - 3xy + y^2 + x - 1 = 0$$

defines y implicitly as a function of x. Solving for y, we have

$$y^2 - 3xy + (2x^2 + x - 1) = 0,$$
$$[y - (x + 1)][y - (2x - 1)] = 0,$$

so that $y = x + 1$, or $y = 2x - 1$,

showing that y is a two-valued function of x.

222

Its graph consists of two straight lines (Fig. 57), the one having the equation $y = x + 1$, the other $y = 2x - 1$.

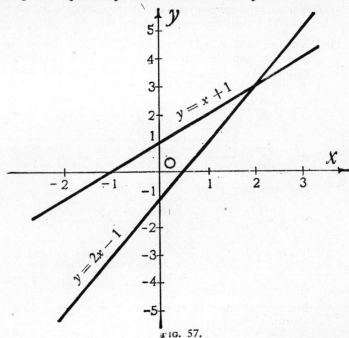

Fig. 57.

Many functions exist such that to each value of the independent variable for which the function exists there correspond more than two values of the function. Such functions are said to be **many-valued**. Thus, if $y = \sin^{-1} x$, then to each value of x between -1 and $+1$, there corresponds an infinite number of values of y. For example, if $x = 0$, $y = 0$, $\pm \pi$, $\pm 2\pi$, $\pm 3\pi$, ... radians (see Fig. 45).

Examples (continued)

4. Sketch the curve $y^2 = x^2 (x + 1)$.

    (i) Since y^2 is never negative, $x^2 (x + 1)$ cannot be negative, and therefore $x + 1 \geqq 0$, that is, $x \geqq -1$. No part of the curve lies to the left of the line $x = -1$.

223

(ii) The curve cuts the coordinate axes in the points $(-1, 0)$, $(0, 0)$.

(iii) The curve is symmetrical about the x-axis, since a given value of x gives two equal and opposite values of y.

(iv) Since $y^2 = x^2 (x + 1)$, $y = \pm x \sqrt{(x + 1)}$. But we need consider only the curve $y = + x \sqrt{(x + 1)}$, since the graph of $y = - x \sqrt{(x + 1)}$ will clearly be the reflection of this curve in the x-axis. Thus,

$$\frac{dy}{dx} = \sqrt{(x + 1)} + \frac{x}{2\sqrt{(x + 1)}} = \frac{3x + 2}{2\sqrt{(x + 1)}},$$

and $\quad \dfrac{d^2y}{dx^2} = \dfrac{3\sqrt{(x + 1)} - \dfrac{3x + 2}{2\sqrt{(x + 1)}}}{2 (x + 1)} = \dfrac{3x + 4}{4 (x + 1)^{\frac{3}{2}}}.$

For stationary points, $\dfrac{dy}{dx} = 0$; that is, $x = -\frac{2}{3}$.

When $x = -\dfrac{2}{3}, y = -\dfrac{2}{3\sqrt{3}} = -\dfrac{2\sqrt{3}}{9}$, and $\dfrac{d^2y}{dx^2}$ is positive.

Therefore $\left(-\dfrac{2}{3}, -\dfrac{2\sqrt{3}}{9}\right)$ is a minimum turning point.

At points of inflexion, $\dfrac{d^2y}{dx^2} = 0$; that is, $x = -\frac{4}{3}$.

But for real values of y, x cannot be less than -1 (see (i) above). Therefore there is no point of inflexion.

(v) We observe that $\dfrac{dy}{dx}$ is infinite when $x = -1$, showing that the tangent to the curve at the point $(-1, 0)$ is perpendicular to the x-axis ; we also see that when $x = 0$ (that is, at the other point where the curve cuts the x-axis) $\dfrac{dy}{dx} = 1.$

(vi) Again, $\dfrac{d^2y}{dx^2}$ is positive for all values of x greater than $-\frac{4}{3}$ (except $x = -1$ for which $\dfrac{d^2y}{dx^2}$ is infinite), and therefore for all values of x greater than -1 (which are the only values which yield real values of y). Therefore the curve is concave upwards at all points (except where $x = -1$).

We can now sketch the curve $y = x \sqrt{(x+1)}$ (Fig. 58).

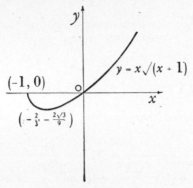

FIG. 58.

We have already noted that the curve $y = -x \sqrt{(x+1)}$ will be the reflection of the above curve in the x-axis. The original curve $y^2 = x^2(x+1)$ has therefore the form shown in Fig. 59.

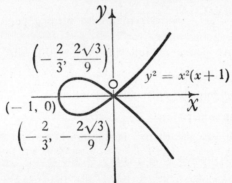

$\left(-\frac{2}{3}, \frac{2\sqrt{3}}{9}\right)$

$y^2 = x^2(x+1)$

$(-1, 0)$

$\left(-\frac{2}{3}, -\frac{2\sqrt{3}}{9}\right)$

FIG. 59.

At the origin, where the two branches of the curve intersect, there are two distinct tangents. Such a point is called a **node**.

5. Sketch the curve $y^2 = x^2(1 - x^2)$.

(i) The equation shows that the curve is symmetrical about both coordinate axes and that it cuts these axes in the points $(-1, 0)$, $(0, 0)$, $(1, 0)$. Also the curve is confined to the range $-1 \leqq x \leqq 1$, since $1 - x^2$ must be positive.

(ii) Let us consider the single-valued function
$$y = + x \sqrt{(1 - x^2)}.$$
We have
$$\frac{dy}{dx} = \sqrt{(1 - x^2)} - \frac{x^2}{\sqrt{(1 - x^2)}} = \frac{1 - 2x^2}{\sqrt{(1 - x^2)}},$$
and $\dfrac{d^2y}{dx^2} = \dfrac{-4x\sqrt{(1 - x^2)} + \dfrac{x(1 - 2x^2)}{\sqrt{(1 - x^2)}}}{(1 - x^2)} = \dfrac{x(2x^2 - 3)}{(1 - x^2)^{\frac{3}{2}}}.$

For stationary points, $\dfrac{dy}{dx} = 0$; that is, $x^2 = \frac{1}{2}$, or $x = \pm \dfrac{\sqrt{2}}{2}.$

When $x = + \dfrac{\sqrt{2}}{2}$, $y = \frac{1}{2}$, and $\dfrac{d^2y}{dx^2}$ is negative ;

when $x = - \dfrac{\sqrt{2}}{2}$, $y = -\frac{1}{2}$, and $\dfrac{d^2y}{dx^2}$ is positive.

Therefore $(\dfrac{\sqrt{2}}{2}, \frac{1}{2})$ is a maximum turning point, and $(-\dfrac{\sqrt{2}}{2}, -\frac{1}{2})$ is a minimum turning point.

At points of inflexion, $\dfrac{d^2y}{dx^2} = 0$; that is, $x = 0$ or $x^2 = \frac{3}{2}$ (which is impossible since $x^2 \leqq 1$). The origin is therefore the only point of inflexion, $\dfrac{d^2y}{dx^2}$ clearly changing sign when $x = 0$.

(iii) We note also that $\dfrac{dy}{dx}$ is infinite when $x = \pm 1$, showing that the tangents to the curve at the points $(\pm 1, 0)$ are perpendicular to the x-axis ; also that when $x = 0$, $\dfrac{dy}{dx} = 1$, so that the inflexional tangent at the origin has gradient 1.

(iv) For the range $-1 < x < 1$, $\dfrac{d^2y}{dx^2}$ has the opposite sign from that of x, since $2x^2 - 3$ is negative in this range and $(1 - x^2)^{\frac{3}{2}}$ is positive. Thus,

for $0 < x < 1$, the curve is concave downwards ;
for $-1 < x < 0$, the curve is concave upwards.

The general form of the curve $y^2 = x^2 (1 - x^2)$ may now be sketched (Fig. 60). The continuous portion represents the curve $y = x \sqrt{(1 - x^2)}$, and the dotted portion, obtained by symmetry, represents the curve $y = - x \sqrt{(1 - x^2)}$.

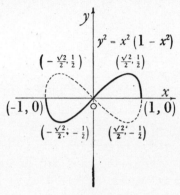

Fig. 60.

Asymptotes

The reader was introduced to asymptotes during the study of the curve $y = \dfrac{1}{x}$. He would be well advised to re-read pages 165-167 before proceeding further.

If the function $f(x)$ which we wish to graph has a fractional form $\dfrac{F(x)}{\Phi(x)}$, where $F(x)$ and $\Phi(x)$ are polynomials in x, with no factor in common, then it is clear that the function $f(x)$ cannot have a finite value for those values of x (if any) for which the denominator $\Phi(x)$ has the value zero. If $x = a$ is one such value, then as x approaches the value a, $f(x)$ will tend to infinity; and the graphical interpretation of this situation is that the straight line $x = a$ will be an asymptote to the curve. Thus, the values of x for which the denominator vanishes give asymptotes of the form $x = k$, that is, asymptotes parallel to the y-axis.

For example,

the curve $y = \dfrac{x\,(x-1)}{x+1}$ has one such asymptote, namely the

line $x = -1$;

the curve $y = \dfrac{x^2}{4-x^2}$ has two such asymptotes, namely the

lines $x = \pm 2$;

the curve $y = \dfrac{x^2}{1+x^2}$ has no asymptote parallel to the y-axis.

It is possible, however, for a curve to have an asymptote which is not parallel to the y-axis, for not only must we consider large values of y but also large values of x. The circumstances under which such asymptotes exist are probably most easily seen by examining particular curves.

(i) If $y = \dfrac{x}{1+x^2}$, then $y = \dfrac{\dfrac{1}{x}}{\dfrac{1}{x^2}+1}$, provided $x \neq 0$, and as x

tends to infinity, y tends to zero. The line $y = 0$ (that is, the x-axis) is therefore an asymptote to the curve, for as x increases numerically, the curve approaches more and more closely to the x-axis.

(ii) If $y = \dfrac{x^2}{4+x^2}$, then $y = \dfrac{1}{\dfrac{4}{x^2}+1}$, provided $x \neq 0$, and as x

tends to infinity, y tends to the value 1. The line $y = 1$ is therefore an asymptote to this curve.

(iii) If $y = \dfrac{(x-1)\,(x+2)}{x}$, then $y = x + 1 - \dfrac{2}{x}$, provided

$x \neq 0$. When x is numerically large, $\dfrac{2}{x}$ is numerically small, and the ordinate of the curve differs only slightly from the corresponding ordinate of the straight line $y = x + 1$, the difference becoming increasingly smaller as x tends to infinity. The straight line $y = x + 1$ is therefore an asymptote to the curve. (Clearly, of course, the line $x = 0$ is also an asymptote to this curve.)

(iv) If $y = \dfrac{x^3 + 1}{x}$, then $y = x^2 + \dfrac{1}{x}$, provided $x \neq 0$. When x is numerically large, $\dfrac{1}{x}$ is numerically small, and the ordinate of the curve differs only slightly from the corresponding ordinate of the parabola $y = x^2$. We may, if we like, refer to the curve $y = x^2$ as a *curvilinear* asymptote to the given curve, but there is certainly no straight line asymptote to which the curve approaches as x tends to infinity. (The line $x = 0$ is, however, an asymptote to this curve.)

A careful scrutiny of these results will reveal that, for the curve $y = \dfrac{F(x)}{\Phi(x)}$, the existence of an asymptote (other than those parallel to the y-axis) depends entirely on the relative degrees of $F(x)$ and $\Phi(x)$. The general results may be expressed thus :

(a) If $F(x)$ is of lower degree than $\Phi(x)$, then the x-axis is an asymptote to the curve.

(b) If $F(x)$ and $\Phi(x)$ are of equal degree, then there is an asymptote parallel to the x-axis.

(c) If $F(x)$ is of degree one higher than $\Phi(x)$, then there is a slant asymptote found by division.

(d) If $F(x)$ is of degree two or more higher than $\Phi(x)$, then there is no straight line asymptote (apart from those given by the equation $\Phi(x) = 0$).

It is not intended that the above results be committed to memory ; it is more instructive (and equally effective) if particular examples be tackled from first principles. The illustrations quoted above show the appropriate procedure.

Examples (continued)

6. Sketch the curve $y = \dfrac{x^2}{4 - x^2}$.

    (i) The equation shows that the curve passes through the origin and is symmetrical about the y-axis. Also since the numerator is always positive, y has the same sign as $4 - x^2$, and is therefore negative everywhere, except in the range $-2 < x < 2$.

    (ii) The lines $x = \pm 2$ are asymptotes since as $x \longrightarrow \pm 2$, $y \longrightarrow \infty$. The approach of the curve to these asymptotes is clear from the sign of y as noted in (i) above.

    (iii) Since $y = \dfrac{1}{\dfrac{4}{x^2} - 1} = \dfrac{-1}{1 - \dfrac{4}{x^2}}$, as $x \longrightarrow \infty$, $y \longrightarrow -1$.

The line $y = -1$ is therefore an asymptote, to which the approach of the curve is from below at both ends (for the denominator $1 - \dfrac{4}{x^2}$ is always less than 1 and therefore y is negative and numerically greater than 1).

    (iv) We have $\dfrac{dy}{dx} = \dfrac{(4 - x^2)\,2x - x^2 \cdot (-2x)}{(4 - x^2)^2} = \dfrac{8x}{(4 - x^2)^2}$,

and $\dfrac{d^2y}{dx^2} = \dfrac{(4 - x^2)^2 \cdot 8 - 8x\,(-4x)\,(4 - x^2)}{(4 - x^2)^4}$

$$= \dfrac{8\,(4 + 3x^2)}{(4 - x^2)^3} .$$

For stationary points, $\dfrac{dy}{dx} = 0$; that is, $x = 0$.

When $x = 0$, $y = 0$, and $\dfrac{d^2y}{dx^2}$ is positive ; therefore the origin is a minimum turning point.

    Also, since $\dfrac{d^2y}{dx^2}$ cannot equal zero for any real value of x, there are no points of inflexion.

    (v) We see that $\dfrac{d^2y}{dx^2}$ has the same sign as $4 - x^2$, and is therefore negative except in the range $-2 < x < 2$. Thus, the curve is concave downwards everywhere except between $x = -2$

and $x = 2$, where it is concave upwards.

We now have sufficient (indeed, more than sufficient) information to enable us to sketch the curve (Fig. 61).

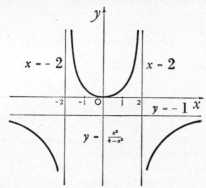

$x = -2$ $x = 2$

$y = -1$

$y = \dfrac{x^2}{4 - x^2}$

FIG. 61.

7. Sketch the curve $y = \dfrac{(x - 1)(x - 4)}{x}$.

(i) The curve cuts the x-axis in the points $(1, 0)$, $(4, 0)$.

(ii) The line $x = 0$ (that is, the y-axis) is an asymptote, for as $x \longrightarrow 0$, $y \longrightarrow \infty$. The approach of the curve to the asymptote is given by the table of signs

x	$0 -$	0	$0 +$
y	$-$	∞	$+$

(iii) Since $y = x - 5 + \dfrac{4}{x}$, the line $y = x - 5$ is an asymptote

(by the argument of pages 228-9). The term $+ \dfrac{4}{x}$ shows that the curve approaches the asymptote from above as $x \longrightarrow + \infty$, and from below as $x \longrightarrow - \infty$.

(iv) Differentiating, we have

$$\frac{dy}{dx} = 1 - \frac{4}{x^2} = \frac{x^2 - 4}{x^2} , \text{ and } \frac{d^2y}{dx^2} = \frac{8}{x^3} .$$

For stationary points, $\dfrac{dy}{dx} = 0$; that is, $x = \pm 2$.

When $x = 2$, $y = -1$, and $\dfrac{d^2y}{dx^2}$ is positive ;

when $x = -2$, $y = -9$, and $\dfrac{d^2y}{dx^2}$ is negative.

Therefore $(2, -1)$ is a minimum turning point, and $(-2, -9)$ is a maximum turning point.

At points of inflexion, $\dfrac{d^2y}{dx^2} = 0$; but $\dfrac{d^2y}{dx^2} = \dfrac{8}{x^3} \neq 0$ for finite values of x. There is therefore no point of inflexion.

(v) We see also that $\dfrac{d^2y}{dx^2}$ has the same sign as x. Therefore,

for $x > 0$, the curve is concave upwards ;
for $x < 0$, the curve is concave downwards.
Fig. 62 shows a sketch of the curve.

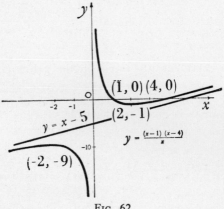

FIG. 62.

Periodic functions

It is assumed that the reader is familiar with the graphs of the trigonometric functions $\sin x$, $\cos x$, and $\tan x$. It will be recalled that the complete graph of any one of these functions, for negative and positive values of x, consists of an endless number of repetitions of the portion of the graph between $x = 0$ and $x = 2\pi$ radians. Such functions are said to be **periodic**.

More precisely, if $f(x)$ denote one of these functions, then

$$f(x) = f(x \pm 2\pi) = f(x \pm 4\pi) = f(x \pm 6\pi) = \ldots,$$

or $f(x) = f(x + 2n\pi)$, where n is any integer, positive or negative.

This means that no matter what particular value is given to x, if this value is increased (or diminished) by any multiple of 2π, the value of the function is unaltered. The number 2π is called the **period** of these functions. (Actually, the function $\tan x$ has also the shorter period π, for $\tan x = \tan(x + n\pi)$, for positive and negative integral values of n.)

In sketching the graph of any trigonometrical function, it is therefore sufficient if we sketch one complete portion or **cycle** which is typical of the complete graph. Thus, if we wish to graph the function $\sin 4x$, all we need do is graph the portion from $x = 0$ to $x = \dfrac{\pi}{2}$, for one cycle will be completed when $4x$ increases by 2π, that is, when x increases by $\dfrac{\pi}{2}$. The period of the function $\sin 4x$ is therefore $\dfrac{\pi}{2}$. Similarly, if we wish to sketch the curve $y = \cos 4x + \cos 3x$, we may confine ourselves to the range $0 \leqq x \leqq 2\pi$, for $\cos 4x$ has a period $\dfrac{\pi}{2}$ (or any multiple thereof), and $\cos 3x$ has a period of $\dfrac{2\pi}{3}$ (or any multiple thereof), and the smallest common multiple of $\dfrac{\pi}{2}$ and $\dfrac{2\pi}{3}$ is 2π. *

On the other hand, although the function $\sin x \sin 5x$ has clearly a period which is a common multiple of 2π and $\dfrac{2\pi}{5}$, that is, 2π,

---

* The reader may find it helpful at this stage to transfer temporarily from radians to degrees.

since

$$\sin x \sin 5x = \tfrac{1}{2} (\cos 4x - \cos 6x),$$

the function has in fact a shorter period π, the least common

multiple of $\dfrac{\pi}{2}$ and $\dfrac{\pi}{3}$.

Examples (continued)

8. Sketch the curve $y = \dfrac{3 \sin x}{2 + \cos x}$.

    (i) The curve has a period 2π, and is symmetrical about the origin.

    (ii) The denominator is always positive (since the smallest value of $\cos x$ is -1) ; therefore y has always the same sign as $\sin x$.

    (iii) The curve cuts the x-axis where $\sin x = 0$, that is, where $x = 0$, π, 2π, etc.

    (iv) Differentiating, we have

$$\frac{dy}{dx} = \frac{(2 + \cos x) \, 3 \cos x + 3 \sin^2 x}{(2 + \cos x)^2} = \frac{3 (1 + 2 \cos x)}{(2 + \cos x)^2} ,$$

and

$$\frac{d^2y}{dx^2} = 3 . \frac{(2+\cos x)^2(-2 \sin x)-(1+2 \cos x)(-2 \sin x)(2+\cos x)}{(2 + \cos x)^4}$$

$$= \frac{6 \sin x \, (\cos x - 1)}{(2 + \cos x)^3} .$$

For stationary points, $\dfrac{dy}{dx} = 0$; that is, $\cos x = -\tfrac{1}{2}$.

Therefore, in the range $0 \leqq x \leqq 2\pi$, $x = \dfrac{2\pi}{3}$ or $\dfrac{4\pi}{3}$.

When $x = \dfrac{2\pi}{3}$, $y = \sqrt{3}$, and $\dfrac{d^2y}{dx^2}$ is negative ;

when $x = \dfrac{4\pi}{3}$, $y = - \sqrt{3}$, and $\dfrac{d^2y}{dx^2}$ is positive.

Therefore $\left(\dfrac{2\pi}{3} , \sqrt{3}\right)$ is a maximum turning point, and

$\left(\dfrac{4\pi}{3} , - \sqrt{3}\right)$ is a minimum turning point.

At points of inflexion, $\dfrac{d^2y}{dx^2} = 0$; that is $\sin x = 0$ or $\cos x = 1$.

Therefore, in the range $0 \leqq x \leqq 2\pi$, $x = 0$, π, or 2π ; and the points $(0, 0)$, $(\pi, 0)$, $(2\pi, 0)$ are points of inflexion, since at each of these points $\dfrac{d^2y}{dx^2}$ changes sign.

(v) When $x = 0$ or 2π, $\dfrac{dy}{dx} = 1$; therefore the inflexional tangents at the points $(0, 0)$, $(2\pi, 0)$ have gradient 1.

When $x = \pi$, $\dfrac{dy}{dx} = -3$; therefore the inflexional tangent at the point $(\pi, 0)$ has gradient -3.

Fig. 63 shows a sketch of the curve from $x = 0$ to $x = 2\pi$

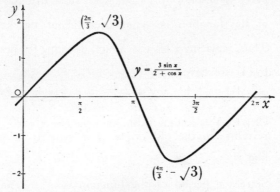

FIG. 63.

9. Prove that the function $\cos^2 2x + 3 \sin^2 x$ has a period π and that its graph is symmetrical about the line $x = \dfrac{\pi}{2}$. Find the stationary values of the function for the range $0 \leqq x \leqq \dfrac{\pi}{2}$, and hence sketch the graph of the function from $x = 0$ to $x = 2\pi$.

(i) Clearly the function is always positive, and its graph is symmetrical about the line $x = 0$.

(ii) Let $y = \cos^2 2x + 3 \sin^2 x$;   then
$$y = \tfrac{1}{2}(1 + \cos 4x + 3 - 3\cos 2x) = \tfrac{1}{2}(4 - 3\cos 2x + \cos 4x).$$

The period of $\cos 2x$ is π, that of $\cos 4x$ is $\dfrac{\pi}{2}$; therefore y is a function of period π.

(iii) To show that the graph of the function is symmetrical about the line $x = \dfrac{\pi}{2}$, we can show that the values of y are the same for $x = \dfrac{\pi}{2} - a$ as for $x = \dfrac{\pi}{2} + a$, where a is any constant. Alternatively, we can imagine the origin changed to the point $\left(\dfrac{\pi}{2}, 0\right)$—this will entail reducing every value of x by $\dfrac{\pi}{2}$—and then show that the new form of the function is symmetrical about the new y-axis. Thus, replacing x by $x - \dfrac{\pi}{2}$, and denoting the new function by Y, we have
$$Y = \tfrac{1}{2}\left\{ 4 - 3\cos(2x - \pi) + \cos(4x - 2\pi) \right\},$$
$$= \tfrac{1}{2}(4 + 3\cos 2x + \cos 4x).$$
Clearly, Y is symmetrical about the line $x = 0$; therefore, reverting to the old origin, y is symmetrical about the line $x = \dfrac{\pi}{2}$.

(iv) Since the period of the function is π, and its graph is symmetrical about the line $x = \dfrac{\pi}{2}$, we need only investigate the variation of the function for the range $0 \leq x \leq \dfrac{\pi}{2}$. The extension to the range $0 \leq x \leq 2\pi$ can then be done by symmetry.

(v) Differentiating, we have
$$\frac{dy}{dx} = 3\sin 2x - 2\sin 4x = \sin 2x(3 - 4\cos 2x),$$

and $\dfrac{d^2y}{dx^2} = 6\cos 2x - 8\cos 4x$.

For stationary points, $\dfrac{dy}{dx} = 0$; that is, $\sin 2x = 0$ or $\cos 2x = \tfrac{3}{4}$.

Therefore, in the range $0 \leqq x \leqq \dfrac{\pi}{2}$, that is, $0 \leqq 2x \leqq \pi$,

$$2x = 0, \text{ or } \pi, \text{ or } 41° 24' ;$$

that is, $x = 0$, or $\dfrac{\pi}{2}$, or $20° 42'$ $\left(\text{approx. } \dfrac{\pi}{9}\right)$.

When $x = 0$, $y = 1$, and $\dfrac{d^2y}{dx^2}$ is negative ;

when $x = \dfrac{\pi}{2}$, $y = 4$, and $\dfrac{d^2y}{dx^2}$ is negative ;

when $x = \dfrac{\pi}{9}$, $y = \tfrac{15}{16}$, and $\dfrac{d^2y}{dx^2}$ is positive.

Therefore, the points $(0, 1)$, $\left(\dfrac{\pi}{4}, 4\right)$ are maximum turning points, and the point $\left(\dfrac{\pi}{9}, \tfrac{15}{16}\right)$ is a minimum turning point.

We may now sketch the curve $y = \cos^2 2x + 3\sin^2 x$ for the given range (Fig. 64).

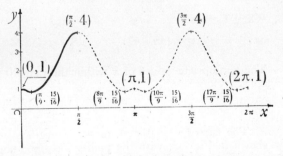

FIG. 64.

10. Sketch the curve $y = e^{-\frac{1}{4}x} \sin 3x$ from $x = 0$ to $x = 2\pi$.

(i) Because of the exponential factor, y is *not* a periodic function.

(ii) Whatever the value of x, the value of $\sin 3x$ never exceeds $+ 1$; the required curve is therefore never above the curve $y = e^{-\frac{1}{4}x}$, and meets it at points given by

$$e^{-\frac{1}{4}x} = e^{-\frac{1}{4}x} \sin 3x,$$

that is, $\sin 3x = 1$,

$$3x = \frac{\pi}{2} + 2n\pi, \text{ where } n \text{ is a positive or negative}$$

integer,

or $\qquad x = (4n + 1)\frac{\pi}{6}.$

The appropriate values of x within the given range $0 \leq x \leq 2\pi$ are therefore

$$x = \frac{\pi}{6}, \frac{5\pi}{6}, \frac{3\pi}{2}.$$

Similarly, since the least value of $\sin 3x$ is $- 1$, the required curve is never below the curve $y = - e^{-\frac{1}{4}x}$, and meets it at points given by

$$- e^{-\frac{1}{4}x} = e^{-\frac{1}{4}x} \sin 3x,$$

that is, $\sin 3x = - 1$,

$$3x = \frac{3\pi}{2} + 2n\pi, \text{ where } n \text{ is a positive or}$$

negative integer,

or $\qquad x = (4n + 3)\frac{\pi}{6}.$

The appropriate values of x within the range $0 \leq x \leq 2\pi$ are therefore

$$x = \frac{\pi}{2}, \frac{7\pi}{6}, \frac{11\pi}{6}.$$

The curves $y = \pm e^{-\frac{1}{4}x}$, for the range $0 \leq x \leq 2\pi$ are shown in Fig. 65, with the points corresponding to these six values of x marked by crosses.

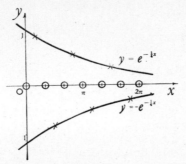

Fig. 65.

Apart from these six points (within the range $0 \leqq x \leqq 2\pi$), the required curve lies wholly between the two curves shown.

(iii) The required curve intersects the x-axis where $e^{-\frac{1}{4}x} \sin 3x = 0$, that is, where $\sin 3x = 0$. This means that the curve crosses the x-axis an indefinitely large number of times, at points given by

$3x = n\pi$, where n is a positive or negative integer,

or $x = \dfrac{n\pi}{3}$.

The appropriate values of x within the given range $0 \leqq x \leqq 2\pi$ are therefore

$$x = 0,\ \frac{\pi}{3},\ \frac{2\pi}{3},\ \pi,\ \frac{4\pi}{3},\ \frac{5\pi}{3},\ 2\pi.$$

These points are also marked (by circles) in Fig. 65.

It is therefore already clear that the given curve must " swing " to and fro between the curves $y = \pm\, e^{-\frac{1}{4}x}$, the extent of the swings diminishing steadily.

(iv) Since $y = e^{-\frac{1}{4}x} \sin 3x$,

$$\frac{dy}{dx} = -\tfrac{1}{4}\, e^{-\frac{1}{4}x} \sin 3x + 3e^{-\frac{1}{4}x} \cos 3x$$

$$= e^{-\frac{1}{4}x} (3 \cos 3x - \tfrac{1}{4} \sin 3x).$$

239

For stationary points, $\dfrac{dy}{dx} = 0$;   that is,

$$3 \cos 3x - \tfrac{1}{4} \sin 3x = 0,$$
or $$\tan 3x = 12.$$

Hence, $3x = 85° \ 14' + n . 180°$, where n is a positive or negative integer,
or $x = 28° \ 25' + n . 60°$.

The appropriate values* within the range $0 \leqq x \leqq 2\pi$ are given by
$x = 28° \ 25', 88° \ 25', 148° \ 25', 208° \ 25', 268° \ 25', 328° \ 25'.$

From what has already been derived, it is clear that these values give alternately maximum and minimum turning points of the given curve, which appears in Fig. 66.

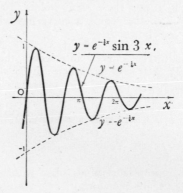

FIG. 66.

It should be noted carefully, for the scale of the graph may not make this clear, that the turning points are *not* the points where the curve meets the curves $y = \pm e^{-\frac{1}{4}x}$, but have abscissæ which are slightly smaller than the abscissæ of these points.

This curve is of particular interest to engineers for, if the independent variable represents time, it illustrates the phenomenon of **damped oscillations.** The curve may be regarded as of sine form—or *sinusoidal*—with constantly decreasing " amplitude " ; the greater the damping, the more rapidly does the amplitude diminish.

---

* These values, obtained from tables, are quoted in degrees and minutes; they should, of course, be converted to radians.

11. Sketch, on the same diagram, the graphs of the functions
$$\tfrac{1}{2}\,(e^x + e^{-x}), \qquad \text{(ii)} \ \tfrac{1}{2}\,(e^x - e^{-x}).$$

(i) Let $f(x) = \tfrac{1}{2}\,(e^x + e^{-x})$, and $F(x) = \tfrac{1}{2}\,(e^x - e^{-x})$.
Then $f(-x) = \tfrac{1}{2}\,(e^{-x} + e^x) = f(x)$, so that the graph of $f(x)$ is symmetrical about the y-axis.
   Again, $F(-x) = \tfrac{1}{2}\,(e^{-x} - e^x) = -F(x)$, so that the graph of $F(x)$ is symmetrical about the origin.

(ii) Since e is positive, both e^x and e^{-x} are positive for all values of x. It follows that $f(x)$ is positive for all values of x. Moreover, $f(0) = 1$.
   Since $e > 1$, then $e^x > e^{-x}$ for all positive values of x; hence $F(x)$ is positive for all positive values of x, and negative for all negative values of x, $F(0)$ being zero.

(iii) Differentiating, we have
$$f'(x) = \tfrac{1}{2}\,(e^x - e^{-x}) = F(x),$$
$$f''(x) = \tfrac{1}{2}\,(e^x + e^{-x}) = F'(x),$$
$$\tfrac{1}{2}\,(e^x - e^{-x}) = F''(x).$$

The reader will find no difficulty in deducing from these results that

(a) $f(x)$ is always concave upwards, with a minimum turning value of 1 when $x = 0$;

(b) $F(x)$ is concave upwards for $x > 0$, and concave downwards for $x < 0$, with an inflexional value at the origin, where the gradient is 1.

The graphs of the two functions are shown in Fig. 67.

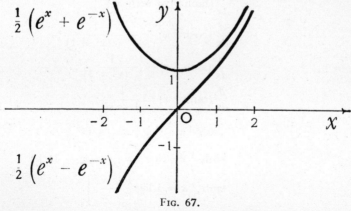

FIG. 67.

241

The graph of $f(x)$ is the curve taken up by a heavy, uniform chain suspended at its ends. For this reason, the curve is called a **catenary** (Latin, *catena* = chain).

[The functions $f(x)$ and $F(x)$ are linked to the hyperbola in much the same way as the trigonometric (or " circular ") functions are connected with the circle. They are therefore called respectively the **hyperbolic cosine** (written " cosh ") and the **hyperbolic sine** (written " sinh "), that is,

$$\cosh x = \tfrac{1}{2}(e^x + e^{-x}), \; \sinh x = \tfrac{1}{2}(e^x - e^{-x}).$$

All the trigonometric formulæ have counterparts relating to hyperbolic functions ; thus, we have

$$\tanh x = \frac{\sinh x}{\cosh x}, \; \cosh^2 x - \sinh^2 x = 1,$$

$$\sinh(x \pm y) = \sinh x \cosh y \pm \cosh x \sinh y,$$
$$\cosh(x \pm y) = \cosh x \cosh y \pm \sinh x \sinh y,$$

and many others.

The reader is invited to verify for himself these results and also those which follow :

$$\frac{d}{dx}(\cosh x) = \sinh x ;$$

$$\frac{d}{dx}(\sinh x) = \cosh x ;$$

$$\frac{d}{dx}(\tanh x) = \operatorname{sech}^2 x ;$$

$$\frac{d}{dx}(\cosh^{-1} x) = \pm \frac{1}{\sqrt{(x^2 - 1)}} ;$$

$$\frac{d}{dx}(\sinh^{-1} x) = \frac{1}{\sqrt{(x^2 + 1)}} ;$$

$$\frac{d}{dx}(\tanh^{-1} x) = \frac{1}{1 - x^2} ;$$

$$\cosh^{-1} x = \log\{ x \pm \sqrt{(x^2 - 1)} \} ;$$

$$\sinh^{-1} x = \log\{ x + \sqrt{(x^2 + 1)} \} ;$$

$$\tanh^{-1} x = \tfrac{1}{2}\log\frac{1 + x}{1 - x}.]$$

12. For what ranges of values of x are the following curves
    (a) concave upwards, (b) concave downwards ?
    Sketch the shape of each curve at its point(s) of inflexion, if any.

    (i) $y = 2 - 3x - x^6$,   (ii) $y = x^5 - 10x^2 + 16x - 7$,

    (iii) $y = 3 (5 - 2x)^4$,   (iv) $y = 3x^5 - 5x^4 + 5x - 3$,

    (v) $xy = x^2 - 5x + 4$,   (vi) $y = \dfrac{x (x + 1)}{(x - 1) (x + 2)}$,

    (vii) $y = e^{-x^2}$,   (viii) $yx^3 = 4 - 6x^2$.

13. Find the equations of the asymptotes of the following curves, and show by means of diagrams how each curve approaches its asymptote(s).

    (i) $y = \dfrac{2x + 3}{3 - x}$,   (ii) $y = \dfrac{x (x + 1)}{(x - 1) (x + 2)}$,

    (iii) $y = \dfrac{4x^2 + 5x + 6}{x^2 + 3x + 2}$,   (iv) $y = \dfrac{3 - 2x}{4 + x^2}$,

    (v) $y = \left(\dfrac{3 - 2x}{2 - x}\right)^2$,   (vi) $y = x + \dfrac{1}{x^2 - 3}$,

    (vii) $xy = x^2 - 5x + 4$,   (viii) $y = \dfrac{(x + 1) (x - 2)^2}{x^2}$,

    (ix) $y = \dfrac{x^3}{x + 2}$,   (x) $y^2 (2 - x) = x$,

    (xi) $y^2 (x - 2) = x$,   (xii) $y^2 (2 + x) = x^2 (1 - x)$.

14. Find the periods of the following functions of x :

    (i) $\sin 3x$,   (ii) $\cos \tfrac{1}{2}x$,

    (iii) $\tfrac{2}{3} \sin \tfrac{2}{3}x$,   (iv) $\sin \dfrac{\pi x}{4}$,

    (v) $4 \cos 5x$,   (vi) $\sin \tfrac{1}{3}\pi (x + \tfrac{1}{2})$,

    (vii) $\tfrac{1}{2} \cos \left(\dfrac{3}{4}x - \dfrac{2\pi}{3}\right)$,   (viii) $a \sin 2\pi (bx + c)$,

    (ix) $\sin \dfrac{1}{\pi} (2x - 3)$,   (x) $2 \sin 2x - 4 \cos 4x$,

    (xi) $\sin 2\pi x + \sin \tfrac{1}{2}\pi x$,   (xii) $2 \cos \dfrac{\pi x}{5} + 3 \sin \dfrac{\pi x}{6}$,

    (xiii) $\cos x \cos 3x$,   (xiv) $\tfrac{3}{4} \sin 2x \cos 6x$,

    (xv) $\cos x \cos 2x \cos 3x$.

15. Write down the ranges of values within which x must lie in order that y, defined by the following equations, should be real :

   (i) $y^2 = x (x - 4)^2$, 　　　　　(ii) $y^2 = (1 - x) (x - 2)^2$,

   (iii) $y^2 = 4x^2 (1 - x^2)$, 　　　(iv) $y^2 = x^2 (x^2 - 4)$,

   (v) $y^2 = x^4 (3 - 2x)^2$, 　　　(vi) $y^2 = \frac{2}{3} v^3 (2 - x)$,

   (vii) $y^2 = (2 - x^2)^3$, 　　　(viii) $y^2 = x^3 (2x - 3)$,

   (ix) $ay^2 = x^2 (a - x)$, 　　　(x) $a^2y^2 = x^2 (a^2 - x^2)$,

   (xi) $a^4y^2 = x^5 (2a - x)$, 　　(xii) $16a^2y^2 = x^2 (32a^2 - x^2)$.

16. Find the turning values of the following functions and quote the corresponding values of the independent variable :

   (i) $x \log x$, 　　　　　(ii) $t^2 \log \frac{1}{t}$,

   (iii) $x^3 e^{-x^2}$, 　　　　(iv) $\dfrac{\sin x}{2 + \sqrt{3} \cos x}$,

   (v) $\sin 3\theta + 3 \sin \theta$, 　(vi) $\sin^2 2x + 2 \cos^2 x$,

   (vii) $9 \sec^2 \theta + \operatorname{cosec}^2 \theta$, 　(viii) $\dfrac{3x - 5}{(x^2 - 4x + 5)^{\frac{3}{2}}}$.

17. Find the stationary points and the points of inflexion of the following curves, and sketch each curve :

   (i) $4y = 3x^5 - 20x^3 + 60x$,

   (ii) $81y = (x - 2)^3 (x + 4)$,

   (iii) $y = (x - 1)^3 (3x^2 - 6x - 2)$,

   (iv) $y = \dfrac{1}{x^2 + 1}$, 　　　(v) $y = \dfrac{x^3}{x^2 + 1}$,

   (vi) $y = e^{-x^2}$, 　　　　(vii) $y = xe^{-x^2}$,

   (viii) $y = \sin 2x - 4 \sin x$.

18. Find the equations of the asymptotes of the following curves, and sketch each curve :

   (i) $y = \dfrac{2x - 3}{3x - 2}$, 　　　(ii) $y = \dfrac{x^2}{x - 1}$,

   (iii) $y = \dfrac{27 (1 - x)}{x^3}$, 　　(iv) $y = \dfrac{x^4 - 3}{x}$,

   (v) $y = \left(\dfrac{x}{x - 1}\right)^2$, 　　(vi) $y = \dfrac{2x^2}{x^2 - 1}$,

   (vii) $y = \dfrac{x}{x^2 + 4}$ 　　　(viii) $y = \dfrac{x^4 + x^2 + 4}{x^3}$,

(ix) $y = \dfrac{9x}{(3-x)^2}$,   (x) $y = \dfrac{x^3}{x^2+3}$,

(xi) $y = \dfrac{x^3}{2-x}$,   (xii) $y = \dfrac{x^4}{x^2-4}$

19. Sketch the graphs of the two-valued functions defined by the following equations :

(i) $12y^2 = x(x-4)^2$,   (ii) $16y^2 = x^2(2-x^2)$,

(iii) $y^2 = (x+1)(x-2)^2$,   (iv) $3y^2 = (x-3)^3$,

(v) $y^2 = x^3(4-x)$,   (vi) $9y^2 = 4(1-x^2)^3$,

(vii) $y^2 = x^2(x^2-4)$,   (viii) $y^2 = \dfrac{x}{2-x}$,

(ix) $y^2 = \dfrac{x}{x-2}$.   (x) $y^2 = x^2\left(\dfrac{2+x}{2-x}\right)$.

20. Sketch the curves whose freedom equations are given below. (Do *not* derive the corresponding constraint equations.)

(i) $x = 3t^2$, $y = t(3-t^2)$;

(ii) $x = t - \dfrac{1}{t}$, $y = t + \dfrac{1}{t}$;

(iii) $x = \sqrt{2}.\sin t$, $y = \frac{1}{4}\sin 2t$;

(iv) $x = \cos^3 t$, $y = \sin^3 t$;

(v) $x = \dfrac{4t}{(1+t^2)^2}$, $y = \dfrac{4t^2}{(1+t^2)^2}$.

21. Sketch complete cycles of the following curves :

(i) $y = 8\sin x \cos^3 x$,   (ii) $y = \sin 3x \cos x$,

(iii) $y = 3\cos x - \cos 3x$,   (iv) $y = \sin x \sin 2x$,

(v) $y = \log(\sin x + \cos x)$.

22. Sketch the graphs of the following functions of x :

(i) e^{2x},   (ii) $e^{-\frac{1}{2}x}$,

(iii) xe^x,   (iv) $x^2 e^{-x}$,

(v) $(2x+1)(x-1)e^{-x}$,   (vi) $e^{1/x}$,

(vii) $x \log x$,   (viii) $\dfrac{1}{x}\log x$.

23. Find the values of t for which the function $e^{-kt} \sin(at + b)$ is stationary, and use your result to sketch the graph of the function $e^{-\frac{1}{3}t} \cos 2t$.

24. Draw *rough* sketches showing the general outlines of the graphs of the following functions of x :

   (i) $x \sin x$,   (ii) $x^2 \cos x$,   (iii) $\dfrac{1}{x} \sin x$.

25. Sketch the curve whose freedom equations are
$$x = a\,(\theta - \sin \theta),$$
$$y = a\,(1 - \cos \theta).$$

   [This curve, which is of some importance in certain branches of Applied Mathematics, is called the **cycloid.** It is the locus of a point on the circumference of a circle (of radius a) which rolls without slipping on a fixed straight line (the x-axis).]

26. The output power (P) of a triode valve is given by the formula
$$P = \frac{RV^2}{2\,(2r + R)^2},$$
where R, the resistance of the output stage, is variable. Show that the maximum output power is $V^2/16r$, and that this occurs when $R = 2r$.

27. The perimeter of an isosceles triangle is 12 inches. Find the lengths of the sides in order that the area of the triangle should be a maximum.

28. A person in a boat exactly 1 mile east of A, a point on a coast-line which runs due north and south, wishes to reach a point on the shore some distance north of A. If he can row at 3 m.p.h. and walk at 4 m.p.h., show that in order to reach his destination in the least possible time, he should row in a direction $\sin^{-1} \frac{3}{4}$ north of west, and then walk.

29. A lamp A is hung vertically above the centre C, of a circular carpet of diameter a feet. Assuming that at any point B on the carpet, the intensity of illumination is proportional to the cosine of angle CAB, and inversely proportional to the square of AB, find the height at which the lamp should be hung so that the circumference of the carpet may best be illuminated.

30. A solid, right circular cylinder of variable radius r, and height h, has a hemisphere, also of radius r, hollowed out from each end. If the total surface area of the solid so formed is given, prove that the volume is a maximum when $h = 8r$.

31. Concentric with a square of side $2a$, a circle of variable radius R is described, $(R < a)$; then in each corner of the square a circle is described touching two sides of the square and the first circle. Show that the sum of the areas of the five circles is a minimum when $R = \dfrac{4a\sqrt{2}}{7 + 2\sqrt{2}}$.

32. A point P starts from $(-3, 0)$ and moves along the x-axis in the positive direction with velocity 1 unit per second; another point Q starts from the origin at the same instant, and moves along the y-axis in the positive direction so that at time t seconds, its distance from the origin is $\frac{1}{4}t^2$. Show that the minimum distance between P and Q is $\sqrt{2}$, and that the maximum angle which PQ makes with the positive direction of the x-axis is $\dfrac{\pi}{2} + \tan^{-1}\frac{1}{3}$.

§ 29. EXPANSION OF FUNCTIONS IN POWER SERIES

Let us begin this section by examining the general cubic function

$$f(x) = a + bx + cx^2 + dx^3, \qquad . \qquad . \quad (1)$$

where the terms are arranged in ascending powers of x. Differentiating, we have

$$f'(x) = b + 2cx + 3dx^2,$$
$$f''(x) = 2c + 3 \cdot 2dx,$$
$$f'''(x) = 3 \cdot 2d,$$
$$f^{iv}(x) = f^v(x) = \ldots = 0.$$

Clearly

$$f(0) = a, \qquad f'(0) = b,$$
$$f''(0) = 2c, \quad f'''(0) = 3 \cdot 2d,$$
$$f^{iv}(0) = f^v(0) = \ldots = 0.$$

Therefore, it is true to say that for the particular function defined by (1),

$$f(x) = f(0) + x \cdot f'(0) + \frac{x^2}{2} \cdot f''(0) + \frac{x^3}{3 \cdot 2} \cdot f'''(0),$$

$$= f(0) + x \cdot f'(0) + \frac{x^2}{2!} \cdot f''(0) + \frac{x^3}{3!} \cdot f'''(0).$$

Let us now treat in similar fashion the binomial function $f(x) = (1 + x)^n$, where n is a positive integer. Since

$$f(x) = (1 + x)^n, \text{ then } f(0) = 1,$$

and by differentiation we have

$f'(x) = n(1 + x)^{n-1}$, so that $f'(0) = n$;

$f''(x) = n(n - 1)(1 + x)^{n-2}$, so that $f''(0) = n(n - 1)$;

$f'''(x) = n(n - 1)(n - 2)(1 + x)^{n-3}$, so that

$$f'''(0) = n(n - 1)(n - 2) ;$$

and so on.

Ultimately,
$$f^n(x) = n(n-1)(n-2)\dots 2.1, \text{ so that } f^n(0) = n!$$
and $f^{n+1}(x) = f^{n+2}(x) = \dots = 0.$

But, by the Binomial Theorem,
$$f(x) = 1 + nx + n(n-1).\frac{x^2}{2!} + n(n-1)(n-2).\frac{x^3}{3!}$$
$$+ \dots \text{ to } (n+1) \text{ terms}, \qquad . \qquad . \qquad . \qquad (2)$$

the last term being $n(n-1)(n-2)\dots[n-(n-1)].\frac{x^n}{n!}$, or x^n;

reference to the results obtained above shows that it may therefore be said of the function defined by (2) that

$$f(x) = f(0) + x.f'(0) + \frac{x^2}{2!}.f''(0) + \frac{x^3}{3!}.f'''(0) + \dots$$
$$+ \frac{x^n}{n!}.f^n(0).$$

In the Binomial Theorem (see footnote, page 172), the index need not be a positive integer. If $f(x) = (1+x)^n$, where n is a positive or negative fraction, or a negative integer, then

$$f(x) = 1 + nx + n(n-1).\frac{x^2}{2!} + n(n-1)(n-2).\frac{x^3}{3!} + \dots, \quad (3)$$

provided that x is numerically less than 1, that is, provided that the value of x is confined to the range $-1 < x < 1$ (or $|x| < 1$). Whereas the expansion (2) terminates after $(n+1)$ terms, the expansion (3) does not terminate but continues indefinitely. Clearly the series of differentiations carried out with function (2) could be repeated with function (3), and therefore it is easy to see that this time we may write

$$f(x) = f(0) + x.f'(0) + \frac{x^2}{2!}.f''(0) + \frac{x^3}{3!}.f'''(0) + \dots$$
$$+ \frac{x^n}{n!}.f^n(0) + \dots.$$

Let us consider one more example. The reader has already (page 186) been introduced to the exponential function, e^x, which it was stated could be expressed in the form of an infinite series. Denoting, for the sake of uniformity, the exponential function by $f(x)$, we have

$$f(x) = 1 + x + \frac{x^2}{2!} + \frac{x^3}{3!} + \dots + \frac{x^n}{n!} + \dots \quad . \quad . \quad . \quad (4)$$

Remembering that for the exponential function

$$f(x) = f'(x) = f''(x) = \dots = f^n(x) = \dots = e^x,$$

we see that

$$f(0) = f'(0) = f''(0) = \dots = f^n(0) = \dots = 1 \; ;$$

and once more, though very artificially in this case,

$$f(x) = f(0) + x \cdot f'(0) + \frac{x^2}{2!} \cdot f''(0) + \frac{x^3}{3!} \cdot f'''(0) + \dots$$

$$+ \frac{x^n}{n!} \cdot f^n(0) + \dots .$$

Each of the expanded forms of the functions (1), (2), (3), (4) is a **power series,** that is, an expression of the general form

$$a_0 + a_1 x + a_2 x^2 + a_3 x^3 + \dots ,$$

where a_0, a_1, a_2, ... are constants (some of which may be zero). Series (1) and (2) are finite, and terminate after 4 and $(n + 1)$ terms, respectively : series (3) and (4) do not terminate and are said to be ' infinite.'

The reader can hardly have failed to observe that in each of the four cases considered, it was found that the function could be expressed in the form

$$f(0) + x \cdot f'(0) + \frac{x^2}{2!} \cdot f''(0) + \frac{x^3}{3!} \cdot f'''(0) + \dots ,$$

and the question at once suggests itself—Can *any* function (for example, $\sin x$ or $\log(1 + x)$), which can be differentiated as often as we please (and for which the values of $f(0)$, $f'(0)$, $f''(0)$, ... , can therefore be found), be expressed as a power series of the above form ? The answer is that *under certain circumstances* such expansions are possible. This result is known as **Maclaurin's Theorem.***

Consideration of the circumstances under which such expansions can be established are beyond the scope of this book, and for further information the enquiring reader is referred to G. A. Gibson, *Elementary Treatise on the Calculus* (Macmillan), Chapter XVIII. All that can be stated here is that in order that Maclaurin's Theorem should apply

(i) $f(x)$ and all its derivatives must be continuous, and therefore finite, where $x = 0$;

(ii) the remainder after the first n terms, that is,

$$\frac{x^n}{n!} \cdot f^n(0) + \frac{x^{n+1}}{(n+1)!} \cdot f^{n+1}(0) + \frac{x^{n+2}}{(n+2)!} \cdot f^{n+2}(0) + \dots,$$

must tend to zero as n tends to infinity, for only then will the series for $f(x)$ be convergent and have a finite sum to infinity.

Thus, it is impossible to find power series expansions for $\log x$ or $x^{\frac{1}{2}}$ or $\cot x$, for in each case $f'(0)$, $f''(0)$, ... are all infinite.

Examples

1. Find an expansion for $\sin x$ in ascending powers of *x*.

Let $\qquad f(x) = \sin x$, so that $\qquad f(0) = 0.$

Also $\qquad f'(x) = \cos x$, $\qquad$ and $f'(0) = 1$;

$\qquad f''(x) = -\sin x$, $\qquad$ and $f''(0) = 0$;

$\qquad f'''(x) = -\cos x$, $\qquad$ and $f'''(0) = -1$;

$\qquad f^{iv}(x) = \sin x$, $\qquad$ and $f^{iv}(0) = 0$;

and so on. Therefore, by Maclaurin's Theorem,

$$\sin x = x - \frac{x^3}{3!} + \frac{x^5}{5!} - \frac{x^7}{7!} + \dots,$$

---

* Colin Maclaurin (1698-1746) was a mathematical prodigy from Kilmodan, Argyllshire, who entered the University of Glasgow at the age of 11, and eight years later, as a result of a competitive examination, was appointed to the Chair of Mathematics at Aberdeen University. In 1742, he formulated the theorem which bears his name, but it is now known that the theorem had already been established some years earlier by James Stirling.

for those values of x for which this series is convergent. It is not possible to investigate this aspect of the problem without a lengthy digression on infinite series.* Suffice it to state that the above series is convergent for all values of x, and therefore the expansion is valid for all values of x.

2. Expand $\cos x$ in ascending powers of x.

We may proceed exactly as in the previous example, but the result is more quickly found by differentiating the expansion for $\sin x$ term by term. This procedure is valid since the series in question is convergent. Thus, we have

$$\cos x = 1 - \frac{3x^2}{3!} + \frac{5x^4}{5!} - \frac{7x^6}{7!} + \dots,$$

$$= 1 - \frac{x^2}{2!} + \frac{x^4}{4!} - \frac{x^6}{6!} + \dots.$$

This expansion holds for all values of x.

3. Expand $\log (1 + x)$ as a series in ascending powers of x.

Let $f(x) = \log (1 + x)$, so that $f(0) = \log 1 = 0$.

Then $f'(x) = \dfrac{1}{1 + x}$, and $f'(0) = 1$;

$f''(x) = \dfrac{-1}{(1 + x)^2}$, and $f''(0) = -1$;

$f'''(x) = \dfrac{2.1}{(1 + x)^3}$, and $f'''(0) = 2!$;

$f^{iv}(x) = \dfrac{-3.2.1}{(1 + x)^4}$, and $f^{iv}(0) = -3!$;

and so on. Therefore

$$\log (1 + x) = x - \frac{x^2}{2!} + \frac{2!}{3!} \cdot x^3 - \frac{3!}{4!} \cdot x^4 + \dots,$$

$$= x - \frac{x^2}{2} + \frac{x^3}{3} - \frac{x^4}{4} + \dots,$$

the expansion holding for those values for which the above series is convergent.

Alternatively, since $f'(x) = \dfrac{1}{1 + x} = (1 + x)^{-1}$, we may

_____

* For further information on the convergency and divergency of infinite series, the reader is referred to McArthur and Keith, *Intermediate Algebra* (Methuen), Chapter XV.

expand using the Binomial Theorem. Thus,
$$f'(x) = 1 - x + x^2 - x^3 + \dots,$$
provided x is confined to the range $-1 < x < 1$, or $|x| < 1$.
Within this range, the series is convergent and therefore we may
integrate term by term, obtaining
$$f(x) = C + x - \frac{x^2}{2} + \frac{x^3}{3} - \frac{x^4}{4} + \dots,$$

where C is a constant of integration. This expansion will be
valid for all values of x within the stated range $-1 < x < 1$,
and therefore, in particular, for $x = 0$. Hence, putting $x = 0$,
we have
$$C = f(0) = \log 1 = 0.$$
Hence,
$$\log(1 + x) = x - \frac{x^2}{2} + \frac{x^3}{3} - \frac{x^4}{4} + \dots.$$

From what has gone before, one would expect this expansion
to hold for values of x within the range $-1 < x < 1$; in fact,
the expansion is valid for values within the range $-1 < x \leq 1$.
Integration of a convergent series produces a series which is
even "more convergent" than the original series, and which
may therefore, as in this case, be convergent over a wider range
than that of the original series.

[This series does not provide a very practical means for obtaining
the numerical values of particular logarithms, since its range is
limited to values of $1 + x$ between 0 and 2, and since its convergence
is so slow that many terms must be considered before reasonably
accurate results are obtained. A more convenient series is
obtained as follows.

In the above series, let us replace x by $-x$; we have
$$\log(1 - x) = -x - \frac{x^2}{2} - \frac{x^3}{3} - \frac{x^4}{4} - \dots,$$
provided $-1 \leq x < 1$. Hence
$$\log \frac{1+x}{1-x} = \log(1 + x) - \log(1 - x)$$
$$= \left(x - \frac{x^2}{2} + \frac{x^3}{3} - \frac{x^4}{4} + \dots \right)$$
$$- \left(-x - \frac{x^2}{2} - \frac{x^3}{3} - \frac{x^4}{4} - \dots \right)$$

$$= 2 \left(x + \frac{x^3}{3} + \frac{x^5}{5} + \dots \right),$$

the series being valid for all values of x within the range $-1 < x < 1$, or $|x| < 1$. If we now write $\frac{m}{n}$ for $\frac{1+x}{1-x}$, so that

$$m(1-x) = n(1+x),$$

that is,

$$x = \frac{m-n}{m+n},$$

this last expansion becomes

$$\log \frac{m}{n} = 2 \left\{ \frac{m-n}{m+n} + \frac{1}{3} \left(\frac{m-n}{m+n} \right)^3 + \frac{1}{5} \left(\frac{m-n}{m+n} \right)^5 + \dots \right\}.$$

Not only does this series converge much more rapidly than that for $\log(1+x)$, but $\frac{m}{n}$ can be given any (positive) value whatever, for although x must still be numerically less than unity, as x varies from -1 to 1, the expression $\frac{1+x}{1-x}$, and therefore $\frac{m}{n}$, varies from 0 to infinity.

Thus if we wish to calculate $\log 2$ (to the base e, let it be remembered), we let $m = 2$, $n = 1$; then

$$\log 2 = 2 \{ \tfrac{1}{3} + \tfrac{1}{3} (\tfrac{1}{3})^3 + \tfrac{1}{5} (\tfrac{1}{3})^5 + \tfrac{1}{7} (\tfrac{1}{3})^7 + \dots \}$$
$$= 2 (0 \cdot 33333 + 0 \cdot 01234 + 0 \cdot 00082 + 0 \cdot 00006 + \dots)$$
$$\fallingdotseq 0 \cdot 6931.$$

Similarly, if we let $m = 3$, $n = 2$, we have

$$\log 3 - \log 2 = 2 \{ \tfrac{1}{5} + \tfrac{1}{3} (\tfrac{1}{5})^3 + \tfrac{1}{5} (\tfrac{1}{5})^5 + \dots \}$$
$$= 2 (0 \cdot 2 + 0 \cdot 00266 + 0 \cdot 00006 + \dots)$$
$$\fallingdotseq 0 \cdot 4054.$$

Hence $\log 3 \fallingdotseq 0 \cdot 4054 + 0 \cdot 6931 = 1 \cdot 0985.$

Since $\log_e x = \log_{10} x \cdot \log_e 10$, if we wish to convert these *natural* logarithms to the *common* logarithms used in arithmetical calculations, we must divide by $\log_e 10$, that is, $2 \cdot 3026$, or multiply by its reciprocal, $0 \cdot 4343$.

Thus, $\log_{10} 2 = 0.6931 \times 0.4343 = 0.3010$.]

4. Expand $\tan^{-1} x$ in ascending powers of x.

Let $f(x) = \tan^{-1} x$, so that $f(0) = \tan^{-1} 0 = 0$.

Then $f'(x) = \dfrac{1}{1 + x^2} = (1 + x^2)^{-1}$, and, by the Binomial Theorem,

$$f'(x) = 1 - x^2 + x^4 - x^6 + \ldots,$$

provided $x^2 < 1$, that is, $-1 < x < 1$, or $|x| < 1$.

Integrating, we have

$$\tan^{-1} x = C + x - \frac{x^3}{3} + \frac{x^5}{5} - \frac{x^7}{7} + \ldots.$$

This expansion is valid for values of x within the range $-1 < x < 1$ (at least); therefore we are justified in putting $x = 0$, in which case we have $C = \tan^{-1} 0 = 0$, hence

$$\tan^{-1} x = x - \frac{x^3}{3} + \frac{x^5}{5} - \frac{x^7}{7} + \ldots.$$

This expansion, known as **Gregory's Series,*** holds for values of x within the range $-1 \leqq x \leqq 1$, or $|x| \leqq 1$.

[When $x = 1$, we have, since $\tan^{-1} 1 = \dfrac{\pi}{4}$,

$$\frac{\pi}{4} = 1 - \tfrac{1}{3} + \tfrac{1}{5} - \tfrac{1}{7} + \ldots,$$

a series by which we could find the value of π to as many decimal places as we pleased. Unfortunately several thousand terms must be considered before we get a value correct even to four decimal places. In other words, the above series though convergent does not converge rapidly enough for practical purposes. A fairly good approximation to the value of π may, however, be found by expanding the right-hand side of the relationship

$$\frac{\pi}{4} = 2 \tan^{-1} \tfrac{1}{3} + \tan^{-1} \tfrac{1}{7}$$

using Gregory's Series.

---

* Named after James Gregory (1638-1675) who was born at Drumoak, Aberdeenshire, and who became Professor of Mathematics at St. Andrews, and later at Edinburgh.

The truth of this relationship is readily established. Let $\tan^{-1} \frac{1}{3} = \alpha$, and $\tan^{-1} \frac{1}{7} = \beta$; then

$$\tan \alpha = \tfrac{1}{3}, \ \tan \beta = \tfrac{1}{7}, \ \text{and} \ \tan 2\alpha = \frac{\frac{2}{3}}{1 - \frac{1}{9}} = \tfrac{3}{4} \ ;$$

so that

$$\tan (2\alpha + \beta) = \frac{\frac{3}{4} + \frac{1}{7}}{1 - \frac{3}{28}} = 1 = \tan \frac{\pi}{4}.$$

Hence $\dfrac{\pi}{4} = 2\alpha + \beta = 2\tan^{-1} \frac{1}{3} + \tan^{-1} \frac{1}{7}$

$$= 2 \{ \ \tfrac{1}{3} - \tfrac{1}{3}(\tfrac{1}{3})^3 + \tfrac{1}{5}(\tfrac{1}{3})^5 - \tfrac{1}{7}(\tfrac{1}{3})^7 + \ldots \ \}$$
$$+ \{ \ \tfrac{1}{7} - \tfrac{1}{3}(\tfrac{1}{7})^3 + \tfrac{1}{5}(\tfrac{1}{7})^5 - \ldots \ \},$$
$$= 2 (0 \cdot 33333 - 0 \cdot 01234 + 0 \cdot 00082 - 0 \cdot 00006 + \ldots)$$
$$+ (0 \cdot 14285 - 0 \cdot 00097 + 0 \cdot 00001 - \ldots),$$
$$\doteqdot 0 \cdot 64350 + 0 \cdot 14189 = 0 \cdot 78539.$$

Therefore $\pi \doteqdot 3 \cdot 14159$

$= 3 \cdot 1416$, correct to four decimal places.]

5. Expand $e^{-2x} \sin 3x$ in ascending powers of x as far as the term in x^4.

The required expansion may be found by a direct application of Maclaurin's Theorem. Alternatively, it may be deduced from the known expansions of e^x and $\sin x$. Adopting the latter procedure, we have, in the first place,

$$e^x = 1 + x + \frac{x^2}{2!} + \frac{x^3}{3!} + \frac{x^4}{4!} + \ldots .$$

Therefore the expansion for e^{-2x} is found by replacing x in the above expansion by $-2x$; thus

$$e^{-2x} = 1 + (-2x) + \frac{(-2x)^2}{2!} + \frac{(-2x)^3}{3!} + \frac{(-2x)^4}{4!} + \ldots ,$$
$$= 1 - 2x + 2x^2 - \tfrac{4}{3}x^3 + \tfrac{2}{3}x^4 - \ldots .$$

Similarly, since

$$\sin x = x - \frac{x^3}{3!} + \frac{x^5}{5!} - \ldots ,$$

it follows that

$$\sin 3x = (3x) - \frac{(3x)^3}{3!} + \frac{(3x)^5}{5!} - \ldots ,$$
$$= 3x - \tfrac{9}{2}x^3 + \tfrac{81}{40}x^5 - \ldots .$$

Hence

$$e^{-2x} \sin 3x = (1 - 2x + 2x^2 - \tfrac{4}{3}x^3 + \tfrac{2}{3}x^4 - \dots)(3x - \tfrac{9}{2}x^3 + \dots)$$
$$= 3x - 6x^2 + 6x^3 - 4x^4 + \dots - \tfrac{9}{2}x^3 + 9x^4 - \dots,$$
$$= 3x - 6x^2 + \tfrac{3}{2}x^3 + 5x^4 + \dots.$$

This expansion can hold only for those values of x for which the expansions of e^{-2x} and $\sin 3x$ are both valid. But the expansions of both e^x and $\sin x$ hold for all values of x; therefore so also does the expansion we have derived for $e^{-2x} \sin 3x$.

6. Expand $\log (\cos x)$ in ascending powers of x as far as the term in x^6.

The only logarithmic expansion we have available is that of $\log (1 + x)$. This suggests that the first step must be to find an expansion for $\cos x$ in the form " $1 +$ something." At once, the relationship $\cos x = 1 - 2 \sin^2 \dfrac{x}{2}$ springs to mind, and indeed this relationship could be used, but the arithmetic is simpler if we merely rewrite $\cos x$ in the artificial form $1 + (\cos x - 1)$; thus

$$\log (\cos x) = \log \{ 1 + (\cos x - 1) \}$$
$$= (\cos x - 1) - \tfrac{1}{2} (\cos x - 1)^2 + \tfrac{1}{3} (\cos x - 1)^3 - \dots,$$
$$= \left(-\frac{x^2}{2!} + \frac{x^4}{4!} - \frac{x^6}{6!} + \dots \right) - \frac{1}{2} \left(-\frac{x^2}{2!} + \frac{x^4}{4!} - \dots \right)^2$$
$$+ \frac{1}{3} \left(-\frac{x^2}{2!} + \dots \right)^3 - \dots,$$
$$= -\frac{x^2}{2} + \frac{x^4}{24} - \frac{x^6}{720} + \dots - \frac{1}{2} \left(\frac{x^4}{4} - \frac{x^6}{24} + \dots \right)$$
$$+ \frac{1}{3} \left(-\frac{x^6}{8} + \dots \right) - \dots,$$
$$= -\frac{x^2}{2} - \frac{x^4}{12} - \frac{x^6}{45} - \dots.$$

The expansion for $\log (1 + x)$ holds only if $-1 < x \leq 1$; therefore the above expansion is valid only if

$$-1 < \cos x - 1 \leq 1,$$

that is, $$0 < \cos x \leq 2.$$

This inequality is clearly satisfied at the upper limit, whatever be the value of x, for the value of $\cos x$ cannot exceed 1; the lower limit implies that $\cos x$ must be positive, which is obviously essential in order that $\log (\cos x)$ may be real. Thus, the above expansion holds for all values of x for which $\cos x$ is positive.

7. Find, without using tables, the value of $\sin 10°$, correct to four decimal places.

The first step is to convert $10°$ into radians. Remembering that $180° = \pi$ radians, we have

$$10° = \frac{\pi}{18} \text{ radian} = 0\cdot1745 \text{ radian}.$$

If, as in the present example, x is small, then x^3 must be much smaller, x^5 must be still smaller, and so on. Indeed, when x is small, we may write as successive approximations to the value of $\sin x$:

first approximation . . . x ;

second approximation . . $x - \dfrac{x^3}{3!}$;

third approximation . . . $x - \dfrac{x^3}{3!} + \dfrac{x^5}{5!}$;

and so on.

In the present example, $x = 0\cdot1745$, and we are interested in an approximation which is correct to four decimal places. We find that we need retain only the first two terms ; thus

$$\sin 10° = 0\cdot1745 - \frac{(0\cdot1745)^3}{3!} + \dots,$$
$$= 0\cdot1745 - 0\cdot0009 + \dots,$$
$$\doteqdot 0\cdot1736.$$

Maclaurin's theorem is but a particular case of a more general result which we shall now consider. If $f(x)$ is a function of x, it is possible, *under certain circumstances*, to expand $f(x + h)$ as a power series in h. Let us *assume* that such an expansion is possible, and that

$$f(x + h) = a_0 + a_1 h + a_2 h^2 + a_3 h^3 + \dots,$$

where $a_0, a_1, a_2, \dots$ are functions of x alone, not containing h.

Before we proceed further, it must be stressed that, in the arguments which follow, h should be regarded as variable, and x as some known, fixed, but unstated value. Unless these ideas are kept in mind, confusion may result.

Differentiating with regard to h, we have

$$f'(x+h)\dagger = a_1 + 2a_2h + 3a_3h^2 \quad + \ldots,$$
$$f''(x+h) = \qquad 2a_2 + 3 \cdot 2a_3h + \ldots,$$
$$f'''(x+h) = \qquad\qquad 3 \cdot 2a_3 \quad + \ldots,$$

and so on.

These expansions are to hold for all values of h, and, in particular, for $h = 0$. Hence, putting $h = 0$, we have

$$f(x) = a_0, \qquad f'(x) = a_1,$$
$$f''(x) = 2a_2, \qquad f'''(x) = 3 \cdot 2a_3,$$

and so on.

Hence, provided such an expansion is possible,

$$f(x+h) = f(x) + h \cdot f'(x) + \frac{h^2}{2!} \cdot f''(x) + \frac{h^3}{3!} \cdot f'''(x) + \ldots .$$

This result is known as **Taylor's Theorem.*** ✳

Once more, it must be emphasised that discussion of the circumstances under which such expansions are possible are beyond the scope of this book. It may be stated, however, that Taylor's theorem applies only if

(i) $f(x)$ and all its derivatives are continuous, and therefore finite, throughout the particular range of values of x under consideration ;

---

† This step is not as obvious as it seems. The real meaning of $f'(x+h)$ is the derivative of $f(x+h)$ *with respect to* $x+h$. But

$$\frac{d}{dh}\Big[f(x+h)\Big] = \frac{d}{d(x+h)}\Big[f(x+h)\Big] \cdot \frac{d(x+h)}{dh} = f'(x+h),$$

since $\dfrac{d(x+h)}{dh} = 1$.

Similarly $\dfrac{d^2}{dh^2}\Big[f(x+h)\Big] = f''(x+h)$, and so on.

---

* Brook Taylor (1685-1731), who was born at Edmonton, Middlesex, and educated at Cambridge, was among the most ardent of Newton's admirers. At the age of 30, he published his most important work which contained a proof of the theorem which now bears his name.

✳ Taylor's Theorem may also
be written

$$f(x) = f(a) + \frac{x-a}{1} \cdot f'(a) + \frac{(x-a)^2}{2!} f''(a) + \cdots$$

(ii) the remainder after the first n terms, that is,

$$\frac{h^n}{n!} \cdot f^n(x) + \frac{h^{n+1}}{(n+1)!} \cdot f^{n+1}(x) + \frac{h^{n+2}}{(n+2)!} \cdot f^{n+2}(x) + \ldots,$$

tends to zero as n tends to infinity, so that the series approaches a finite limit.

Maclaurin's theorem may be derived at once from Taylor's theorem by writing 0 for x, and x for h. The relationship between the two theorems may be put in another way. In Maclaurin's theorem we expand from $x = 0$ (the first term in the expansion, it will be remembered is $f(0)$) ; in Taylor's theorem, we start expanding from a known but unspecified value x of the independent variable (the first term in the expansion being $f(x)$). Maclaurin's theorem enables us to find a set of approximations to the value of $f(x)$ when x is small (see Example 7, page 258) ; Taylor's theorem provides a similar set of approximations to the value of $f(x + h)$ when the value of $f(x)$ is known, and h is small. These approximations are given by the following expressions :—

first approximation . . $f(x)$;
second approximation . $f(x) + h \cdot f'(x)$;

third approximation . . $f(x) + h \cdot f'(x) + \frac{h^2}{2!} \cdot f''(x)$;

and so on. If we wish to calculate the value of cos 1°, we use Maclaurin's theorem; if we wish to find the value of cos 61° from the known value of cos 60°, we use Taylor's theorem (see Example 8, page 261).

The first and second approximations quoted above are capable of simple graphical illustration. Let us consider the form of the curve $y = f(x)$ between the point P, whose abscissa is x, and the neighbouring point Q, whose abscissa is $x + h$ (Fig. 68).

If h is sufficiently small, then NQ ($= f(x + h)$) will differ only slightly from MP. The first approximation to $f(x + h)$ may therefore be taken as $f(x)$.

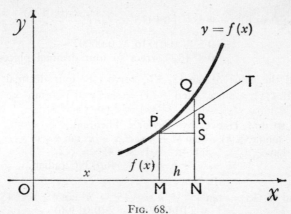

FIG. 68.

At P, the rate of increase of $f(x)$ is given by $f'(x)$; this means that at P, $f(x)$ is increasing at the rate of $f'(x)$ units per unit increase of x. If this rate be assumed uniform over the range x to $x + h$, then the actual increase in $f(x)$ in this range would be $h \cdot f'(x)$, indicated in the figure by SR, and $f(x + h)$ would be given by

$$f(x + h) = f(x) + h \cdot f'(x),$$

which is the second approximation given by Taylor's theorem.

But the rate of increase of $f(x)$ is not uniform; therefore the above result is not exact and it is possible to obtain closer approximations to the exact value of $f(x + h)$. Taylor's theorem provides the means whereby these approximations may be obtained to any required degree of accuracy.

8. Find, correct to four decimal places, the value of $\cos 61°$.

If $f(x) = \cos x$, then $f'(x) = -\sin x$, $f''(x) = -\cos x$, and so on. Hence, by Taylor's theorem,

$$\cos(x + h) = \cos x - h \sin x - \frac{h^2}{2} \cos x + \dots .$$

We have $\cos 60° = \dfrac{1}{2}$, $\quad \sin 60° = \dfrac{\sqrt{3}}{2}$,

and $\qquad h = 1° = \dfrac{\pi}{180}$ radian $= 0 \cdot 0175$ radian.

261

Hence $\cos 61° = 0\cdot5 - \left(0\cdot0175 \times \dfrac{\sqrt{3}}{2}\right) - \dfrac{(0\cdot0175)^2}{2} \cdot \dfrac{1}{2} + \dots ,$

$$= 0\cdot5 - 0\cdot01516 - 0\cdot00007 + \dots ,$$

$$= 0\cdot4848, \text{ correct to four decimal places.}$$

9. Find the value of $\tan 45° 48'$, correct to four decimal places.

If $f(x) = \tan x$, then $f'(x) = \sec^2 x = 1 + \tan^2 x,$
$$f''(x) = 2 \tan x \sec^2 x,$$

and so on. Hence, by Taylor's Theorem,

$$\tan (x + h) = \tan x + h \sec^2 x + h^2 \tan x \sec^2 x + \dots .$$

We have $\tan 45° = 1, \sec 45° = \sqrt{2},$
and $h = 48' = 0\cdot01396 \text{ radian.}$

Hence

$$\tan 45° 48' = \tan 45° + h \sec^2 45° + h^2 \tan 45° \sec^2 45° + \dots ,$$

$$= 1 + 2 (0\cdot01396) + 2 (0\cdot01396)^2 + \dots ,$$

$$= 1 + 0\cdot02792 + 0\cdot00039 + \dots ,$$

$$= 1\cdot0283, \text{ correct to four decimal places.}$$

10. If $F(x)$ and $f(x)$ are functions of x such that $F(a) = f(a) = 0$, prove, by Taylor's theorem, that

$$\mathop{L}_{x \to a} \frac{F(x)}{f(x)} = \frac{F'(a)}{f'(a)} .$$

We have

$$\mathop{L}_{x \to a} \frac{F(x)}{f(x)} = \mathop{L}_{h \to 0} \frac{F(a + h)}{f(a + h)} ,$$

$$= \mathop{L}_{h \to 0} \frac{F(a) + h \cdot F'(a) + \dfrac{h^2}{2!} \cdot F''(a) + \dots}{f(a) + h \cdot f'(a) + \dfrac{h^2}{2!} \cdot f''(a) + \dots} ,$$

assuming that Taylor's theorem may be applied to the two functions in question.

But $F(a) = f(a) = 0$; hence, dividing numerator and denominator by h, we have

$$\mathop{L}_{x \to a} \frac{F(x)}{f(x)} = \mathop{L}_{h \to 0} \frac{F'(a) + \dfrac{h}{2!} \cdot F''(a) + \dots}{f'(a) + \dfrac{h}{2!} \cdot f''(a) + \dots} = \frac{F'(a)}{f'(a)} .$$

If, however, $F'(a)$ and $f'(a)$ are both zero, the limit becomes clearly $\dfrac{F''(a)}{f''(a)}$; if, further, $F''(a) = f''(a) = 0$, the limit is $\dfrac{F'''(a)}{f'''(a)}$, and so on.

[This result, known as **L'Hospital's Theorem***, is sometimes useful in enabling us to find the limit of a quotient of two functions both of which vanish for the limiting value of the independent variable. For example, let us evaluate

$$\mathcal{L}_{x \to \theta} \; \frac{x - \theta}{\sin x - \sin \theta} \; .$$

Here, $F(x) = x - \theta$, and $f(x) = \sin x - \sin \theta$,
so that $\qquad\qquad F(\theta) = 0 = f(\theta)$.
Since, however, $F'(x) = 1$ and $f'(x) = \cos x$,
it follows that $F'(\theta) = 1$ and $f'(\theta) = \cos \theta$,
and the required limit is $\dfrac{1}{\cos \theta}$.]

11. Find the first four terms of the expansions in ascending powers of x of the following functions of x:

    (i) $\sin^{-1} x$,   (ii) $e^{\sin x}$,

    (iii) $\log(1 + \sin x)$,   (iv) $e^x \sin x$,

    (v) $\log(1 + e^x)$,   (vi) $e^{\tan^{-1} x}$,

    (vii) $\dfrac{e^x}{1 - \sin x}$,   (viii) $\log(\sec x)$,

    (ix) $\tan x$,   (x) $\dfrac{\sin x}{1 + x}$.

12. Calculate, correct to four decimal places:

    (i) $\tan 29°$,   (ii) $\cos 5°$,

    (iii) $\sin 31°$,   (iv) $\sqrt[5]{e}$,

    (v) $\log_{10} 1·05$ (given $\log_e 10 = 2·3026$).

13. Given $\log_{10} 87 = 1·9395$, find the value of $\log_{10} 87·5$, correct to four decimal places.

---

* Named after the French mathematician, Marquis de L'Hospital (1661-1704), who wrote what was probably the first textbook on the Calculus.

14. Establish Machin's formula,

$$\frac{\pi}{4} = 4 \tan^{-1}\frac{1}{5} - \tan^{-1}\frac{1}{239} ,$$

and use it to find the value of π, correct to six decimal places.

15. Using the definitions quoted on page 242, establish expansions for $\cosh x$, $\sinh x$, and $\tanh x$, in ascending powers of x.

16. If
$$y = x + \frac{x^2}{2!} + \frac{x^3}{3!} + \frac{x^4}{4!} + \dots , \text{ where } x \leqq \log 2,$$
show that
$$x = y - \frac{y^2}{2} + \frac{y^3}{3} - \frac{y^4}{4} + \dots .$$

17. Draw on the same diagram graphs of the functions
$$x, \ x - \frac{x^3}{3!} , \text{ and } \sin x,$$
in the neighbourhood of $x = 0$.

18. Prove that if $|x| < \frac{1}{2}$,
$$\log (1 + 3x + 2x^2) = 3x - \tfrac{5}{2}x^2 + 3x^3 - \tfrac{17}{4}x^4 + \dots .$$

19. If x is so small that the fourth and higher powers of αx and βx may be neglected, show that
$$\log \left\{ \frac{(1 + \alpha x)(1 + \beta x)}{1 + (\alpha + \beta) x} \right\} = \alpha \beta x^2 \{ 1 - (\alpha + \beta) x \}.$$

20. Show that, if $x^2 > 1$,
$$\log x^2 - \log (x + 1) - \log (x - 1) = \frac{1}{x^2} + \frac{1}{2x^4} + \frac{1}{3x^6} + \dots .$$

21. If x is so small that x^5 and higher powers may be neglected, prove that
$$\log (\cos^2 x) + x \sin x = - \tfrac{1}{3}x^4.$$

22. Find the first four terms of the expansion of $\tan^{-1}(1 + x)$ in ascending powers of x. If $\tan y = 1 + px + qx^2$, where x is small, use the above expansion to obtain an approximate value for y in the form $a_0 + a_1x + a_2x^2$.

23. Show that, for small values of x,
$$(1 + x)^{1+x} \doteqdot 1 + x + x^2.$$

24. Prove that
$$\frac{e^{\sin^{-1}x}}{\sqrt{(1 - x^2)}} = 1 + x + x^2 + \frac{5x^3}{6} + \dots .$$

25. If x is so small that x^8 and higher powers may be neglected, prove that
$$x^3 \log \sqrt{\left(\frac{1+x+x^2}{1-x+x^2}\right)} = \sin^4 x.$$

26. If $xy + \log(x+y+1) = 0$, find the values of y, y', y'', y''' when $x = 0$, and deduce a power series for y as far as the term in x^3.

27. Use the expansions established in this section to evaluate the following limits:

   (i) $\dfrac{1 - \cos x}{x^2}$, as $x \longrightarrow 0$;

   (ii) $\dfrac{e^x - 1}{x}$, as $x \longrightarrow 0$;

   (iii) $\dfrac{\sin x - x}{x^3}$, as $x \longrightarrow 0$;

   (iv) $\dfrac{2 \cos x - 2 + x^2}{x^4}$, as $x \longrightarrow 0$;

   (v) $\dfrac{\log x}{x - 1}$, as $x \longrightarrow 1$.

28. Use L'Hospital's theorem to evaluate the following limits:

   (i) $\dfrac{\sin x}{x}$, as $x \longrightarrow 0$;

   (ii) $\dfrac{x^n - a^n}{x - a}$, as $x \longrightarrow a$;

   (iii) $\dfrac{x^{\frac{1}{2}} - 1}{x^{\frac{1}{3}} - 1}$, as $x \longrightarrow 1$;

   (iv) $\dfrac{x \sin a - a \sin x}{x - a}$, as $x \longrightarrow a$;

   (v) $\dfrac{x^2 \log a - a^2 \log x}{x^2 - a^2}$, as $x \longrightarrow a$.

29. The approximate length of a circular arc ABC is sometimes taken to be $\frac{1}{3}(8b - a)$, where a, b are the lengths of the chords AC, AB, respectively, and B is the mid-point of the arc AC. Prove that if θ is the angle subtended by the arc ABC at the centre of the circle, the above formula assumes that the fourth and higher powers of θ may be neglected.

30. The length of an endless belt passing round two pulleys of
diameters D and d, with their centres at distance l apart, is given
approximately by the formula
$$2l + 1 \cdot 57 (D + d) + \frac{(D - d)^2}{4l} \,.$$

Show that, if $\theta = \sin^{-1} \dfrac{D - d}{2l}$, this formula assumes that the
cube and higher powers of θ may be neglected.

§ 30. INTEGRATION.

Integration has already (**§ 19**) been defined as the process inverse to differentiation ; that is, if we are told that $F(x)$ is the derivative of a certain function $f(x)$, then integration is the process whereby we find that function.   The two statements

$$\frac{d}{dx}\left\{ f(x) \right\} = F(x),$$

and

$$\int F(x)\, dx = f(x)$$

are but two ways of saying the same thing.   Since, however, the derivative of a constant is zero, the most general form of the integral of $F(x)$ is $f(x) + C$, where C is an arbitrary constant. For example,

$$\frac{d}{dx}(x^4) = 4x^3, \text{ but } \int 4x^3 dx = x^4 + C \text{ ;}$$

and x^4, $x^4 + \frac{2}{3}$, $x^4 - 16$, $x^4 + \sqrt{2}$ are all " particular " integrals of $4x^3$.   It will be recalled that the expression $4x^3$ to be integrated is called the " integrand," and the particular integral x^4, obtained by omitting the arbitrary constant, is called the " indefinite " integral of $4x^3$.

While we are concentrating on the mere *technique* of integration, we shall, in order to avoid tedious repetition, omit the constant of integration and quote only the indefinite integral.   But the reader must realise that we are taking a liberty in so doing, and that as soon as we apply the operation of integration to the solution of practical problems, the constant of integration must be inserted. The data of such problems will generally include information which will enable us to calculate the appropriate value of this constant.

Direct processes, such as addition, evolution, and differentiation, are operations which can *always* be performed, by the mere application of certain clearly defined rules.   For example, we can find the sum of *any* two integers, we can square *any* integer, we can differentiate *any* function—even such an absurdly involved one as

$$e^{-z^2}, \text{ where } z = \sqrt[3]{\left\{ \log \left[\sin^{-1} \left(x^{\frac{7}{2}} - 5x^{-\frac{3}{2}} \right) \right] \right\}}.$$

On the other hand, inverse processes, such as subtraction, involution, and integration, are not always possible—at least, not unless we are prepared to introduce new types of numbers and new types of functions. For example, we cannot subtract 5 from 3, without the introduction of negative numbers ; we cannot find the square root of -1, without the use of imaginary numbers. Similarly, so long as we confine ourselves to the elementary functions of Mathematics, we cannot integrate every function which we come across. It may be remembered that in Part I of this book we found that we could integrate x^n for every value of n *except* $n = -1$, for we knew of no **algebraic** function having $\dfrac{1}{x}$ as its derivative. We can now integrate $\dfrac{1}{x}$, for we have since been introduced to the non-algebraic, or **transcendental,** function, $\log x$; but we cannot integrate even such apparently innocuous functions as $\dfrac{1}{x} \cos x$, or $\sqrt{(1 + x^3)}$, for there is no known function—algebraic or transcendental*—which has either of these expressions as its derivative. (See, however, Example **12.**)

With integration it is therefore not possible to lay down general rules of procedure. Some functions may be integrated by inspection, by recognising from previous experience of

---

* Algebraic functions are those in which the only operations performed on the variable (and known constants) are addition, subtraction, multiplication, division, evolution (raising to a known power), and involution (root-extraction). Transcendental functions are those which involve other operations. The commonest transcendental functions are trigonometric functions, exponential functions, and logarithmic functions. The number of operations involved in an algebraic function must be finite, for, as we have already seen in the case of the exponential function, it is possible to express certain transcendental functions in the form of an infinite series of algebraic functions.

differentiation the function which has the given integrand as its derivative. Other functions may be integrated by means of special methods, two of the most powerful of which are described in the next sections. And some functions, as we have already seen, cannot be integrated at all.

The first step must clearly be to compile a list of known integrals. Such a list may be obtained from the set of standard derivatives quoted on page 188. Thus we have

Function	Integral
x^n	$\dfrac{x^{n+1}}{n+1}$, $n \neq -1$
$\dfrac{1}{x}$	$\log x$
$\sin x$	$-\cos x$
$\cos x$	$\sin x$
$\sec^2 x$	$\tan x$
e^x	e^x
$\dfrac{1}{\sqrt{(1 - x^2)}}$	$\sin^{-1} x$ or $-\cos^{-1} x$
$\dfrac{1}{1 + x^2}$	$\tan^{-1} x$
$\dfrac{1}{\sqrt{(a^2 - x^2)}}$	$\sin^{-1}\left(\dfrac{x}{a}\right)$ or $-\cos^{-1}\left(\dfrac{x}{a}\right)$
$\dfrac{1}{a^2 + x^2}$	$\dfrac{1}{a}\tan^{-1}\left(\dfrac{x}{a}\right)$
$\dfrac{1}{\sqrt{(x^2 + a^2)}}$	$\log\{x + \sqrt{(x^2 + a^2)}\}$ or $\sinh^{-1}\left(\dfrac{x}{a}\right)$
$\dfrac{1}{\sqrt{(x^2 - a^2)}}$	$\log\{x + \sqrt{(x^2 - a^2)}\}$ or $\cosh^{-1}\left(\dfrac{x}{a}\right)$

The last four integrals are obtained from the results established
in Example 3, page 200, and Example 4, page 201, and are
included because of their general usefulness.

The independent variable so often occurs in functions in the
form ax or $ax + b$, that the following simple extensions (which
can all be easily checked by differentiation) may be added to the
above list and regarded as standard forms.

Function	Integral
$(ax + b)^n$	$\dfrac{(ax + b)^{n+1}}{a(n + 1)}, \ n \neq -1$
$\dfrac{1}{ax + b}$	$\dfrac{1}{a} \log (ax + b)$
$\sin (ax + b)$	$-\dfrac{1}{a} \cos (ax + b)$
$\cos (ax + b)$	$\dfrac{1}{a} \sin (ax + b)$
$\sec^2 (ax + b)$	$\dfrac{1}{a} \tan (ax + b)$
e^{ax+b}	$\dfrac{1}{a} e^{ax+b}$

The reader should make himself completely familiar with all
these results for the normal procedure in integration is to
reduce, if possible, the given integrand to one of the above
standard forms. The integral may then be written down at
once. To begin with, the reader is advised to test every indefinite
integral by differentiation in order to check that the derivative
so obtained does in fact equal the original integrand.

Examples

1. Integrate $\dfrac{1}{x^{\frac{1}{3}}}$.

   Such integrals as $\displaystyle\int \dfrac{1}{x^{\frac{1}{3}}}\, dx$ are often written more concisely in

   the form $\displaystyle\int \dfrac{dx}{x^{\frac{1}{3}}}$; similarly, $\displaystyle\int \dfrac{x\, dx}{x+1}$ is merely a shorter form of

   $\displaystyle\int \dfrac{x}{x+1}\, dx.$

   Thus, $\displaystyle\int \dfrac{dx}{x^{\frac{1}{3}}} = \int x^{-\frac{1}{3}}\, dx = \dfrac{x^{-\frac{1}{3}+1}}{-\frac{1}{3}+1} = \tfrac{3}{2}x^{\frac{2}{3}}.$

   [Check. $\dfrac{d}{dx}\left(\tfrac{3}{2}x^{\frac{2}{3}}\right) = \tfrac{3}{2}\cdot\tfrac{2}{3}x^{-\frac{1}{3}} = \dfrac{1}{x^{\frac{1}{3}}}$].

2. Integrate $\sqrt{(3-2x)}$.

   $$\int \sqrt{(3-2x)}\, dx = \int (3-2x)^{\frac{1}{2}}\, dx = \dfrac{(3-2x)^{\frac{3}{2}}}{\tfrac{3}{2}\cdot(-2)},$$

   $$= -\tfrac{1}{3}(3-2x)^{\frac{3}{2}}.$$

   [Check. $\dfrac{d}{dx}\left[-\tfrac{1}{3}(3-2x)^{\frac{3}{2}}\right] = -\tfrac{1}{3}\cdot\tfrac{3}{2}\cdot(-2)(3-2x)^{\frac{1}{2}}$

   $$= \sqrt{(3-2x)}.]$$

3. Integrate $\dfrac{6x^2+1}{2x-1}$.

   If the integrand is a rational function of the form $\dfrac{F(x)}{\Phi(x)}$, and

   if $F(x)$ is of degree equal to or higher than that of $\Phi(x)$, the
   first step always is to divide out. The situation is analogous to
   that of expressing an improper fraction, such as $\tfrac{13}{5}$ in the form
   of a mixed number, namely $2 + \tfrac{3}{5}$.

   By division, we have
   $$\dfrac{6x^2+1}{2x-1} = 3x + \dfrac{3}{2} + \dfrac{5}{2(2x-1)}.$$

   Therefore, $\displaystyle\int \dfrac{6x^2+1}{2x-1}\, dx = \int \left\{3x + \dfrac{3}{2} + \dfrac{5}{2(2x-1)}\right\}\, dx,$

$$= \frac{3x^2}{2} + \frac{3}{2}x + \frac{5}{4} \log (2x - 1).$$

The reader is left to check this result by differentiation.

4. Integrate $\sin \left(\frac{1}{2}x + \frac{2\pi}{3} \right)$.

$$\int \sin \left(\frac{1}{2}x + \frac{2\pi}{3} \right) dx = \frac{-\cos \left(\frac{1}{2}x + \frac{2\pi}{3} \right)}{\frac{1}{2}} = -2 \cos \left(\frac{1}{2}x + \frac{2\pi}{3} \right).$$

5. Integrate $\sin^2 x$.

Since $2 \sin^2 x = 1 - \cos 2x$, we have

$$\int \sin^2 x \, dx = \tfrac{1}{2} \int (1 - \cos 2x) \, dx = \tfrac{1}{2} \left(x - \tfrac{1}{2} \sin 2x \right).$$

6. Integrate $\sin 3x \sin 4x$.

A product of two sines, or of two cosines, or of a sine and a cosine, can always be expressed as a sum or difference of two cosines or sines. For example,

$$2 \sin A \sin B = \cos (A - B) - \cos (A + B).$$

Thus, $$\int \sin 3x \sin 4x \, dx = \tfrac{1}{2} \int (\cos x - \cos 7x) \, dx,$$

$$= \tfrac{1}{2} \left(\sin x - \tfrac{1}{7} \sin 7x \right).$$

7. Integrate $\frac{1}{\sqrt{(9 - 4x^2)}}$.

The denominator may be changed to the standard form $\sqrt{(a^2 - x^2)}$ by the removal of the unwanted factor 4 ; thus $\sqrt{(9 - 4x^2)} = 2\sqrt{(\tfrac{9}{4} - x^2)}$.

Therefore, $$\int \frac{dx}{\sqrt{(9 - 4x^2)}} = \tfrac{1}{2} \int \frac{dx}{\sqrt{(\tfrac{9}{4} - x^2)}} = \tfrac{1}{2} \sin^{-1} \left(\frac{x}{\tfrac{3}{2}} \right).$$

$$= \tfrac{1}{2} \sin^{-1} \left(\frac{2x}{3} \right).$$

8. Integrate $\frac{1}{x^2 + 2x + 4}$.

The denominator may be written in the form $(x + 1)^2 + 3$, that is, $(x + 1)^2 + (\sqrt{3})^2$. Thus

$$\int \frac{dx}{x^2 + 2x + 4} = \int \frac{dx}{(x + 1)^2 + (\sqrt{3})^2} = \frac{1}{\sqrt{3}} \tan^{-1} \left(\frac{x + 1}{\sqrt{3}} \right).$$

Although the last integral does not conform to any of the standard types, it is clearly a straight-forward extension of

$$\int \frac{dx}{x^2 + a^2}.$$

9. Integrate $\dfrac{1}{\sqrt{(x^2 - x + 1)}}$.

Since $x^2 - x + 1 = (x - \frac{1}{2})^2 + \frac{3}{4}$, we have

$$\int \frac{dx}{\sqrt{(x^2 - x + 1)}} = \int \frac{dx}{\sqrt{\{(x - \frac{1}{2})^2 + \frac{3}{4}\}}}$$
$$= \log \{(x - \tfrac{1}{2}) + \sqrt{(x^2 - x + 1)}\}.$$

10. Integrate $\dfrac{x + 3}{x^2 + 3x + 2}$.

This expression has the form of a proper fraction, for the degree of the numerator is less than that of the denominator. Moreover, the denominator can be expressed as the product of two first degree factors, $x + 1$ and $x + 2$. The expression can therefore be written as the sum (or difference) of two **partial fractions***, one a proper fraction with denominator $x + 1$, and one a proper fraction with denominator $x + 2$. The numerators, being of degree less than one (the degree of the denominators), must be constants. Thus,

if $\dfrac{x + 3}{(x + 1)(x + 2)} = \dfrac{A}{x + 1} + \dfrac{B}{x + 2}$, where A and B are constants,

then $\qquad x + 3 = A(x + 2) + B(x + 1),$

and this is an identity which holds for all values of x.

To find the appropriate values of A and B we may equate corresponding coefficients :

from the coefficient of x, ... $1 = A + B$;
from the constant term, ... $3 = 2A + B$.

Hence $A = 2$, $B = -1$.

It is often quicker, however, to substitute particular values of x in the identity, especially if we choose in turn those values which make the factors within the brackets vanish. Thus,

let $x = -1$; then $-1 + 3 = A(-1 + 2) + B(0)$, or $A = 2$;
let $x = -2$; then $-2 + 3 = A(0) + B(-2 + 1)$, or $B = -1$.

---

* For fuller information on partial fractions, see McArthur and Keith, *Intermediate Algebra* (Methuen), Chapter V.

10

Therefore, $\int \dfrac{(x+3)\,dx}{x^2+3x+2} = \int \left(\dfrac{2}{x+1} - \dfrac{1}{x+2}\right) dx$

$$= 2 \log (x+1) - \log (x+2),$$

$$= \log \frac{(x+1)^2}{x+2}.$$

11. Integrate $\dfrac{x^4 - x^3 - 2}{(x^2+1)(x-1)}$.

By division, $\dfrac{x^4 - x^3 - 2}{(x^2+1)(x-1)} = x - \dfrac{x^2 - x + 2}{(x^2+1)(x-1)}$.

Now let us resolve the proper fraction $\dfrac{x^2 - x + 2}{(x^2+1)(x-1)}$ into

partial fractions. These fractions will have denominators $x^2 + 1$ and $x - 1$. The numerator of the first fraction will be of lower degree than two (the degree of $x^2 + 1$), and therefore of the form $Ax + B$, where A and B are constants; the numerator of the second fraction will be of lower degree than one (the degree of $x - 1$), and therefore a constant, say C. Thus

if $\qquad \dfrac{x^2 - x + 2}{(x^2+1)(x-1)} = \dfrac{Ax + B}{x^2 + 1} + \dfrac{C}{x - 1},$

then $\qquad x^2 - x + 2 = (Ax + B)(x - 1) + C(x^2 + 1),$
for all values of x.

Let $x = 1$; then $2 = 2C$, or $C = 1$.

Let $x = 0$; then $2 = -B + C = -B + 1$, so that $B = -1$.

From the coefficient of x^2, $1 = A + C = A + 1$, so that $A = 0$.

Thus, $\int \dfrac{x^4 - x^3 - 2}{(x^2+1)(x-1)}\,dx = \int \left(x + \dfrac{1}{x^2 + 1} - \dfrac{1}{x - 1}\right) dx,$

$$= \tfrac{1}{2}x^2 + \tan^{-1} x - \log (x - 1).$$

12. Find, using Simpson's Rule (page 120), an approximate value for the definite integral

$$\int_0^5 \sqrt{(1 + x^3)}\,dx.$$

It has already been observed (page 268) that we cannot integrate $\sqrt{(1 + x^3)}$ exactly, for we know of no function which, when differentiated, yields $\sqrt{(1 + x^3)}$. From geometrical considerations, however, we can find an approximate value for the above definite integral using Simpson's Rule, for all we have to do is to find a value for the area under the curve $y = \sqrt{(1 + x^3)}$ from $x = 0$ to $x = 5$.

We choose values of x which will subdivide the range $x = 0$ to $x = 5$ into an *even* number of equal parts, say 10, and then we calculate the corresponding values of y. Thus

x	0	0·5	1	1·5	2	2·5	3	3·5	4	4·5	5
y	1	1·06	1·41	2·09	3	4·08	5·29	6·62	8·06	9·60	11·23

Using Simpson's Rule, we have
the required area $= \frac{1}{3} . \frac{1}{2} [(1 + 11·23)$
$$+ 2 (1·41 + 3 + 5·29 + 8·06)$$
$$+ 4 (1·06 + 2·09 + 4·08 + 6·62 + 9·60)]$$
$$= \frac{1}{6} [12·23 + 35·52 + 93·80]$$
$$= \frac{1}{6} . 141·55 \doteqdot 23·6 \text{ sq. units.}$$

Hence
$$\int_0^5 \sqrt{(1 + x^3)} \, dx \doteqdot 23·6.$$

To obtain a more accurate value for this integral, we subdivide the range $x = 0$ to $x = 5$ into a still greater number of equal parts (but, in order that Simpson's Rule may be applied, that number must always be even).

13. Integrate the following functions of x, and verify your results by differentiation :

(i) $x^{\frac{1}{4}}$,

(ii) $6x^{-\frac{2}{3}}$,

(iii) $\sqrt{\left(\dfrac{3}{2x^3}\right)}$,

(iv) $1 - e^{-2x/3}$,

(v) $\sqrt{(1 - 3x)}$,

(vi) $\dfrac{1}{(2x - 5)^{\frac{1}{2}}}$,

(vii) $\dfrac{2x^2 - 1}{\sqrt{x}}$,

(viii) $3e^{\frac{2}{3}(1-x)}$,

(ix) $\dfrac{1}{1 - x}$,

(x) $\dfrac{x}{x + 1}$,

(xi) $\dfrac{1 + x^2}{1 - x}$,

(xii) $\dfrac{6x^2 - x + 7}{2x + 1}$,

(xiii) $\dfrac{x^2}{1 - 2x}$,

(xiv) $\dfrac{3 - 4x^2}{2 - 3x}$,

(xv) $\dfrac{3x + 2}{\sqrt{(2x + 1)}}$.

Try without substitution

14. Integrate with regard to x:

✓(i) $\cos\left(\dfrac{2\pi}{3} - \dfrac{3x}{2}\right)$,

(ii) $\sin\frac{3}{4}(\pi - x)$,

✓(iii) $\cos^2 x$,

(iv) $2\sin^2 x - 3\cos^2 x$,

✓(v) $\cos x \cos 2x$,

(vi) $\sin 3x \cos 5x$,

✓(vii) $\sin\dfrac{5}{2}x \cos\dfrac{3}{2}x$,

(viii) $3\sin 2x \cos^2 x$,

✓(ix) $\cos^3 x$,

(x) $\sin^3(1 - x)$.

15. Evaluate the following definite integrals:

✗(i) $\displaystyle\int_0^1 \sqrt{(3 - 2x)^3}\,dx$,

(ii) $\displaystyle\int_1^4 \left(\sqrt{x} - \dfrac{1}{\sqrt{x}}\right)^3 dx$,

✓(iii) $\displaystyle\int_{-a}^a \left\{\dfrac{1}{\sqrt{(2a + x)}} + \dfrac{1}{\sqrt{(2a - x)}}\right\} dx$,

(iv) $\displaystyle\int_{-a}^a \left(\sin\dfrac{\pi x}{2a} - 3\cos\dfrac{5\pi x}{2a}\right) dx$,

✗(v) $\displaystyle\int_{-l}^l \left(\sin\dfrac{\pi x}{l} + \sin^2\dfrac{\pi x}{l}\right) dx$,

(vi) $\displaystyle\int_0^{\frac{\pi}{4}} (\cos x - 2\sin x)^2\,dx$,

✓(vii) $\displaystyle\int_0^{\frac{\pi}{2}} \sin^2 x \cos^2 x\,dx$,

(viii) $\displaystyle\int_0^\pi \sin x\,(3 + 2\sin x + 4\cos x)\,dx$,

✓(ix) $\displaystyle\int_3^5 \dfrac{5 - 2x^2}{2 - x}\,dx$,

(x) $\displaystyle\int_7^{15} \dfrac{x\,dx}{\sqrt{(2x - 5)}}$.

276

16. Integrate the following functions of x:

(i) $\dfrac{1}{1 + 4x^2}$,   (ii) $\dfrac{1}{\sqrt{(4x^2 + 1)}}$,   (iii) $\dfrac{1}{\sqrt{(4x^2 - 1)}}$,

(iv) $\dfrac{1}{\sqrt{(1 - 4x^2)}}$,   (v) $\dfrac{1}{x^2 + x + 1}$,   (vi) $\dfrac{1}{\sqrt{(x^2 + x + 1)}}$,

(vii) $\dfrac{1}{5 - 4x - x^2}$,   (viii) $\dfrac{1}{\sqrt{(5 - 4x - x^2)}}$,

(ix) $\dfrac{1}{2x^2 - 3x + 4}$,   (x) $\dfrac{1}{\sqrt{(2 - 3x - 4x^2)}}$.

17. Evaluate the following indefinite integrals :

(i) $\displaystyle\int \dfrac{29dx}{(x^2 + 4)(x + 5)}$,   (ii) $\displaystyle\int \dfrac{5dx}{(x - 1)(3x^2 + 2)}$,

(iii) $\displaystyle\int \dfrac{x^2 + 5x + 16}{x^2 + 4x + 13}\,dx$,   (iv) $\displaystyle\int \dfrac{(x^2 + 1)\,dx}{(2x - 1)(4x^2 + 9)}$,

(v) $\displaystyle\int \dfrac{(x + 3)\,dx}{x^3 + x^2 + x}$,   (vi) $\displaystyle\int \dfrac{3xdx}{1 + x^3}$.

18. Evaluate the following definite integrals :

(i) $\displaystyle\int_1^2 \dfrac{2x^3 + 1}{x^2(2x + 1)}\,dx$,   (ii) $\displaystyle\int_{-1}^1 \dfrac{8 - 3x}{(73 - 48x)^{\frac{3}{2}}}\,dx$,

(iii) $\displaystyle\int_{-2}^3 \dfrac{xdx}{x^2 + 2x + 5}$,   (iv) $\displaystyle\int_0^1 \dfrac{x^2 + 1}{x^2 + x + 1}\,dx$,

(v) $\displaystyle\int_0^2 \dfrac{x^2 + x + 1}{x^2 - x + 1}\,dx$.

19. Express $8 \cos x + \sin x$ in the form
$$A (2 \cos x - \sin x) + B (2 \sin x + \cos x).$$
and hence find the value of

$$\int_0^{\frac{\pi}{4}} \dfrac{8 \cos x + \sin x}{2 \cos x - \sin x}\,dx.$$

20. Show in a diagram the area represented by the integral

$$\int_1^3 \sqrt{\{ (x - 1)(5 - x) \}}\,dx,$$

and hence find the value of the integral.

21. Prove geometrically that, if $b > a$,

$$\int_a^b \sqrt{\{(x-a)(b-x)\}}\, dx = \tfrac{1}{8}\pi\, (b-a)^2.$$

22. If $\dfrac{dy}{dx} = \dfrac{1}{(3-2x)^{\frac{3}{2}}}$, and if $y = 3$ when $x = 1$, prove that
$(3 - 2x)(y - 2)^2 = 1$.

23. If $\dfrac{dy}{dx} = \dfrac{x}{(x-1)^{\frac{3}{2}}}$, and if $y = 2$ when $x = 5$, prove that
$(y + 1)^2 (x - 1) = 4 (x - 2)^2$.

24. If $\dfrac{dy}{dx} = 1 - 4e^{-3x}$, and if $y = 1$ when $x = 0$, find an expression
for y in terms of x.

25. If $\dfrac{d^2y}{dx^2} = 4 \cos 2x - 12$, and if $y = -1$ and $\dfrac{dy}{dx} = 1$ when $x = 0$,
find an expression for y in terms of x.

26. Use Simpson's Rule to find an approximate value for each of
the definite integrals :

    (i) $\displaystyle\int_2^8 \frac{dx}{x\,(9-x)}$,   (ii) $\displaystyle\int_{\frac{\pi}{4}}^{\frac{\pi}{3}} (\tan x + \cot x)\, dx$,

    (iii) $\displaystyle\int_0^{\frac{\pi}{2}} \sqrt{(10 \sin x)}\, dx$,   (iv) $\displaystyle\int_0^{\frac{\pi}{2}} \sqrt{(\tan \tfrac{1}{2}x)}\, dx$.

§31. SPECIAL METHODS OF INTEGRATION—
BY CHANGE OF VARIABLE.

Reference has been made in the previous section to two special methods which are of great value in integration. These may be described as

(i) integration by change of variable,

(ii) integration by " parts."

We devote the major part of this section to an examination of the first of these two powerful methods. But before we do so, we must digress slightly in order to establish a result which will greatly simplify the change of variable in integration.

Differentials

In **§ 17** we saw that if y is a function of x, and if δy is the increment in y corresponding to the *small* increment δx in x, then

$$\delta y \fallingdotseq \frac{dy}{dx}\,\delta x.$$

When the symbol " $\fallingdotseq$ " is used in place of the more usual " $=$ ", it indicates that the relationship in question is one of practical equivalence and not one of absolute equality. As a rule, such an equation holds only under specified conditions, and in the above case the condition is that δx must be small.

It is possible by means of *Taylor's Theorem* (see page 259) to obtain better approximations for δy, and, in fact, we may find δy to any desired degree of accuracy by means of the series

$$\delta y = \frac{dy}{dx}\,\delta x + \frac{1}{2!}\frac{d^2y}{dx^2}(\delta x)^2 + \frac{1}{3!}\frac{d^3y}{dx^3}(\delta x)^3 + \cdots \qquad . \qquad . \quad (1)$$

Clearly, if δx is small, the terms of this series are of successively smaller orders of magnitude, and by considering one, two, three ... terms we obtain successively closer approximations for δy.

By way of illustration let us consider the function $y = x^4$. Let x increase from 1 to 1·1, so that y increases from 1 to 1·4641 ; thus $\delta x = 0\cdot1$, and $\delta y = 0\cdot4641$. It should be observed that 0·4641 is the *exact* value of δy and not an approximation. Using the series (1) we obtain approximate values for δy, as follows.

Since $y = x^4$, $\dfrac{dy}{dx} = 4x^3$, $\dfrac{d^2y}{dx^2} = 12x^2$, and $\dfrac{d^3_y}{dx^3} = 24x$,

we have, when $x = 1$ and $\delta x = 0\cdot1$,

the first approximation to $\delta y \quad = \dfrac{dy}{dx}\,\delta x = 4 \times 0\cdot1 = 0\cdot4$;

the second approximation to $\boldsymbol{\delta} y = 0\cdot4 + \dfrac{1}{2}\dfrac{d^2y}{dx^2}(\delta x)^2$

$= 0\cdot4 + \tfrac{1}{2} . 12 . 0\cdot01$

$= 0\cdot46$;

the third approximation to $\delta y \quad = 0\cdot46 + \dfrac{1}{6}\dfrac{dy^3}{dx^3}(\delta x)^3$

$= 0\cdot46 + \tfrac{1}{6} . 24 . 0\cdot001$

$= 0\cdot464.$

The exact value of δy is 0·4641 ; the first term of (1) gives the value of δy to within about 12 per cent., the first two terms to within about 1 per cent., the first three terms to within about 0·02 per cent. Expressed otherwise, the first term by itself contributes about 88 per cent. of the value of δy.

The series (1) thus consists of terms of decreasing magnitude. The first term, $\dfrac{dy}{dx}\,\delta x$, is therefore the most important in the sense that by itself it gives a very good approximation to the value of δy. It is therefore given a special name—the **differential** of y—and is denoted dy.

Thus

$$dy = \frac{dy}{dx}\,\delta x \quad \cdot \quad \cdot \quad \cdot \quad \cdot \quad (2)$$

Similarly, if $y = f(x)$, we may write

$$d[f(x)] = f'(x)\,\delta x,$$

using $f'(x)$ to denote the derivative of $f(x)$ (see footnote, page 41).

The function x has the derivative 1, and therefore its differential is $1\,.\,\delta x$, or δx. Thus,

$$d[f(x)] = \delta x, \text{ when } f(x) = x,$$

or

$$dx = \delta x,$$

so that, for the *independent* variable, dx and δx may be considered to be identical, and we may rewrite (2) as follows :—

$$dy = \frac{dy}{dx}\,dx \quad \cdot \quad \cdot \quad \cdot \quad \cdot \quad (3)$$

It is because of the position which $\frac{dy}{dx}$ occupies in this formula that the derivative is sometimes known as the " differential coefficient."

The implications of (3) are most important, especially in integration. Formerly we have consistently regarded $\frac{dy}{dx}$ as one quantity, *not* a ratio itself, although it is the limiting value of the ratio $\frac{\delta y}{\delta x}$ as δx tends to zero. Now, however, we may, if we find it convenient to do so, consider $\frac{dy}{dx}$ to be the ratio of the differentials dy and dx. Thus, if $y = x^3$, we are authorised to write $dy = 3x^2 dx$, instead of $\frac{dy}{dx} = 3x^2$. Similarly,

if $y = \dfrac{1}{ax+b}$, we may write $\dfrac{dy}{dx} = \dfrac{-a}{(ax+b)^2}$,

or, if we prefer, $\qquad dy = -\dfrac{a\,dx}{(ax+b)^2}$,

or
$$d\left(\frac{1}{ax+b}\right) = -\frac{a\,dx}{(ax+b)^2}.$$

A very little practice will soon bring the necessary skill in the alternative mode of writing the results of a differentiation. The value of this device in integration will be appreciated only once this skill has been acquired. The reader should therefore check the following results carefully before proceeding further.

If $u = \sin x$,　　then $du = \cos x\,dx$;

if $u = \dfrac{1}{x^2}$,　　then $du = -\dfrac{2dx}{x^3}$;

if $u = \log x$,　　then $du = \dfrac{dx}{x}$;

if $u = \sqrt{(1-x)}$, then $du = -\dfrac{dx}{2\sqrt{(1-x)}}$;

and conversely

$$x\,dx = d\left(\tfrac{1}{2}x^2\right) ;$$
$$\sin x\,dx = -d\left(\cos x\right);$$
$$\frac{dx}{x^2} = -d\left(\frac{1}{x}\right) ;$$
$$\sec^2 x\,dx = d\left(\tan x\right).$$

Integration by change of variable

It sometimes happens that an integrand which is difficult to reduce directly to one of the standard forms given on page 269, may be so reduced more easily by the choice of a suitable new independent variable. Consider, for example,

$$\int \frac{x\,dx}{\sqrt{(1+4x^2)}}.$$

There is no obvious way of reducing the integrand to one of the standard forms. The form of the denominator, however, together with the combination $x\,dx$ in the numerator at once suggests the substitution $u = x^2$, for then $du = 2x\ dx$, and the integral assumes the form

$$\int \frac{du}{2\sqrt{(1 + 4u)}},$$

which can be integrated without difficulty. But the denominator of the original integrand is also a function of $1 + 4x^2$, and $d(1 + 4x^2) = 8x\ dx$, so that the substitution $u = 1 + 4x^2$ will yield an even simpler integrand, namely

$$\int \frac{du}{8\sqrt{u}}.$$

Thus, the given integral $= \frac{1}{4}\sqrt{u}$, where $u = 1 + 4x^2$,
$$= \frac{1}{4}\sqrt{(1 + 4x^2)},$$
as may easily be verified by differentiation.

The original integral might, of course, have been a definite integral, say,

$$\int_0^{\sqrt{2}} \frac{x\ dx}{\sqrt{(1 + 4x^2)}};$$

that is, we have to integrate the given function over the range $x = 0$ to $x = \sqrt{2}$. The upper and lower limits of integration are values of the independent variable, and therefore when we change this variable to u by means of the substitution $u = 1 + 4x^2$, we must also change the limits of integration. We note, however, that

when $x = 0$, $u = 1 + 0 = 1$;
when $x = \sqrt{2}$, $u = 1 + 8 = 9$;

and that when x varies continuously from 0 to $\sqrt{2}$, u varies continuously from 1 to 9. Therefore,

$$\int_0^{\sqrt{2}} \frac{x\ dx}{\sqrt{(1 + 4x^2)}} = \int_1^9 \frac{du}{8\sqrt{u}} = \left[\frac{1}{4}\sqrt{u} \right]_1^9 = \frac{3}{4} - \frac{1}{4} = \frac{1}{2}.$$

There is no need in the case of a definite integral to return to the original independent variable (as was done with the indefinite integral above). We merely carry out the integration of the transformed integral over the appropriate range, in this case from $u = 1$ to $u = 9$.

The example just considered illustrates better than any general arguments all that is entailed in changing the independent variable in integration. The main difficulty for the beginner is in deciding what the new variable is to be. The decision is not alway an easy one, and only with considerable experience— and possibly a little mathematical " insight "—can the student acquire any real facility in finding the correct transformation. A study of the variety of worked exercises which follow will, however, show that in practically every case the *form* of the original integrand gives a clue as to what the new independent variable should be.

Examples

1. Evaluate $\int \sin^3 x \cos x \, dx$.

   The combination $\cos x \, dx$ suggests the substitution

   $$u = \sin x \; ; \quad \text{then } du = \cos x \, dx.$$

   Therefore, the required integral $= \int u^3 \, du = \dfrac{u^4}{4} = \tfrac{1}{4} \sin^4 x$.

2. Evaluate $\int x^3 \, (2 + x^4)^5 \, dx$.

   The presence of the x^4, together with the combination $x^3 \, dx$, suggests the substitution $u = x^4$, or, better still,
   $$u = 2 + x^4 \; ; \quad \text{then } du = 4x^3 \, dx.$$

   Therefore, the required integral $= \int \tfrac{1}{4} u^5 \, du = \tfrac{1}{24} u^6$,

   $$= \tfrac{1}{24} (2 + x^4)^6.$$

3. Evaluate $\int \tan x \, dx$.

   We have $\int \tan x \, dx = \int \dfrac{\sin x \, dx}{\cos x}$.

   Let $u = \cos x$; then $du = - \sin x \, dx$,

   and the required integral $= \int \dfrac{- du}{u} = - \log u$,

   $$= - \log \cos x,$$

   $$= \log \sec x.$$

284

4. Evaluate $\int \dfrac{x\, dx}{\sqrt{(1-x^4)}}$.

Let $u = x^2$; then $du = 2x\, dx$, and

the required integral $= \displaystyle\int \dfrac{du}{2\sqrt{(1-u^2)}} = \tfrac{1}{2}\sin^{-1} u,$

$$= \tfrac{1}{2}\sin^{-1}(x^2).$$

5. Evaluate $\displaystyle\int_0^{\frac{\pi}{2}} \dfrac{\cos^3 x\, dx}{\sqrt{\sin x}}$.

We have $\displaystyle\int_0^{\frac{\pi}{2}} \dfrac{\cos^3 x\, dx}{\sqrt{\sin x}} = \int_0^{\frac{\pi}{2}} \dfrac{(1-\sin^2 x)\cos x\, dx}{\sqrt{\sin x}}$.

Let $u = \sin x$; then $du = \cos x\, dx$.

Also, when $x = 0$, $u = \sin 0 = 0$; when $x = \dfrac{\pi}{2}$, $u = \sin\dfrac{\pi}{2} = 1$.

Therefore, the required integral $= \displaystyle\int_0^1 \dfrac{(1-u^2)\, du}{\sqrt{u}},$

$$= \left[2u^{\frac{1}{2}} - \tfrac{2}{5}u^{\frac{5}{2}} \right]_0^1,$$

$$= 1\tfrac{3}{5}.$$

6. Evaluate $\displaystyle\int_1^{\frac{3}{2}} \dfrac{(x+1)\, dx}{\sqrt{(x^2+2x-3)}}$.

Let $u = x^2 + 2x - 3$; then $du = 2(x+1)\, dx$.
Also when $x = 1$, $u = 0$; when $x = \tfrac{3}{2}$, $u = \tfrac{9}{4}$.

Therefore, the required integral $= \displaystyle\int_0^{\frac{9}{4}} \dfrac{du}{2\sqrt{u}} = \left[\sqrt{u} \right]_0^{\frac{9}{4}},$

$$= \tfrac{3}{2}.$$

7. Evaluate $\displaystyle\int \dfrac{(5+x)\, dx}{\sqrt{(9+8x-x^2)}}$.

Since $\dfrac{5+x}{\sqrt{(9+8x-x^2)}} = \dfrac{9 - \tfrac{1}{2}(8-2x)}{\sqrt{(9+8x-x^2)}}$,

(where the reason for this artificial rearrangement will presently be clear) we have the required integral

$$= \int \dfrac{9dx}{\sqrt{\{25-(x-4)^2\}}} - \tfrac{1}{2}\int \dfrac{(8-2x)\, dx}{\sqrt{(9+8x-x^2)}},$$

$$= 9 \sin^{-1}\left(\frac{x-4}{5}\right) - \tfrac{1}{2} \int \frac{du}{\sqrt{u}},$$
$$\text{where } u = 9 + 8x - x^2,$$
$$= 9 \sin^{-1}\left(\frac{x-4}{5}\right) - \sqrt{(9 + 8x - x^2)}.$$

8. Evaluate $\int \dfrac{x^3\, dx}{\sqrt{(1 + x^2)}}$.

The combination $x^3\, dx$ may suggest the substitution $u = x^4$, but the form of the denominator shows at once that that would be unprofitable. Observing, however, that $x^3\, dx$ may be written $x^2 \times x\, dx$, we substitute $u = x^2$, or better still,

$$u = 1 + x^2, \text{ so that } du = 2x\, dx.$$

The required integral $= \tfrac{1}{2} \int \dfrac{(u-1)\, du}{\sqrt{u}}$,

$$= \tfrac{1}{2} \int \left(\sqrt{u} - \frac{1}{\sqrt{u}}\right) du,$$
$$= \tfrac{1}{3}u^{\frac{3}{2}} - u^{\frac{1}{2}} = \tfrac{1}{3}u^{\frac{1}{2}}(u - 3),$$
$$= \tfrac{1}{3}\sqrt{(1 + x^2)} \cdot (x^2 - 2).$$

9. Evaluate $\int_1^\infty \dfrac{dx}{x\sqrt{(x^2 + 1)}}$.

The required integral $= \displaystyle\int_1^\infty \dfrac{dx}{x^2\sqrt{\left(1 + \dfrac{1}{x^2}\right)}}$.

Let $u = \dfrac{1}{x}$; then $du = -\dfrac{dx}{x^2}$.

Also when $x = 1$, $u = 1$;
and when $x \longrightarrow \infty$, $u \longrightarrow 0$.

Therefore, the required integral $= \displaystyle\int_1^0 \dfrac{-du}{\sqrt{(1 + u^2)}}$,

$$= \int_0^1 \frac{du}{\sqrt{(1 + u^2)}},$$
$$= \left[\log\{u + \sqrt{(u^2 + 1)}\}\right]_0^1,$$
$$= \log(1 + \sqrt{2}).$$

[The reader will have observed that at one stage in the argument we changed the order of the limits of integration and at the same time deleted a minus sign. In general,

$$\int_a^b F(x)\,dx = -\int_b^a F(x)\,dx,$$

for if the indefinite integral of $F(x)$ is $f(x)$, the left-hand integral is $f(b) - f(a)$, and the right-hand integral is $f(a) - f(b)$.]

10. Evaluate $\displaystyle\int_{\frac{1}{3}}^{\frac{2}{5}} \frac{dx}{x\,\sqrt{(1-x)(1-2x)}}$.

The required integral $= \displaystyle\int_{\frac{1}{3}}^{\frac{2}{5}} \frac{dx}{x^2\,\sqrt{\left(\frac{1}{x}-1\right)\left(\frac{1}{x}-2\right)}}$,

$$= \int_3^{\frac{5}{2}} \frac{-\,du}{\sqrt{(u-1)(u-2)}}, \text{ where } u = \frac{1}{x},$$

$$= \int_{\frac{5}{2}}^3 \frac{du}{\sqrt{\{(u-\frac{3}{2})^2 - \frac{1}{4}\}}},$$

$$= \left[\log\{(u-\tfrac{3}{2}) + \sqrt{(u-1)(u-2)}\}\right]_{\frac{5}{2}}^3,$$

$$= \log\left(\tfrac{3}{2} + \sqrt{2}\right) - \log\left(1 + \sqrt{\tfrac{3}{4}}\right),$$

$$= \log \frac{3 + 2\sqrt{2}}{2 + \sqrt{3}},$$

11. Evaluate $\displaystyle\int \frac{dx}{(x^2+2)^{\frac{3}{2}}}$.

The required integral $= \displaystyle\int \frac{dx}{x^3\left(1 + \dfrac{2}{x^2}\right)^{\frac{3}{2}}}$,

$$= \tfrac{1}{2}\int \frac{-\,du}{(1+2u)^{\frac{3}{2}}}, \text{ where } u = \frac{1}{x^2}.$$

so that $du = \dfrac{-2dx}{x^3}$;

$$= \frac{1}{2\sqrt{(1+2u)}} = \frac{x}{2\sqrt{(x^2+2)}}.$$

287

12. Evaluate $\displaystyle\int \frac{dx}{(x^2 + 2x - 3)^{\frac{3}{2}}}$,

The required integral $\displaystyle= \int \frac{dx}{\{(x + 1)^2 - 4\}^{\frac{3}{2}}}$,

$$= \int \frac{dx}{(x + 1)^3 \left\{1 - \dfrac{4}{(x + 1^2)}\right\}^{\frac{3}{2}}},$$

$$= \tfrac{1}{2} \int \frac{- du}{(1 - 4u)^{\frac{3}{2}}}, \text{ where } u = \frac{1}{(x + 1)^2},$$

$$= -\tfrac{1}{4} \cdot \frac{1}{\sqrt{(1 - 4u)}},$$

$$= -\frac{x + 1}{4\sqrt{(x^2 + 2x - 3)}}.$$

Integrands which involve the square root of a quadratic function may often be rationalised by means of a suitable trigonometric substitution, the particular transformation being suggested by the form of the quadratic expression. Thus

$\sqrt{(a^2 - x^2)}$ suggests the substitution $x = a \sin\theta$,

since $\sqrt{(1 - \sin^2\theta)} = \cos\theta$;

$\sqrt{(a^2 + x^2)}$ suggests the substitution $x = a \tan\theta$,

since $\sqrt{(1 + \tan^2\theta)} = \sec\theta$;

$\sqrt{(x^2 - a^2)}$ suggests the substitution $x = a \sec\theta$,

since $\sqrt{(\sec^2\theta - 1)} = \tan\theta$.

Similarly, *any* function of the form $\sqrt{(ax^2 + bx + c)}$ can be expressed in one of the following ways, the factor a having first been removed :

$\sqrt{\{(x \pm p)^2 + q\}}$, for which the substitution is

$x \pm p = \sqrt{q} \cdot \tan\theta$;

$\sqrt{\{(x \pm p)^2 - q\}}$, for which the substitution is

$$x \pm p = \sqrt{q} \,.\, \sec\theta \;;$$

$\sqrt{\{q - (x \pm p)^2\}}$, for which the substitution is

$$x \pm p = \sqrt{q} \,.\, \sin\theta.$$

Even a troublesome square root of a linear function, such as $\sqrt{(a - x)}$ or $\sqrt{(a + x)}$, which for some reason cannot be manipulated in some more direct way, may be rationalised by means of a trigonometric substitution such as $x = a \sin^2\theta$ or $x = a \tan^2\theta$.

The trigonometric substitutions mentioned above are all of particular value in the evaluation of definite integrals.

Examples (continued)

13. Evaluate $\displaystyle\int_0^1 x^2 \sqrt{(1 - x^2)} \, dx$.

Let $x = \sin \theta$; then $dx = \cos \theta \, d\theta$.

When $x = 0$, $\sin \theta = 0$, and $\theta = 0$;

when $x = 1$, $\sin \theta = 1$, and $\theta = \dfrac{\pi}{2}$.

Therefore, the required integral $= \displaystyle\int_0^{\frac{\pi}{2}} \sin^2 \theta \,.\, \cos \theta \,.\, \cos \theta \, d\theta$,

$$= \tfrac{1}{4} \int_0^{\frac{\pi}{2}} \sin^2 2\theta \, d\theta,$$

$$= \tfrac{1}{8} \int_0^{\frac{\pi}{2}} (1 - \cos 4\theta) \, d\theta,$$

$$= \tfrac{1}{8} \left[\theta - \tfrac{1}{4} \sin 4\theta \right]_0^{\frac{\pi}{2}},$$

$$= \frac{\pi}{16} \,.$$

14. Evaluate $\displaystyle\int \frac{x^2 \, dx}{(4 + x^2)^{\frac{5}{2}}}$.

Let $x = 2 \tan \theta$; then $dx = 2 \sec^2 \theta \, d\theta$.

Therefore, the required integral $= \displaystyle\int \frac{4 \tan^2 \theta}{32 \sec^5 \theta} \cdot 2 \sec^2 \theta \, d\theta$,

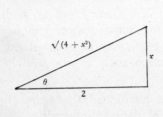

$$= \tfrac{1}{4} \int \sin^2 \theta \cos \theta \, d\theta,$$

$$= \tfrac{1}{4} \int \sin^2 \theta \, d (\sin \theta),$$

$$= \tfrac{1}{12} \sin^3 \theta,$$

$$= \frac{x^3}{12 \, (4 + x^2)^{\frac{3}{2}}} .$$

15. Evaluate $\displaystyle\int \frac{dx}{(x^2 + 2x - 3)^{\frac{3}{2}}}$.

Since $x^2 + 2x - 3 = (x + 1)^2 - 4$,

we let $x + 1 = 2 \sec \theta$, so that $dx = 2 \tan \theta \sec \theta \, d\theta$.

Therefore, the required integral $= \displaystyle\int \frac{1}{8 \tan^3 \theta} \cdot 2 \tan \theta \sec \theta \, d\theta$,

$$= \tfrac{1}{4} \int \frac{\cos \theta}{\sin^2 \theta} \, d\theta,$$

$$= - \frac{1}{4 \sin \theta},$$

$$= - \frac{x + 1}{4 \sqrt{(x^2 + 2x - 3)}} .$$

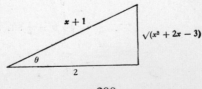

16. Evaluate $\displaystyle\int_0^a \sqrt{\left(\frac{a-x}{x}\right)}\, dx.$

Let $x = a \sin^2 \theta$; then $dx = 2a \sin \theta \cos \theta\, d\theta.$
When $x = 0,$ $\sin^2 \theta = 0,$ and $\theta = 0$;

when $x = a,$ $\sin^2 \theta = 1,$ and $\theta = \dfrac{\pi}{2}.$

Therefore, the required integral $= \displaystyle\int_0^{\frac{\pi}{2}} \frac{\cos \theta}{\sin \theta} \cdot 2a \sin \theta \cos \theta\, d\theta,$

$$= a \int_0^{\frac{\pi}{2}} 2 \cos^2 \theta\, d\theta,$$

$$= a \int_0^{\frac{\pi}{2}} (1 + \cos 2\theta)\, d\theta,$$

$$= a \left[\theta + \tfrac{1}{2} \sin 2\theta \right]_0^{\frac{\pi}{2}},$$

$$= \tfrac{1}{2}\pi a.$$

17. Evaluate $\displaystyle\int \frac{(5 + x)\, dx}{\sqrt{(9 + 8x - x^2)}}.$

Since $9 + 8x - x^2 = 25 - (x - 4)^2,$
we let $x - 4 = 5 \sin \theta,$ so that $dx = 5 \cos \theta\, d\theta.$

Therefore, the required integral $= \displaystyle\int \frac{9 + 5 \sin \theta}{5 \cos \theta} \cdot 5 \cos \theta\, d\theta,$

$$= \int (9 + 5 \sin \theta)\, d\theta,$$

$$= 9\theta - 5 \cos \theta,$$

$$= 9 \sin^{-1} \left(\frac{x - 4}{5} \right)$$

$$- \sqrt{(9 + 8x - x^2)}.$$

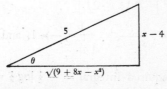

If the integrand is a rational function involving $\sin x$ and $\cos x$, or any combinations of these, *to the first power only*, or can be reduced to such a form, then the substitution $t = \tan \frac{1}{2}x$ converts it into a rational algebraic function of t, for which the various methods of integration already examined are available.

Examples (continued)

18. Evaluate $\displaystyle\int_{\frac{\pi}{2}}^{\pi} \frac{dx}{1 - \cos x + 2 \sin x}$.

Let $t = \tan \frac{1}{2}x$; then, from trigonometry,

$$\cos x = \frac{1 - t^2}{1 + t^2}, \text{ and } \sin x = \frac{2t}{1 + t^2}.$$

Also $dt = \frac{1}{2} \sec^2 \frac{1}{2}x \, dx = \frac{1}{2}(t^2 + 1) \, dx$, so that $dx = \dfrac{2dt}{1 + t^2}$.

When $x = \dfrac{\pi}{2}$, $t = \tan \dfrac{\pi}{4} = 1$;

when $x = \pi$, $t = \tan \dfrac{\pi}{2} = \infty$.

Therefore, the required integral

$$= \int_1^{\infty} \frac{1}{1 - \dfrac{1 - t^2}{1 + t^2} + \dfrac{4t}{1 + t^2}} \cdot \frac{2}{1 + t^2} \, dt,$$

$$= \int_1^{\infty} \frac{dt}{t^2 + 2t},$$

$$= \frac{1}{2} \int_1^{\infty} \left(\frac{1}{t} - \frac{1}{t + 2}\right) dt,$$

$$= \frac{1}{2} \left[\log \left(\frac{t}{t + 2}\right) \right]_1^{\infty}$$

When $t \longrightarrow \infty$, $\dfrac{t}{t + 2} = \dfrac{1}{1 + \dfrac{2}{t}} \longrightarrow 1$, and $\log 1 = 0$.

Therefore, the required integral $= -\frac{1}{2} \log \frac{1}{3} = \frac{1}{2} \log 3$.

19. Evaluate $\int \sec x \, dx$.

Let $t = \tan \frac{1}{2}x$; then $\sec x = \dfrac{1}{\cos x} = \dfrac{1 + t^2}{1 - t^2}$, and $dx = \dfrac{2dt}{1 + t^2}$

(see previous example).

$$\text{Therefore, the required integral} = \int \frac{1 + t^2}{1 - t^2} \cdot \frac{2}{1 + t^2} \, dt,$$

$$= \int \frac{2 \, dt}{1 - t^2},$$

$$= \int \left(\frac{1}{1 + t} + \frac{1}{1 - t} \right) dt,$$

$$= \log (1 + t) - \log (1 - t),$$

$$= \log \left(\frac{1 + \tan \frac{1}{2}x}{1 - \tan \frac{1}{2}x} \right).$$

20. Evaluate $\displaystyle\int_0^{\frac{\pi}{2}} \frac{dx}{\cos^2 x + 4 \sin^2 x}$.

Since $\cos^2 x = \frac{1}{2} (1 + \cos 2x)$, and $\sin^2 x = \frac{1}{2} (1 - \cos 2x)$, we can express the denominator of the integrand in the form $a + b \cos 2x$, which is of the required form, with $2x$ in place of x. The appropriate substitution in this case is therefore $t = \tan \frac{1}{2} (2x)$, or $t = \tan x$. But it is quicker to divide the numerator and denominator of the integrand by $\cos^2 x$.

$$\text{Therefore, the required integral} = \int_0^{\frac{\pi}{2}} \frac{\sec^2 x \, dx}{1 + 4 \tan^2 x}$$

$$= \int_0^{\infty} \frac{dt}{1 + 4t^2}, \text{ where } t = \tan x,$$

$$= \frac{1}{4} \int_0^{\infty} \frac{dt}{t^2 + \frac{1}{4}},$$

$$= \frac{1}{2} \left[\tan^{-1} \frac{t}{\frac{1}{2}} \right]_0^{\infty},$$

$$= \frac{\pi}{4}.$$

The reader may be forgiven if at this stage he feels rather depressed with the somewhat haphazard nature of integration. Unfortunately, it is not possible to give for integration a set of clear-cut rules such as was done for differentiation. All inverse processes are essentially tentative, and integration is no exception. Some consolation may be found, however, in the knowledge that for any particular integrand there is usually more than one mode of procedure available. Thus, for example, it may have been observed that Examples 12 and 15 worked out above (also Examples 7 and 17) illustrate two methods of integrating the same function. The best advice for the beginner is to re-examine all the examples already given in this section, and then tackle boldly the exercises which follow. The Answers at the end of the book include the most suitable substitutions for each exercise. It is no exaggeration to say that with a little experience he will, by merely glancing at the integrand, be able to recognise at once whether a change of variable is necessary, and if so what form the appropriate transformation should take.

Examples (continued)

Integrate the following functions of x (Examples 21–50) :—

21. $\dfrac{\sqrt{x}}{2 + \sqrt{x}}$.

22. $\dfrac{x}{\sqrt{(1 - x^2)}}$.

23. $x\sqrt{(2x^2 + 3)}$.

24. $\dfrac{\sin x}{1 + \cos x}$.

25. $\dfrac{1 - 2\sin x}{x + 2\cos x}$.

26. $\cot x$.

27. $\sin x \cos^4 x$.

28. $\sin^5 x$.

29. $\sin^3 x \cos^2 x$.

30. $\dfrac{1}{e^{3x} - e^{-3x}}$.

31. $\dfrac{1}{\sin^3 x \cos x}$.

32. $\dfrac{\cos x \sin x}{\sqrt{(2 + 3\cos^2 x)}}$.

33. $\tan x \sec^3 x$.

34. $\dfrac{\sin 2x}{a + b\cos^2 x}$.

35. $x^5 \sqrt{(1 - x^2)}$.

36. $\dfrac{x^2 + 1}{x\sqrt{(x^2 - 1)}}$.

37. $x^2 \sqrt{(2x+3)}$.

38. $\dfrac{1}{\sin x \cos^2 x}$.

39. $\dfrac{1}{\sin x}$.

40. $\dfrac{1}{12 \cos x + 5 \sin x}$.

41. $\dfrac{1}{\sin x \,(1 + \sin x + \cos x)}$.

42. $\dfrac{1 + 2 \sin x}{3 + 2 \cos x}$.

43. $\sqrt{(4 - x^2)}$.

44. $\dfrac{x^2}{\sqrt{(9 - x^2)}}$.

45. $\dfrac{2 + x}{(1 + x^2)^{\frac{3}{2}}}$.

46. $\sqrt{(2x - x^2)}$.

47. $\sqrt{\left(\dfrac{x}{1-x}\right)}$.

48. $\dfrac{1}{(x^2 + a^2)^{\frac{3}{2}}}$.

49. $\dfrac{1}{\sqrt{(2ax - x^2)}}$.

50. $\dfrac{x\,(x^2 + 1)}{x^4 + 1}$.

Evaluate the following definite integrals (Examples 51-70) :—

51. $\displaystyle\int_5^{12} \dfrac{\sqrt{(x+4)}}{x}\, dx$.

52. $\displaystyle\int_1^5 \dfrac{\sqrt{(x-1)}\, dx}{x^2 + 2x - 3}$.

53. $\displaystyle\int_0^3 \dfrac{\sqrt{(x+1)}\, dx}{x + 10 - 6\sqrt{(x+1)}}$.

54. $\displaystyle\int_0^1 \dfrac{\sin^{-1} x\, dx}{\sqrt{(1 - x^2)}}$.

55. $\displaystyle\int_{\frac{3}{4}}^{\frac{4}{3}} \dfrac{dx}{x\sqrt{(1 + x^2)}}$.

56. $\displaystyle\int_0^\infty \dfrac{x^3\, dx}{(4 + x^2)^{\frac{5}{2}}}$.

57. $\displaystyle\int_0^{\frac{3a}{2}} \sqrt{(2ax - x^2)}\, dx$.

58. $\displaystyle\int_0^1 \dfrac{(1 + x)\, dx}{\sqrt{(1 - x^2)}}$.

59. $\displaystyle\int_a^\infty \dfrac{x^2\, dx}{(a^2 + x^2)^{\frac{5}{2}}}$.

60. $\displaystyle\int_{-\frac{a}{2}}^a x^2\sqrt{(a^2 - x^2)}\, dx$.

61. $\displaystyle\int_{\frac{a}{2}}^a \sqrt{\left(\dfrac{a-x}{x^3}\right)}\, dx$.

62. $\displaystyle\int_0^3 \sqrt{\left(\dfrac{x^3}{3-x}\right)}\, dx$.

63. $\displaystyle\int_{-1}^1 \dfrac{(1 + x^2)\, dx}{\sqrt{(4 - x^2)}}$.

64. $\displaystyle\int_0^{\frac{\pi}{2}} \dfrac{dx}{a^2 + b^2 \sin^2 x}$.

65. $\displaystyle\int_0^{\frac{\pi}{2}} \dfrac{dx}{5 \cos x + 13}$.

66. $\displaystyle\int_{\frac{\pi}{2}}^\pi \dfrac{dx}{3 + \sin x + 2 \cos x}$.

67. $\int_{-\frac{\pi}{2}}^{\frac{\pi}{2}} \frac{dx}{5 + 3 \sin x}$.

68. $\int_{\frac{\pi}{6}}^{\frac{\pi}{3}} \frac{dx}{1 + \tan x}$.

69. $\int_{0}^{\pi} \frac{dx}{3 + 2 \cos x}$.

70. $\int_{0}^{\frac{\pi}{2}} \frac{\cos x \, dx}{3 + \cos^2 x}$.

Evaluate the following integrals (Examples 71-78), using the changes of variable indicated :—

71. $\int \frac{dx}{x \sqrt{(x^2 + x - 1)}}$ $\left[\text{Let } x = \frac{1}{u} \right]$.

72. $\int \frac{dx}{x^2 \sqrt{(2x^2 - 3)}}$ $\left[\text{Let } x^2 = \frac{1}{u} \right]$.

73. $\int \frac{dx}{x \sqrt{(x^4 - a^4)}}$ $\left[\text{Let } \frac{1}{x^2} = \frac{u}{a^2} \right]$.

74. $\int_{0}^{1} x \sqrt{(3 + 2x - x^2)} \, dx$ $\left[\text{Let } 1 - x = 2 \sin \theta \right]$.

75. $\int_{a}^{b} \sqrt{\{(b - x)(x - a)\}} \, dx$ [Let $x = a \cos^2 \theta + b \sin^2 \theta$].

76. $\int_{\frac{4}{5}}^{1} \frac{dx}{(2 - x) \sqrt{(1 - x^2)}}$ $\left[\text{Let } 2 - x = \frac{1}{u} \right]$.

77. $\int \sqrt{\left(\frac{x - a}{x^3} \right)} \, dx$ $\left[\text{Let } x = \frac{a}{1 - u^2} \right]$.

78. $\int_{0}^{\frac{1}{2}} \frac{dx}{(2x + 1) \sqrt{(1 - x - 2x^2)}}$ $\left[\text{Let } x = \frac{1 - u^2}{2 + u^2} \right]$.

79. Prove that

$$\int_{0}^{a} f(x) \, dx = \int_{0}^{a} f(a - x) \, dx,$$

and deduce that

$$\int_{0}^{\frac{\pi}{2}} f(\sin x) \, dx = \int_{0}^{\frac{\pi}{2}} f(\cos x) \, dx.$$

80. Use the result of Example 79 in order to show that

$$\int_{0}^{\pi} \frac{x \sin x \, dx}{1 + \cos^2 x} = \frac{\pi}{2} \int_{0}^{\pi} \frac{\sin x \, dx}{1 + \cos^2 x} = \frac{\pi^2}{4}.$$

§32. SPECIAL METHODS OF INTEGRATION
—BY PARTS

The second of the two special methods of integration referred to in the two preceding sections is known as "integration by parts," and is fundamentally merely an inversion of the formula

$$\frac{d}{dx}(uv) = u\frac{dv}{dx} + v\frac{du}{dx}$$

established on page 190 for the differentiation of the product of two functions u and v. Integrating both sides of the equation, we have

$$uv = \int u\frac{dv}{dx}dx + \int v\frac{du}{dx}dx,$$

or, rearranging the terms,

$$\int u\frac{dv}{dx}dx = uv - \int v\frac{du}{dx}dx. \qquad . \qquad . \quad (1)$$

Thus, if an integrand consists of the product of two functions, one of which, $\frac{dv}{dx}$, is by itself immediately integrable, we can carry out the integration using the above formula—known as the rule of **integration by parts**—always provided, of course, that the second integral $\int v\frac{du}{dx}dx$ is a simpler one than the original integral $\int u\frac{dv}{dx}dx$.

The rule may be expressed in various ways—none of which is really easy—of which the following is probably the simplest:

$$\int u\,dv = uv - \int v\,du. \qquad . \qquad . \qquad . \quad (2)$$

297

This follows at once from (1) since $dv = \dfrac{dv}{dx} dx$, and $du = \dfrac{du}{dx} dx$. It must be stressed, however, that the mere memorising of such a formula is almost futile. The rule can only be fully grasped by a careful study of worked examples.

Examples

1. Evaluate $\displaystyle\int x \cos x \, dx$.

Thinking of formula (2), we may consider either $\cos x \, dx$ as dv, or $x \, dx$ as dv. In the former case $v = \sin x$, in the latter $v = \frac{1}{2}x^2$. Let us examine both these possibilities.

(i) If we think of x as u and $\cos x \, dx$ as dv, we have, without introducing u and v explicitly,

$$\int x \, (\cos x \, dx) = x \sin x - \int \sin x \, . \, 1dx,$$

$$= x \sin x + \cos x.$$

(ii) Alternatively, we have

$$\int \cos x \, (x \, dx) = \cos x \, . \, \tfrac{1}{2}x^2 + \int \tfrac{1}{2}x^2 \sin x \, dx,$$

and we are faced with an integral which is more difficult than the original. The procedure indicated in (i) is therefore the correct one, as, indeed, could have been anticipated from the fact that of the two functions—x and $\cos x$—the former has the simpler derivative ; and the rule of integration by parts demands in the second step the differentiation of one of the two original functions.

2. Evaluate $\displaystyle\int xe^{-x} \, dx$.

Once more, both functions, x and e^{-x}, are immediately integrable, but in order that the second integrand should be as simple as possible, we proceed thus :—

$$\int x \, (e^{-x} \, dx) = x \, (- e^{-x}) - \int (- e^{-x}) \, . \, 1dx,$$

$$= - xe^{-x} + \int e^{-x} \, dx,$$

$$= -xe^{-x} - e^{-x},$$
$$= -e^{-x}(x+1).$$

3. Evaluate $P = \int e^x \cos x \, dx$, and $Q = \int e^x \sin x \, dx$.

We have

$$P = \int e^x (\cos x \, dx), \qquad\qquad Q = \int e^x (\sin x \, dx),$$

$$= e^x \sin x - \int \sin x \cdot e^x \, dx, \quad = e^x (-\cos x) + \int \cos x \cdot e^x \, dx,$$

$$= e^x \sin x - Q. \qquad\qquad\qquad = -e^x \cos x + P.$$

Therefore, $\qquad P + Q = e^x \sin x,$
and $\qquad\qquad P - Q = e^x \cos x,$
so that $\qquad\qquad P = \tfrac{1}{2}e^x (\cos x + \sin x),$
and $\qquad\qquad Q = \tfrac{1}{2}e^x (\sin x - \cos x).$

4. Evaluate $P = \int e^{ax} \cos(bx + c)\, dx$, and $Q = \int e^{ax} \sin(bx + c)\, dx$.

We have

$$P = e^{ax} \cdot \frac{1}{b} \sin(bx + c) - \frac{1}{b} \int \sin(bx + c) \cdot ae^{ax}\, dx,$$

$$= \frac{1}{b} e^{ax} \sin(bx + c) - \frac{a}{b} Q,$$

so that $\qquad\qquad bP + aQ = e^{ax} \sin(bx + c).$
Similarly, $\qquad\qquad aP - bQ = e^{ax} \cos(bx + c).$
Solving for P and Q, we have

$$P = \frac{e^{ax}}{a^2 + b^2} [a \cos(bx + c) + b \sin(bx + c)],$$

and $Q = \dfrac{e^{ax}}{a^2 + b^2} [a \sin(bx + c) - b \cos(bx + c)].$

5. Evaluate $\int x^2 \sin x \, dx$.

We have

$$\int x^2 (\sin x \, dx) = x^2 (-\cos x) + \int \cos x \cdot 2x \, dx,$$

$$= - x^2 \cos x + 2 \int x \cos x \, dx.$$

This last integral is obviously simpler than the original. We now integrate by parts once more.

$$\int x^2 \sin x \, dx = - x^2 \cos x + 2 \left\{ x \sin x - \int \sin x \,.\, 1 dx \right\}$$

$$= - x^2 \cos x + 2x \sin x + 2 \cos x.$$

A useful particular case of the rule of integration by parts is found by considering $v = x$, so that $\dfrac{dv}{dx} = 1$, and $dv = dx$. Formulæ (1) and (2) then become, respectively,

$$\int u \, dx = ux - \int x \frac{du}{dx} \, dx,$$

and

$$\int u \, dx = ux - \int x \, du.$$

These last forms are often useful when the integrand consists of a single function (*not* a product) which cannot be integrated directly, but whose derivative is easily found.

Examples (continued)

6. Evaluate $\displaystyle\int \log x \, dx$.

Here we do not have a product of two functions ; the formulæ just established, however, apply. Alternatively, we may regard $\log x$ as the artificial product, $\log x \times 1$, and then proceed as follows :—

$$\int \log x \,.\, (1 \,.\, dx) = x \log x - \int x \,.\, \frac{1}{x} \, dx,$$

$$= x \log x - x.$$

7. Evaluate $\displaystyle\int \sqrt{(a^2 - x^2)} \, dx$.

Denoting the required integral by I, we have

$$I = \int \sqrt{(a^2 - x^2)} \,.\, (1 \,.\, dx)$$

$$= x\sqrt{(a^2 - x^2)} - \int x \cdot \frac{(-x)}{\sqrt{(a^2 - x^2)}}\, dx,$$

$$= x\sqrt{(a^2 - x^2)} + \int \frac{x^2}{\sqrt{(a^2 - x^2)}}\, dx,$$

$$= x\sqrt{(a^2 - x^2)} + \int \frac{a^2 - (a^2 - x^2)}{\sqrt{(a^2 - x^2)}}\, dx,$$

$$= x\sqrt{(a^2 - x^2)} + \int \frac{a^2}{\sqrt{(a^2 - x^2)}}\, dx - \int \sqrt{(a^2 - x^2)}\, dx,$$

$$= x\sqrt{(a^2 - x^2)} + a^2 \sin^{-1}\left(\frac{x}{a}\right) - I,$$

so that $\quad 2I = x\sqrt{(a^2 - x^2)} + a^2 \sin^{-1}\left(\frac{x}{a}\right),$

and $\qquad I = \tfrac{1}{2}x\sqrt{(a^2 - x^2)} + \tfrac{1}{2}a^2 \sin^{-1}\left(\frac{x}{a}\right).$

[This integral can, of course, be found rather more readily by means of the substitution $x = a \sin \theta$.]

It sometimes happens that through integration by parts, or otherwise, an integral may be made to depend on a simpler integral of the same form. When this occurs, the second integral may similarly be made to depend on a still simpler integral, again of the same form, and this process continued until there is obtained an expression which can be integrated at once. This procedure, known as **integration by successive reduction,** will become clear from an examination of specific examples. It is a particularly useful artifice in the evaluation of many *definite* integrals.

Consider, for example, the integration of $\tan^5 x$.

We have $\displaystyle\int \tan^5 x\, dx = \int \tan^3 x \cdot \tan^2 x\, dx,$

$$= \int \tan^3 x\, (\sec^2 x - 1)\, dx,$$

$$= \int \tan^3 x \sec^2 x\, dx - \int \tan^3 x\, dx,$$

$$= \tfrac{1}{4} \tan^4 x - \int \tan^3 x \, dx.$$

Thus $\int \tan^5 x \, dx$ has been made to depend on $\int \tan^3 x \, dx$, and by a repetition of the argument this latter integral can be made to depend on $\int \tan x \, dx$, which is immediately integrable.

Examples (continued)

8. If $I_n = \int_0^{\frac{\pi}{2}} \sin^n x \, dx$, where n is a positive integer, show that

$$I_n = \frac{n-1}{n} I_{n-2},$$

and deduce the values of the integrals

$$\int_0^{\frac{\pi}{2}} \sin^{10} x \, dx, \quad \text{and} \quad \int_0^{\frac{\pi}{2}} \sin^9 x \, dx.$$

We have

$$I_n = \int_0^{\frac{\pi}{2}} \sin^{n-1} x \, (\sin x \, dx),$$

$$= \left[\sin^{n-1} x \, (- \cos x) \right]_0^{\frac{\pi}{2}} + \int_0^{\frac{\pi}{2}} \cos x \cdot (n-1) \sin^{n-2} x \cos x \, dx,$$

$$= (n-1) \int_0^{\frac{\pi}{2}} \sin^{n-2} x \cos^2 x \, dx,$$

$$= (n-1) \int_0^{\frac{\pi}{2}} \sin^{n-2} x \, (1 - \sin^2 x) \, dx,$$

$$= (n-1) \int_0^{\frac{\pi}{2}} \sin^{n-2} x \, dx - (n-1) \int_0^{\frac{\pi}{2}} \sin^n x \, dx,$$

$$= (n-1) I_{n-2} - (n-1) I_n.$$

Hence $$I_n = \frac{n-1}{n} I_{n-2}.$$

Similarly $$I_{n-2} = \frac{n-3}{n-2} I_{n-4},$$

and so on, each successive application of the above **reduction formula** reducing the index by 2.

302

Thus, $I_n = \dfrac{n-1}{n} \cdot \dfrac{n-3}{n-2} \cdot \dfrac{n-5}{n-4} \cdots ,$

where the last factor is either

$(n \text{ even})\quad I_0 = \displaystyle\int_0^{\frac{\pi}{2}} \sin^0 x \, dx = \int_0^{\frac{\pi}{2}} dx = \frac{\pi}{2},$

or $(n \text{ odd})\quad I_1 = \displaystyle\int_0^{\frac{\pi}{2}} \sin x \, dx = \Big[-\cos x \Big]_0^{\frac{\pi}{2}} = 1.$

Therefore,

if n is an even integer,

$$\int_0^{\frac{\pi}{2}} \sin^n x \, dx = \frac{(n-1)}{n} \cdot \frac{(n-3)}{(n-2)} \cdot \; \cdots \; \frac{3}{4} \cdot \frac{1}{2} \cdot \frac{\pi}{2};$$

if n is an odd integer,

$$\int_0^{\frac{\pi}{2}} \sin^n x \, dx = \frac{(n-1)}{n} \cdot \frac{(n-3)}{(n-2)} \cdot \; \cdots \; \frac{4}{5} \cdot \frac{2}{3}.$$

Thus, $I_{10} = \displaystyle\int_0^{\frac{\pi}{2}} \sin^{10} x \, dx = \frac{9 \cdot 7 \cdot 5 \cdot 3 \cdot 1}{10 \cdot 8 \cdot 6 \cdot 4 \cdot 2} \cdot \frac{\pi}{2} = \frac{63\pi}{512};$

$I_9 = \displaystyle\int_0^{\frac{\pi}{2}} \sin^9 x \, dx = \frac{8 \cdot 6 \cdot 4 \cdot 2}{9 \cdot 7 \cdot 5 \cdot 3} = \frac{128}{315}.$

The same reduction formula applies to $\displaystyle\int_0^{\frac{\pi}{2}} \cos^n x \, dx$, as may easily be verified either by integration by parts, or by means of the substitution $x = \dfrac{\pi}{2} - y$, or from graphical considerations.

9. If $I_{m,\,n} = \displaystyle\int_0^{\frac{\pi}{2}} \sin^m x \cos^n x \, dx$, where m and n are positive integers, show that

$$I_{m,\,n} = \frac{n-1}{m+n} I_{m,\,n-2} = \frac{m+1}{m+n} I_{m-2,\,n},$$

and deduce the values of the integrals

$$\int_0^{\frac{\pi}{2}} \sin^2 x \cos^4 x \, dx, \quad \int_0^{\frac{\pi}{2}} \sin^3 x \cos^4 x \, dx, \quad \int_0^{\frac{\pi}{2}} \sin^3 x \cos^5 x \, dx.$$

We have

$$I_{m, n} = \int_0^{\frac{\pi}{2}} \sin^m x \cos^n x \, dx = \int_0^{\frac{\pi}{2}} \cos^{n-1} x \, (\sin^m x \cos x \, dx),$$

$$= \left[\cos^{n-1} x \cdot \frac{\sin^{m+1} x}{m+1} \right]_0^{\frac{\pi}{2}}$$

$$- \frac{1}{m+1} \int_0^{\frac{\pi}{2}} \sin^{m+1} x \cdot (n-1) \cos^{n-2} x \, (-\sin x) \, dx,$$

$$= \frac{n-1}{m+1} \int_0^{\frac{\pi}{2}} \sin^{m+2} x \cos^{n-2} x \, dx,$$

$$= \frac{n-1}{m+1} \int_0^{\frac{\pi}{2}} \sin^m x \, (1 - \cos^2 x) \cos^{n-2} x \, dx,$$

$$= \frac{n-1}{m+1} \left\{ \int_0^{\frac{\pi}{2}} \sin^m x \cos^{n-2} x - \int_0^{\frac{\pi}{2}} \sin^m x \cos^n x \, dx \right\},$$

$$= \frac{n-1}{m+1} I_{m, n-2} - \frac{n-1}{m+1} I_{m, n} .$$

Hence
$$I_{m, n} = \frac{n-1}{m+n} I_{m, n-2} \qquad . \qquad . \qquad . \qquad \text{(A)}$$

Similarly, by regarding $\sin^m x \cos^n x$ as $\sin^{m-1} x \, (\cos^n x \sin x)$, and integrating by parts, we should find that

$$I_{m, n} = \frac{m-1}{m+n} I_{m-2, n} \qquad . \qquad . \qquad . \qquad \text{(B)}$$

Thus, by repeated application of (A) we can make $I_{m, n}$ depend eventually on either $I_{m, 1}$ or $I_{m, 0}$, according as n is odd or even. We then apply reduction formula (B) until in the end $I_{m, n}$ is reduced to one of the following four forms:

(i) (m and n both even) $I_{0, 0} = \int_0^{\frac{\pi}{2}} dx = \frac{\pi}{2}$;

(ii) (m even, n odd) $\quad I_{0, 1} = \int_0^{\frac{\pi}{2}} \cos x \, dx = 1$;

(iii) (m odd, n even) $\quad I_{1,\,0} = \displaystyle\int_0^{\frac{\pi}{2}} \sin x \, dx = 1$;

(iv) (m and n both odd) $\quad I_{1,\,1} = \displaystyle\int_0^{\frac{\pi}{2}} \sin x \cos x \, dx$

$$= \left[\frac{\sin^2 x}{2} \right]_0^{\frac{\pi}{2}} = \tfrac{1}{2}.$$

These results may be summarised in the following rule :

$$\int_0^{\frac{\pi}{2}} \sin^m x \cos^n x \, dx = \frac{(m-1)(m-3)\ldots(n-1)(n-3)\ldots}{(m+n)(m+n-2)\ldots} \times a,$$

where each of the three sets of factors is continued until one further step would produce a negative factor or zero, and where $a = 1$ except when m and n are both even, in which case $a = \dfrac{\pi}{2}.$

This result should be committed to memory because of its extreme usefulness. It covers the case of the previous Example if we make m (or n) zero.

It follows that

$$\int_0^{\frac{\pi}{2}} \sin^2 x \cos^4 x \, dx = \frac{(1)(3 \cdot 1)}{6 \cdot 4 \cdot 2} \cdot \frac{\pi}{2} = \frac{\pi}{32} \; ;$$

$$\int_0^{\frac{\pi}{2}} \sin^3 x \cos^4 x \, dx = \frac{(2)(3 \cdot 1)}{7 \cdot 5 \cdot 3 \cdot 1} = \frac{2}{35} \; ;$$

$$\int_0^{\frac{\pi}{2}} \sin^3 x \cos^5 x \, dx = \frac{(2)(4 \cdot 2)}{8 \cdot 6 \cdot 4 \cdot 2} = \frac{1}{24}.$$

Examples (continued)

Integrate " **by parts** " the following functions of x (Examples 10-26) :

10. $x \sec^2 x.$
11. $e^x \sin 2x.$
12. $x \log (1 + x).$
13. $(x + 2) \log x.$
14. $x \tan^{-1} x.$
15. $e^{-x} \sin^2 x.$
16. $\sin x \log \cos x.$
17. $\log (4 - 3x).$
18. $x^2 \cos 2x.$
19. $(x + 1)^2 \, e^{-x}.$
20. $\dfrac{\log x}{x^3}.$
21. $x (2 - 3x^2) \, e^{-3x}.$

22. $x^n \log x$.

23. $(\log x)^2$.

24. $\dfrac{\log x}{(x + 1)^2}$.

25. $\dfrac{xe^x}{(1 + x)^2}$.

26. $x\sqrt{(1 - x^2)} \cdot \sin^{-1} x$.

Evaluate the following definite integrals (Examples 27-38), using integration " by parts " :

27. $\displaystyle\int_1^2 x^3 \log x \, dx$.

28. $\displaystyle\int_0^\pi x \cos 3x \, dx$.

29. $\displaystyle\int_0^\pi x \sin^2 x \, dx$.

30. $\displaystyle\int_0^{\frac{\pi}{4}} x^2 \sin 2x \, dx$.

31. $\displaystyle\int_0^{\frac{\pi}{2}} x^2 \cos^2 x \, dx$.

32. $\displaystyle\int_2^3 \frac{\log x}{x^2} \, dx$.

33. $\displaystyle\int_0^{\frac{\pi}{3}} \frac{x}{\cos^2 x} \, dx$.

34. $\displaystyle\int_0^1 x^3 e^{-2x} \, dx$.

35. $\displaystyle\int_0^{\sqrt{3}} \log (1 + x^2) \, dx$.

36. $\displaystyle\int_0^\infty e^{-\frac{x}{3}} \sin 2x \, dx$.

37. $\displaystyle\int_\pi^\infty e^{-2x} \cos 3x \, dx$.

38. $\displaystyle\int_0^\infty e^{-2x} \cos^2 x \, dx$.

Find, using the formula quoted on page 305, the value of each of the definite integrals in Examples 39-45.

39. $\displaystyle\int_0^{\frac{\pi}{2}} \sin^4 \theta \cos^2 \theta \, d\theta$.

40. $\displaystyle\int_0^{\frac{\pi}{2}} \cos^5 \theta \cos 3\theta \, d\theta$.

41. $\displaystyle\int_0^{\frac{\pi}{2}} \sin^2 2\theta \sin^3 \theta \, d\theta$.

42. $\displaystyle\int_0^{\frac{\pi}{2}} \sin^4 2\theta \, d\theta$.

43. $\displaystyle\int_0^{\frac{\pi}{2}} \sin 4\theta \cos^4 \theta \, d\theta$.

44. $\displaystyle\int_0^{\frac{\pi}{2}} \cos^4 \theta \, (1 + 2 \cos \theta) \, d\theta$.

45. $\displaystyle\int_0^1 x^4 \, (1 - x^2)^{\frac{7}{2}} \, dx$.

46. Prove that

  (i) $\int \sqrt{(x^2 + k)}\, dx = \frac{1}{2}x\sqrt{(x^2 + k)} + \frac{1}{2}k \log\{x + \sqrt{(x^2 + k)}\}$,

  (ii) $\int \dfrac{x^2\, dx}{\sqrt{(x^2 + k)}} = \frac{1}{2}x\sqrt{(x^2 + k)} - \frac{1}{2}k \log\{x + \sqrt{(x^2 + k)}\}$;

  and deduce the value of $\displaystyle\int_a^{2a} \dfrac{x^2\, dx}{\sqrt{(x^2 - a^2)}}$.

47. If $I_n = \displaystyle\int_0^{\frac{\pi}{4}} \tan^n x\, dx$, prove that

$$I_n + I_{n-2} = \frac{1}{n-1},$$

  and deduce the value of $\displaystyle\int_0^{\frac{\pi}{4}} \tan^4 x\, dx$.

48. If $I_n = \displaystyle\int x^n \cos x\, dx$, prove that

$$I_n = x^n \sin x + nx^{n-1} \cos x - n(n-1) I_{n-2},$$

  and deduce the value of $\displaystyle\int_0^{\frac{\pi}{2}} x^4 \cos x\, dx$.

49. If $I_n = \displaystyle\int_0^1 (1 - x^2)^n\, dx$, prove that

$$I_n = \frac{2n}{2n+1} I_{n-1} = \frac{2^n\, n!}{(2n+1)(2n-1)\ldots 3}.$$

50. If $I_n = \displaystyle\int \dfrac{x^n\, dx}{\sqrt{(x^2 - a^2)}}$, prove that

$$n\,I_n - (n-1)\,a^2\, I_{n-2} = x^{n-1}\sqrt{(x^2 - a^2)},$$

  and evaluate $\displaystyle\int_a^{2a} \dfrac{x^4\, dx}{\sqrt{(x^2 - a^2)}}$.

51. If $I_n = \displaystyle\int \dfrac{\sin nx}{\sin x}\, dx$, prove that

$$I_n - I_{n-2} = \frac{2}{n-1} \sin(n-1)x,$$

  and hence evaluate $\displaystyle\int \dfrac{\sin 6x}{\sin x}\, dx$.

307

52. If $I_{m,n} = \displaystyle\int_0^1 x^m (1-x)^n \, dx$, where m and n are positive integers, prove that

$$I_{m,n} = \frac{n}{m+1} I_{m+1,\,n-1} = \frac{n!}{(m+1)(m+2) \ldots (m+n+1)}.$$

By substituting $x = \sin^2 \theta$, deduce that

$$\int_0^{\frac{\pi}{2}} \sin^{2m+1} \theta \cos^{2n+1} \theta \, d\theta = \tfrac{1}{2} \cdot \frac{m! \, n!}{(m+n+1)!}.$$

§33. DIFFERENTIAL EQUATIONS.

The reader has already (Example 9, page 203) met differential equations. In those examples, differential equations were obtained from their **complete primitives** by differentiation and elimination of arbitrary constants ; in the present section, the converse problem is investigated, that of passing from a given differential equation to what is known as its **general solution** or **complete integral,** the name " complete primitive " being no longer appropriate. Clearly the process involved will be that of integration. Thus, if

$$y = A \cos nx + B \sin nx, \quad . \quad . \quad . \quad (1)$$

by differentiating twice and eliminating the arbitrary constants A and B, we obtain

$$\frac{d^2y}{dx^2} + n^2y = 0, \quad . \quad . \quad . \quad (2)$$

a differential equation of the second order and of first degree.* The problem in this section is that of integrating or " solving " such a differential equation as (2) in order to obtain the general solution (1).

From what has already been learned about the formation of a differential equation from its complete primitive it might be anticipated that the integration of a differential equation will yield a general solution which involves arbitrary constants equal in number to the order of the differential equation. With some qualification (which need not detain us) this is the case. Thus, if we are given the *second* order differential equation $\frac{d^2y}{dx^2} = 6x$,

---

* The terms " order " and " degree " as applied to differential equations are defined on page 203.

then integrating we have

$$\frac{dy}{dx} = 3x^2 + A,$$

and integrating again, we have the general solution

$$y = x^3 + Ax + B,$$

involving *two* arbitrary constants, A and B. If particular values are assigned to the arbitrary constants, then a **particular solution,** or a **particular integral,** of the differential equation is obtained. Thus, $y = x^3$, $y = x^3 - 1$, $y = x^3 + 5x$, $y = x^3 + x - 1$, are all particular solutions of the equation $\frac{d^2y}{dx^2} = 6x$.

Differential equations of the first order and first degree

The various methods available for the solution of differential equations of the first order and first degree may be examined under several " types."

Type I.—One variable absent

An equation of this sort is immediately integrable ; thus, if

$$\frac{dy}{dx} = f(x),$$

then

$$y = \int f(x)\, dx + C,$$

where C is an arbitrary constant.

Similarly, if

$$\frac{dy}{dx} = f(y),$$

then

$$\frac{dx}{dy} = \frac{1}{f(y)},$$

and

$$x = \int \frac{dy}{f(y)} + C,$$

where C is arbitrary.

Type II.—Variables separable

If a given equation can be arranged in the form

$$f(x) + F(y)\frac{dy}{dx} = 0,$$

then we may " separate the variables " and write

$$f(x)\,dx + F(y)\,dy = 0,$$

the general solution of which is

$$\int f(x)\,dx + \int F(y)\,dy = C,$$

where C is arbitrary.

For example, if $(x-1)\dfrac{dy}{dx} = y,$

then $\qquad\qquad \dfrac{dy}{y} = \dfrac{dx}{x-1},$

and integrating we have $\quad \log y = \log(x-1) + C',$

or $\qquad\qquad\qquad y = C(x-1),$

where, for the sake of elegance, we have replaced the original arbitrary constant C' by C, where $\log C = C'$. Since C' is arbitrary, so also is C.

Type III.—Homogeneous equations

If a given equation can be expressed in the form

$$P + Q\frac{dy}{dx} = 0,$$

where P and Q are *homogeneous polynomials* in x and y *of the same degree*, then it may be solved by changing the dependent variable from y to v where $y = vx$. This substitution is suggested by the fact that

$$\frac{dy}{dx} = -\frac{P}{Q},$$

and since P and Q are homogeneous polynomials in x and y of the same degree, the fraction $\frac{P}{Q}$ may be rearranged as a function of $\frac{y}{x}$. Thus, we may write

311

$$\frac{dy}{dx} = f\left(\frac{y}{x}\right).$$

If we now substitute $\frac{y}{x} = v$, or $y = vx$,

then
$$\frac{dy}{dx} = v + x\frac{dv}{dx},$$

and we have
$$v + x\frac{dv}{dx} = f(v),$$

an equation in which the variables are separable.

For example, if
$$\frac{dy}{dx} = \frac{y(x+y)}{x(y-x)},$$

then, substituting $y = vx$, we have

$$v + x\frac{dv}{dx} = \frac{v(1+v)}{v-1},$$

so that
$$x\frac{dv}{dx} = \frac{2v}{v-1},$$

and, separating the variables,

$$\frac{v-1}{v}\,dv = \frac{2}{x}\,dx.$$

Integrating, we have $v - \log v = 2\log x + C'$

or $v = \log(vx^2) + C'.$

But $v = \frac{y}{x}$, therefore $\frac{y}{x} = \log(xy) + C',$

or $xy = Ce^{\frac{x}{y}}$, where $C = e^{-c'}.$

Type IV.—Linear equations

A differential equation is said to be *linear*, if the dependent variable and its derivatives are present in the first degree only. The linear equation of the first order is therefore of the type

$$\frac{dy}{dx} + Py = Q,$$

where P and Q are functions of x, or constants.

If we multiply throughout by e^R, where $R = \int P dx$, we have

$$e^R \frac{dy}{dx} + Pe^R y = Q e^R,$$

or

$$\frac{d}{dx}(e^R y) = Q e^R, \text{ since } \frac{dR}{dx} = P.$$

Hence

$$e^R y = \int Q e^R dx + C.$$

The factor e^R introduced in this way converts the whole of the left-hand side into the x-derivative of *one* function, and is therefore described as an **integrating factor.**

For example, if $\quad \dfrac{dy}{dx} + \dfrac{y}{x} = 1,$

then comparing this equation with the general linear form

$$\frac{dy}{dx} + Py = Q,$$

we have

$P = \dfrac{1}{x}$, and the integrating factor is e^R, where $R = \displaystyle\int \frac{1}{x} dx = \log x.$

That is, the integrating factor is $e^{\log x}$ or x.*

Multiplying throughout by x, we have

$$x \frac{dy}{dx} + y = x,$$

or

$$\frac{d}{dx}(xy) = x,$$

so that $\qquad xy = \frac{1}{2}x^2 + C'$

or $\qquad 2xy = x^2 + C.$

---

* If this step is not obvious, then the reader may argue thus. Let $e^{\log x} = k$; then, by definition of a logarithm, $\log_e k = \log x = \log_e x$, so that $k = x$.

Examples

1. Solve the differential equation $(1 + x^2)\dfrac{dy}{dx} = 2xy$.

   This equation may be solved either by separating the variables, or by the method for linear equations.

   (i) We have $\qquad\qquad (1 + x^2)\, dy = 2xy\, dx,$

   therefore $\qquad\qquad\qquad \dfrac{dy}{y} = \dfrac{2x\, dx}{1 + x^2},$

   and, integrating, $\qquad \log y = \log (1 + x^2) + C'\,;$

   hence $\qquad\qquad\qquad\quad y = C\,(1 + x^2).$

   (ii) Alternatively, we have

   $$\frac{dy}{dx} - \frac{2x}{1 + x^2}\, y = 0,$$

   the integrating factor of which is e^R,

   where $R = \displaystyle\int \frac{-2x\, dx}{1 + x^2} = -\log (1 + x^2).$

   Hence we multiply throughout by $e^{-\log (1 + x^2)}$ or $\dfrac{1}{1 + x^2}.$

   Thus $\qquad\quad \dfrac{1}{1 + x^2}\dfrac{dy}{dx} - \dfrac{2x}{(1 + x^2)^2}\, y = 0,$

   or $\qquad\qquad\qquad \dfrac{d}{dx}\left(\dfrac{y}{1 + x^2}\right) = 0,$

   and, integrating, we have $\dfrac{y}{1 + x^2} = C,$

   or $\qquad\qquad\qquad\qquad y = C\,(1 + x^2).$

2. Integrate the differential equation $x\dfrac{dy}{dx} + (3x + 2y) = 0.$

   This equation is both linear and homogeneous ; two methods of integration are therefore available.

   (i) Since $\dfrac{dy}{dx} + \dfrac{2}{x}\, y = -3,$

   the integrating factor is e^R,

   where $R = \displaystyle\int \frac{2dx}{x} = 2 \log x = \log x^2\,;$ so that $e^R = x^2.$

Therefore

$$x^2 \frac{dy}{dx} + 2xy = -3x^2,$$

or

$$\frac{d}{dx}(x^2 y) = -3x^2,$$

and

$$x^2 y = -x^3 + C,$$

or

$$x^2 y + x^3 = C.$$

(ii) Alternatively, let $y = vx$, so that $\frac{dy}{dx} = v + x \frac{dv}{dx}$.

The given equation therefore becomes

$$x \left(v + x \frac{dv}{dx} \right) + 3x + 2vx = 0,$$

or

$$v + x \frac{dv}{dx} + 3 + 2v = 0 ;$$

hence

$$x \frac{dv}{dx} + 3(1 + v) = 0,$$

and

$$\frac{dv}{v+1} + \frac{3dx}{x} = 0.$$

Integrating, we have $\log(v + 1) + 3 \log x = C'$,
or $x^3(v + 1) = C.$

But $v = \frac{y}{x}$; the general solution is therefore

$$x^2 y + x^3 = C.$$

3. Find the general solution of the differential equation

$$\frac{dy}{dx} = y \tan x - 2 \sin x.$$

We have $\frac{dy}{dx} - \tan x \cdot y = -2 \sin x.$

The equation is linear, the integrating factor being e^R, where

$$R = \int -\tan x \, dx = \int \frac{-\sin x \, dx}{\cos x} = \log \cos x.$$

Hence, we multiply throughout by $e^{\log \cos x}$, or $\cos x$; thus

$$\cos x \frac{dv}{dx} - \sin x \cdot y = -2 \sin x \cos x,$$

and

$$\frac{d}{dx}(\cos x \cdot y) = -\sin 2x.$$

315

Integrating, we have $y \cos x = \frac{1}{2} \cos 2x + C'$,

$$= \cos^2 x - \frac{1}{2} + C',$$

$$= \cos^2 x + C,$$

so that $y = \cos x + C \sec x$.

4. Solve the differential equation $x \dfrac{dy}{dx} + y = x^3 y^3$.

We have $\dfrac{x}{y^3} \dfrac{dy}{dx} + \dfrac{1}{y^2} = x^3$.

Let $\dfrac{1}{y^2} = u$;   then $-\dfrac{2}{y^3} \dfrac{dy}{dx} = \dfrac{du}{dx}$,

and $-\dfrac{x}{2} \dfrac{du}{dx} + u = x^3$,

or $\dfrac{du}{dx} - \dfrac{2u}{x} = -2x^2$,

which is linear in u.

The integrating factor is e^R,

where $R = \displaystyle\int \frac{-2}{x} \, dx = -2 \log x = \log \frac{1}{x^2}$.

Thus, $\dfrac{1}{x^2} \dfrac{du}{dx} - \dfrac{2}{x^3} u = -2$,

and $\dfrac{u}{x^2} = -2x + C$,

so that, since $u = \dfrac{1}{y^2}$, we have

$$\dfrac{1}{x^2 y^2} = C - 2x,$$

or $y^2 = \dfrac{1}{x^2 (C - 2x)}$.

Any equation of the form $\dfrac{dy}{dx} + Py = Qy^n$ may be made

linear by substituting $\dfrac{1}{y^{n-1}} = u$.

It sometimes happens tha tthe data include information which enables us to find a particular value for the arbitrary constant. Thus, in the previous example, if, besides being given the differential equation, we are further told that when $x = -1$, $y = 1$, we find, by substituting these corresponding values in the general solution, that

$$1 = \frac{1}{C + 2},$$

so that $\qquad\qquad C = -1,$

and the particular solution which satisfies the condition that when $x = -1$, $y = 1$, is

$$y^2 = \frac{-1}{x^2 (1 + 2x)},$$

or, possibly in more elegant form,

$$x^2 y^2 (1 + 2x) + 1 = 0.$$

Differential equations of the second order and first degree

In a book of this scope, we cannot do more than consider the commonest types, and of these, only the simplest. Before passing on to an examination of the most important type of second order differential equation—the linear equation—we consider a few special types.

Type I.—Equations of the form $\frac{d^2y}{dx^2} = f(x)$

Such equations may be solved by two successive integrations. Thus, if

$$x^2 \frac{d^2y}{dx^2} = 1, \text{ then } \frac{d^2y}{dx^2} = \frac{1}{x^2}.$$

Integrating, we have $\qquad\qquad \dfrac{dy}{dx} = \dfrac{-1}{x} + A,$

and, integrating once more, we have

$$y = - \log x + Ax + B,$$

where the constants A, B are arbitrary.

Type II.—Equations of the form $\dfrac{d^2y}{dx^2} = f\left(\dfrac{dy}{dx}\right)$

In this type of equation neither x nor y appears explicitly. Such an equation (and, indeed, any second order equation in which y is absent) may be reduced to one of first order by writing p for $\dfrac{dy}{dx}$. Thus, if

$$\frac{dy}{dx} = p, \text{ then } \frac{d^2y}{dx^2} = \frac{d}{dx}\left(\frac{dy}{dx}\right) = \frac{dp}{dx},$$

and the original equation becomes

$$\frac{dp}{dx} = f(p).$$

If this first order equation is solved, then, when we reintroduce $\dfrac{dy}{dx}$ for p, we obtain yet another first order differential equation to solve.

For example, if

$$\frac{d^2y}{dx^2} - \frac{dy}{dx} = 0,$$

writing p for $\dfrac{dy}{dx}$, we have

$$\frac{dp}{dx} - p = 0,$$

so that

$$\frac{dp}{p} = dx,$$

and

$$\log p = x + C,$$

or

$$\log \frac{p}{A} = x, \text{ where } \log A = C;$$

that is, $\qquad\qquad p = Ae^x,$

or $\qquad\qquad\qquad \dfrac{dy}{dx} = Ae^x,$

and $\qquad\qquad\qquad y = Ae^x + B.$

Type III.—Equations of the form $\dfrac{d^2y}{dx^2} = f(y)$.

Such equations may be solved by means of the integrating factor $2\dfrac{dy}{dx}$. Thus, if

$$\frac{d^2y}{dx^2} + n^2y = 0, \text{ where } n \text{ is a constant,}$$

then $\qquad 2\dfrac{dy}{dx}\cdot\dfrac{d^2y}{dx^2} = -2n^2y\dfrac{dy}{dx},$

or $\qquad \dfrac{d}{dx}\left[\left(\dfrac{dy}{dx}\right)^2\right] = -2n^2y\dfrac{dy}{dx}.$

Integrating, we have $\left(\dfrac{dy}{dx}\right)^2 = -n^2y^2 + n^2C_1,$

where C_1, and therefore n^2C_1, is arbitrary.

Thus $\qquad\qquad \dfrac{dy}{dx} = \pm n\sqrt{(C_1 - y^2)},$

so that $\qquad\qquad \dfrac{dy}{\sqrt{(C_1 - y^2)}} = \pm n dx.$

Integrating once more, we have

$$\sin^{-1}\frac{y}{\sqrt{C_1}} = \pm nx + C_2,$$

or $\qquad\qquad y = \sqrt{C_1}\sin(C_2 \pm nx) \qquad . \qquad . \qquad . \quad (1)$

This is the general solution, but it may be expressed more neatly in the form

$$y = A\cos nx + B\sin nx \qquad . \qquad . \qquad . \quad (2)$$

[The reader should convince himself that *any* solution obtained by giving particular values to C_1, C_2 in (1) could equally well be obtained from (2) by giving appropriate values to A, B. The skill in the choice and forms of the arbitrary constants with a view to obtaining as neat a general solution as possible comes with experience.]

Type IV.—Linear equations

The general linear equation of the second order is of the type

$$\frac{d^2y}{dx^2} + P\frac{dy}{dx} + Qy = R,$$

where P, Q, R are functions of x, or constants, but we shall confine our attention to equations in which P and Q are constants. Such equations are of frequent occurrence in problems in applied mathematics.

Let us consider first of all an equation of the form

$$\frac{d^2y}{dx^2} + a\frac{dy}{dx} + by = 0, \qquad . \qquad . \qquad . \quad (1)$$

in which there is no right-hand member, R.

Let $y = u$, and $y = v$ be *any* two particular solutions of this equation ; then

$$\frac{d^2u}{dx^2} + a\frac{du}{dx} + bu = 0,$$

and

$$\frac{d^2v}{dx^2} + a\frac{dv}{dx} + bv = 0.$$

It can easily be verified by substitution that the original equation (1) is also satisfied by $y = Au + Bv$, where A, B are arbitrary constants. It therefore follows that provided u and v are independent solutions (that is, one is not merely a multiple of the other), $y = Au + Bv$ must be the general solution of (1) since it satisfies the equation and contains *two* arbitrary constants.

Let us now assume* tentatively that equation (1) has a particular solution of the form $y = e^{ax}$; then

$$\frac{dy}{dx} = ae^{ax}, \text{ and } \frac{d^2y}{dx^2} = a^2 e^{ax},$$

and therefore, $e^{ax}(a^2 + aa + b) = 0.$

If, then, a_1 and a_2 are the roots of the equation

$$a^2 + aa + b = 0, \qquad . \quad . \quad . \quad (2)$$

then $e^{\alpha_1 x}$ and $e^{\alpha_2 x}$ are particular solutions of equation (1), and the general solution is

$$y = Ae^{\alpha_1 x} + Be^{\alpha_2 x},$$

where A, B are arbitrary.

The equation (2), obtained by replacing $\frac{d^2y}{dx^2}$ by a^2, $\frac{dy}{dx}$ by a,

and omitting y, is known as the **auxiliary equation.**

Thus, if

$$\frac{d^2y}{dx^2} - 3\frac{dy}{dx} - 4y = 0,$$

the auxiliary equation is $a^2 - 3a - 4 = 0,$
or $(a - 4)(a + 1) = 0,$
so that $a_1 = -1$ and $a_2 = 4$.

The general solution of the differential equation is therefore

$$y = Ae^{-x} + Be^{4x}.$$

It may happen, however, that the auxiliary equation has equal roots, or imaginary roots. The appropriate procedure to follow in these two special cases must now be investigated.

(a) If the auxiliary equation (2) has two equal roots, then by the theory of quadratic equations, $a^2 = 4b$ and the equal roots are

$$a_1 = a_2 = -\tfrac{1}{2}a.$$

---

* The thoughtful reader may ask "why?". It is not possible to answer this question without a lengthy digression, though, of course, the procedure may clearly be justified *a posteriori*.

Now let $y = e^{-\frac{1}{2}ax} u$, where u is a function of x as yet unknown ;

then $\dfrac{dy}{dx} = e^{-\frac{1}{2}ax} \left(-\tfrac{1}{2}au + \dfrac{du}{dx} \right),$

and $\dfrac{d^2y}{dx^2} = e^{-\frac{1}{2}ax} \left(\tfrac{1}{4}a^2u - a\dfrac{du}{dx} + \dfrac{d^2u}{dx^2} \right).$

Substituting in (1), we have

$$e^{-\frac{1}{2}ax}\left\{ \left(\tfrac{1}{4}a^2u - a\dfrac{du}{dx} + \dfrac{d^2u}{dx^2} \right) + a\left(-\tfrac{1}{2}au + \dfrac{du}{dx} \right) \right.$$
$$\left. + bu \right\} = 0,$$

so that $\dfrac{d^2u}{dx^2} + u\left(b - \tfrac{1}{4}a^2\right) = 0,$

or $\dfrac{d^2u}{dx^2} = 0,$ since $a^2 = 4b.$

Hence, by integration, $u = Ax + B,$
and the general solution of the given differential equation in this case is

$$y = e^{-\frac{1}{2}ax}(Ax + B),$$

where A, B are arbitrary.

For example, if $\dfrac{d^2y}{dx^2} + 4\dfrac{dy}{dx} + 4y = 0,$

the auxiliary equation is $a^2 + 4a + 4 = 0$, or $(a+2)^2 = 0$, so that $a_1 = a_2 = -2,$
and the general solution of the differential equation is
$$y = e^{-2x}(A + Bx).$$

(b) If the roots of the auxiliary equation (2) are imaginary, then by the theory of quadratic equations, $a^2 < 4b$, and the roots may be written

$$a_1 = -\tfrac{1}{2}a + ni, \quad a_2 = -\tfrac{1}{2}a - ni,$$
where $i = \sqrt{(-1)}$, and $n^2 = b - \tfrac{1}{4}a^2.$

Now, as in (a), let $y = e^{-\frac{1}{2}ax}u$; equation (1) reduces, as before, to

$$\frac{d^2u}{dx^2} + u\,(b - \tfrac{1}{4}a^2) = 0,$$

or $\qquad \dfrac{d^2u}{dx^2} + n^2u = 0$, since $n^2 = b - \tfrac{1}{4}a^2$.

The general solution of this equation (see page 319) is
$$u = A\cos nx + B\sin nx.$$
Hence, the general solution of the given differential equation in this case is

$$y = e^{-\frac{1}{2}ax}\,(A\cos nx + B\sin nx),$$

where A, B are arbitrary.

For example, if $\dfrac{d^2y}{dx^2} + 2\dfrac{dy}{dx} + 5y = 0$,

the auxiliary equation is $a^2 + 2a + 5 = 0$,
or $\qquad\qquad (a + 1)^2 = -4,$
so that $\qquad a_1 = -1 + 2i,\ a_2 = -1 - 2i,$
and the general solution of the differential equation is
$$y = e^{-x}\,(A\cos 2x + B\sin 2x).$$

We now have to consider the solution of a differential equation of the form

$$\frac{d^2y}{dx^2} + a\frac{dy}{dx} + by = R, \qquad .\qquad .\qquad . \quad (3)$$

where R is a function of x, or a non-zero constant.

Let the general solution of the equation

$$\frac{d^2y}{dx^2} + a\frac{dy}{dx} + by = 0,$$

obtained by replacing R by zero, be $y = Au + Bv$, where A, B are arbitrary, and let $y = w$ be *any* particular solution of the equation (3). Then it can easily be verified by substitution that equation (3) is also satisfied by $y = Au + Bv + w$, which must therefore be its general solution since it contains two arbitrary constants.

Thus, in solving an equation of the above type, two steps are involved. First we find the general solution of the equation when R, (the term independent of y and its derivatives) is zero. This is called the **complementary function,** and contains two arbitrary constants. Then we find a particular solution of the given equation—any solution whatever, the simpler the better. This function—known as the **particular integral**—contains no arbitrary constant. The general solution of the given equation is then found by adding the complementary function and the particular integral.

So far we have not given any guidance as how to set about finding a particular integral. In each case, the simplest way is to decide by inspection of R the likely *form* of the particular integral, and then test by substitution. The most suitable substitutions for certain forms of R are now quoted.

(i) If $R = P(x)$, where $P(x)$ is a polynomial of degree n, we try $y = Q(x)$, where $Q(x)$ is also a polynomial of degree n, and then find the unknown coefficients of this polynomial by substitution in the differential equation.

(ii) If $R = ke^{ax}$, we try $y = Ce^{ax}$, and find C by substitution. This method fails if a is a root of the corresponding auxiliary equation, in which case we try $y = Cxe^{ax}$ or Cx^2e^{ax}, according as a is a single or double root of the auxiliary equation.

(iii) If $R = K \sin px$, or $L \cos px$, or $K \sin px + L \cos px$, we try $y = C \sin px + D \cos px$, and find C, D by substitution. This method fails if the complementary function has the form $A \sin px + B \cos px$, in which case we try $y = Cx \sin px + Dx \cos px$.

(iv) If R consists of a series of terms of the above type, we try a series of similar terms, and find the unknown coefficients by substitution.

These remarks may not seem very helpful to the student ; the following worked examples may help to clear up the difficulties.

Examples (continued)

5. Solve the differential equation $(1 + x^2) \dfrac{d^2y}{dx^2} + 2x \dfrac{dy}{dx} = 0$.

Let $\dfrac{dy}{dx} = p$; then $\dfrac{d^2y}{dx^2} = \dfrac{dp}{dx}$, and the given equation becomes

$$(1 + x^2) \frac{dp}{dx} + 2xp = 0.$$

Hence $\qquad \dfrac{dp}{p} + \dfrac{2x\,dx}{1 + x^2} = 0,$

and $\qquad p\,(1 + x^2) = A,$

that is, $\qquad \dfrac{dy}{dx} = \dfrac{A}{1 + x^2}.$

Integrating once more, we have
$$y = A \tan^{-1} x + B.$$

6. Solve the differential equation

$$\frac{d^2y}{dx^2} + \frac{dy}{dx} - 2y = e^x + e^{-x}.$$

For the complementary function, $\dfrac{d^2y}{dx^2} + \dfrac{dy}{dx} - 2y = 0$,

and the auxiliary equation is $\qquad a^2 + a - 2 = 0,$
or $\qquad (a + 2)(a - 1) = 0,$
so that $\qquad a = 1 \text{ or } -2.$

Hence the complementary function is $y = Ae^x + Be^{-2x}$.

For a particular integral, try $y = axe^x + be^{-x}$.

We have $\qquad \dfrac{dy}{dx} = ae^x + axe^x - be^{-x},$

and $\qquad \dfrac{d^2y}{dx^2} = 2ae^x + axe^x + be^{-x},$

and, substituting in the given differential equation

$$(2ae^x + axe^x + be^{-x}) + (ae^x + axe^x - be^{-x})$$
$$- 2\,(axe^x + be^{-x}) = e^x + e^{-x}.$$

Thus $\qquad 3ae^x - 2be^{-x} = e^x + e^{-x}.$

This last result is not merely an equation which holds for certain values of x. It is an *identity*—true for all values of x; that is, $3ae^x - 2be^{-x}$ and $e^x + e^{-x}$ are one and the same function.

Hence we may equate corresponding coefficients. Therefore
$$3a = 1 \text{ and } -2b = 1,$$
so that $\qquad a = \tfrac{1}{3} \text{ and } \qquad b = -\tfrac{1}{2}.$

Hence a particular integral is $y = \tfrac{1}{3}xe^x - \tfrac{1}{2}e^{-x}.$

The general solution is therefore
$$y = Ae^x + Be^{-2x} + \tfrac{1}{3}xe^x - \tfrac{1}{2}e^{-x}.$$

7. Integrate the differential equation

$$\frac{d^2y}{dx^2} - 4\frac{dy}{dx} + 13y = 29 \sin 2x.$$

For the complementary function, $\dfrac{d^2y}{dx^2} - 4\dfrac{dy}{dx} + 13y = 0,$

and the auxiliary equation is $\qquad\qquad a^2 - 4a + 13 = 0,$
or $\qquad\qquad\qquad\qquad\qquad\qquad (a - 2)^2 = -9,$
so that $\qquad\qquad\qquad a = 2 \pm 3i.$

Hence the complementary function is $e^{2x}(A \cos 3x + B \sin 3x).$

For a particular integral, try $y = a \cos 2x + b \sin 2x.$

We have $\qquad\qquad \dfrac{dy}{dx} = -2a \sin 2x + 2b \cos 2x,$

and $\qquad\qquad \dfrac{d^2y}{dx^2} = -4a \cos 2x - 4b \sin 2x,$

and, substituting in the given equation
$$\cos 2x\,(-4a - 8b + 13a) + \sin 2x\,(-4b + 8a + 13b) = 29 \sin 2x.$$

Hence $\qquad\qquad 9a - 8b = 0, \text{ or } a = \dfrac{8b}{9},$

and $\qquad\qquad\qquad 8a + 9b = 29.$

Eliminating a, we have $\dfrac{64b}{9} + 9b = 29,$

so that $b = \dfrac{261}{145} = \dfrac{9}{5},$ and $a = \dfrac{8}{5}.$

Hence a particular integral is $y = \tfrac{1}{5}(8 \cos 2x + 9 \sin 2x),$ and the general solution is
$$y = e^{2x}(A \cos 3x + B \sin 3x) + \tfrac{1}{5}(8 \cos 2x + 9 \sin 2x).$$

8. Solve the differential equation

$$\frac{d^2y}{dx^2} - 4\frac{dy}{dx} + 4y = 2e^{2x},$$

given that $y = 1$ and $\dfrac{dy}{dx} = 0$, when $x = 0.$

For the complementary function, $\dfrac{d^2y}{dx^2} - 4\dfrac{dy}{dx} + 4y = 0$,

and the auxiliary equation is $a^2 - 4a + 4 = 0$,
so that $a = 2$ (twice),
and the complementary function is $y = e^{2x}(A + Bx)$.

For a particular integral, try $y = ax^2 e^{2x}$.

We have $\qquad \dfrac{dy}{dx} = 2axe^{2x} + 2ax^2 e^{2x}$,

and $\qquad \dfrac{d^2y}{dx^2} = 2ae^{2x} + 8axe^{2x} + 4ax^2 e^{2x}$,

and, substituting in the given equation,

$$e^{2x}(2a + 8ax + 4ax^2 - 8ax - 8ax^2 + 4ax^2) = 2e^{2x}.$$

Hence $a = 1$, a particular integral is $y = x^2 e^{2x}$,
and the general solution is $y = e^{2x}(A + Bx + x^2)$.
But, when $x = 0$, $y = 1$;
therefore, substituting these corresponding values in the general
solution, we have $A = 1$.

Also, $\qquad \dfrac{dy}{dx} = 2e^{2x}(A + Bx + x^2) + e^{2x}(B + 2x)$,

and when $x = 0$, $\dfrac{dy}{dx} = 0$;

therefore $\qquad 0 = 2A + B$, so that $B = -2$.

The required solution is therefore
$$y = e^{2x}(1 - 2x + x^2),$$
or $\qquad\qquad y = e^{2x}(1 - x)^2$.

9. Solve the differential equation
$$\dfrac{d^2y}{dx^2} + y = x^2 + \sin x.$$

For the complementary function, $\dfrac{d^2y}{dx^2} + y = 0$,

and the auxiliary equation is $\qquad a^2 + 1 = 0$,
so that $a = \pm i$,
and the complementary function is $y = A\cos x + B\sin x$.

For a particular integral, try
$$y = x(a\cos x + b\sin x) + cx^2 + dx + e.$$
We have
$$\dfrac{dy}{dx} = a\cos x + b\sin x + x(-a\sin x + b\cos x) + 2cx + d,$$

and
$$\frac{d^2y}{dx^2} = 2\left(-a\sin x + b\cos x\right) + x\left(-a\cos x - b\sin x\right) + 2c.$$

Substituting in the given equation, we have
$$2\left(-a\sin x + b\cos x\right) + x\left(-a\cos x - b\sin x\right) + 2c +$$
$$x\left(a\cos x + b\sin x\right) + cx^2 + dx + e = x^2 + \sin x,$$

that is,
$$-2a\sin x + 2b\cos x + cx^2 + dx + (2c + e) = x^2 + \sin x.$$

Hence $a = -\frac{1}{2}$, $b = 0$, $c = 1$, $d = 0$, $e = -2c = -2$.

Therefore a particular integral is $y = -\frac{1}{2}x\cos x + x^2 - 2$,
and the general solution is
$$y = A\cos x + B\sin x - \tfrac{1}{2}x\cos x + x^2 - 2.$$

10. Solve the differential equation
$$x^2\frac{d^2y}{dx^2} + x\frac{dy}{dx} - y = 0$$

by changing the independent variable to θ, where $x = e^{\theta}$.

If $x = e^{\theta}$, then $\dfrac{dx}{d\theta} = e^{\theta} = x$, and $\dfrac{d\theta}{dx} = \dfrac{1}{x}$.

Also, $\dfrac{dy}{dx} = \dfrac{dy}{d\theta}\cdot\dfrac{d\theta}{dx} = \dfrac{dy}{d\theta}\cdot\dfrac{1}{x}$,

so that $x\dfrac{dy}{dx} = \dfrac{dy}{d\theta}$;

and, differentiating once more,
$$x\frac{d^2y}{dx^2} + \frac{dy}{dx} = \frac{d}{dx}\left(\frac{dy}{d\theta}\right) = \frac{d^2y}{d\theta^2}\cdot\frac{d\theta}{dx} = \frac{d^2y}{d\theta^2}\cdot\frac{1}{x},$$

so that $x^2\dfrac{d^2y}{dx^2} + x\dfrac{dy}{dx} = \dfrac{d^2y}{d\theta^2}$,

and therefore $x^2\dfrac{d^2y}{dx^2} = \dfrac{d^2y}{d\theta^2} - \dfrac{dy}{d\theta}$.

Thus, in the original equation, we may substitute
$$x\frac{dy}{dx} = \frac{dy}{d\theta}, \text{ and } x^2\frac{d^2y}{dx^2} = \frac{d^2y}{d\theta^2} - \frac{dy}{d\theta},$$

giving $\dfrac{d^2y}{d\theta^2} - \dfrac{dy}{d\theta} + \dfrac{dy}{d\theta} - y = 0$,

or $\dfrac{d^2y}{d\theta^2} - y = 0$.

The auxiliary equation is $a^2 - 1 = 0$, so that $a = \pm 1$, and the general solution is

$$y = Ae^\theta + Be^{-\theta},$$
$$= Ax + \frac{B}{x}.$$

11. Solve the simultaneous differential equations

$$\frac{dx}{dt} = x + 2y,$$

$$\frac{dy}{dt} = 2x + y.$$

The form of the given equations implies that x and y are both functions of a third variable, t. To solve these equations, the procedure is exactly that employed in the solution of algebraic simultaneous equations. We manipulate the two given equations so as to eliminate one of the unknowns—either x or y—and derive a single equation involving only one unknown. Thus, from the first equation, we have

$$y = \tfrac{1}{2}\left(\frac{dx}{dt} - x\right),$$

and, differentiating with respect to t,

$$\frac{dy}{dt} = \tfrac{1}{2}\left(\frac{d^2x}{dt^2} - \frac{dx}{dt}\right).$$

Substituting these values for y and $\frac{dy}{dt}$ in the second equation, we have

$$\tfrac{1}{2}\left(\frac{d^2x}{dt^2} - \frac{dx}{dt}\right) = 2x + \tfrac{1}{2}\left(\frac{dx}{dt} - x\right),$$

a differential equation (not involving y) which can be solved by the methods already discussed in this section.

Rearranging, we have

$$\frac{d^2x}{dt^2} - 2\frac{dx}{dt} - 3x = 0\,;$$

hence $\qquad\qquad x = Ae^{-t} + Be^{3t}.$

This is not the entire solution, however, for we have still to find the expression for y as a function of t.

Since $\qquad y = \tfrac{1}{2}\left(\dfrac{dx}{dt}\right) - x$,

then $\qquad y = \tfrac{1}{2}\left(-Ae^{-t} + 3Be^{3t} - Ae^{-t} - Be^{3t}\right)$
$\qquad\qquad = -Ae^{-t} + Be^{3t}.$

That is, the general solution of the given pair of equations is
$$x = Ae^{-t} + Be^{3t}, \quad y = -Ae^{-t} + Be^{3t}.$$

12. Solve the simultaneous differential equations

$$\frac{dy}{dt} + x + 2y = 5,$$

$$\frac{dx}{dt} + \frac{dy}{dt} + x = 2,$$

given that $x = 4$ and $y = \dfrac{3}{2}$, when $t = 0$.

Referring to the equations as (1) and (2), we have, from (2),
$$\frac{dy}{dt} = 2 - x - \frac{dx}{dt},$$

and, substituting this value in (1),

$$2 - x - \frac{dx}{dt} + x + 2y = 5,$$

or $\qquad\qquad 2y = 3 + \dfrac{dx}{dt}.$

Differentiating with respect to t, we have

$$2\frac{dy}{dt} = \frac{d^2x}{dt^2},$$

and the elimination of y is completed by substituting for $\dfrac{dy}{dt}$ the value obtained above, thus

$$\frac{d^2x}{dt^2} = 4 - 2x - 2\frac{dx}{dt},$$

or $\qquad\qquad \dfrac{d^2x}{dt^2} + 2\dfrac{dx}{dt} + 2x = 4.$

For the complementary function, $\dfrac{d^2x}{dt^2} + 2\dfrac{dx}{dt} + 2x = 0,$

and the auxiliary equation is $\qquad a^2 + 2a + 2 = 0,$

or $(a + 1)^2 = -1,$

so that $a = -1 \pm i.$

Hence the complementary function is given by
$$x = e^{-t}(A \cos t + B \sin t).$$

A particular solution is clearly $x = 2$; therefore the general solution is
$$x = e^{-t}(A \cos t + B \sin t) + 2 \qquad . \qquad . \qquad (3)$$

But $2y = 3 + \dfrac{dx}{dt},$

so that $2y = 3 + e^{-t}(-A \cos t - B \sin t - A \sin t + B \cos t)$
$$= 3 + e^{-t}[(B - A) \cos t - (B + A) \sin t],$$

and $y = \tfrac{3}{2} + \tfrac{1}{2}e^{-t}[(B - A) \cos t - (B + A) \sin t] \qquad . \quad (4)$

The general solution of the original pair of differential equations is therefore given by (3) and (4). But we are given further that when $t = 0$, $x = 4$ and $y = \tfrac{3}{2}$; hence
$$4 = A + 2, \text{ or } A = 2,$$
and $\tfrac{3}{2} = \tfrac{3}{2} + \tfrac{1}{2}(B - A), \text{ or } B = A = 2.$

Therefore the particular solution which satisfies the given conditions is
$$x = 2e^{-t}(\cos t + \sin t) + 2,$$
$$y = \tfrac{3}{2} - 2e^{-t} \sin t.$$

Solve the differential equations 13 - 45:

13. $\dfrac{dy}{dx} = \dfrac{x}{y}.$

14. $\dfrac{dy}{dx} = \tan x \tan y.$

15. $x\dfrac{dy}{dx} + y = xy.$

16. $y + x\dfrac{dy}{dx} = x - y\dfrac{dy}{dx}.$

17. $\dfrac{dy}{dx} = \dfrac{2x - y}{x + y}.$

18. $x\dfrac{dy}{dx} - 2y = \sqrt{x}.$

19. $\dfrac{dy}{dx} = y \tan x - 2 \sin x.$

20. $\cot x\dfrac{dy}{dx} = \sin x - y.$

21. $y \left(y - x \dfrac{dy}{dx} \right) = x^2 \dfrac{dy}{dx}.$

22. $y - x \dfrac{dy}{dx} = 3 \left(1 + x^2 \dfrac{dy}{dx} \right).$

23. $xy \left(\dfrac{dy}{dx} - 2 \right) = 2x^2 + y^2.$

24. $\dfrac{dy}{dx} + \dfrac{y}{x} + \dfrac{y^2}{x^2} = 0.$

25. $3x \dfrac{dy}{dx} + 2y^2 = 3 \left(2y - 3 \dfrac{dy}{dx} \right).$

26. $x^2 \dfrac{dy}{dx} = x^2 + xy - y^2.$

27. $1 + y^2 = xy (1 + x^2) \dfrac{dy}{dx}.$

28. $x \dfrac{dy}{dx} = y + \sqrt{(x^2 + y^2)}.$

29. $p (x + a) \dfrac{dy}{dx} + q (y + \beta) = 0.$

30. $(xy - 2y^2) + (3xy - x^2) \dfrac{dy}{dx} = 0.$

31. $\cos^2 x \dfrac{dy}{dx} + y = \tan x.$

32. $x^2 \dfrac{dy}{dx} + y^2 = 2xy$, given that $y = 4$, when $x = -2.$

33. $3x \dfrac{dy}{dx} + y = xy \left(3 + \dfrac{dy}{dx} \right)$, given that $y = 3$, when $x = -1.$

34. $y - x \dfrac{dy}{dx} = x + y \dfrac{dy}{dx}$, given that $y = 0$, when $x = 2.$

35. $(1 + x^2) \dfrac{dy}{dx} = 1 + xy$, given that $y = -2$, when $x = 0.$

36. $(2x + y) \dfrac{dy}{dx} = 2 (y - 2x)$, given that $y = 0$, when $x = -1.$

37. $x \dfrac{dy}{dx} - 4y = x^6 e^x$, given that $y = -1$, when $x = 1.$

38. $\left(\dfrac{3}{x} + \dfrac{2}{y} \right) \dfrac{dy}{dx} = \dfrac{1}{x}$, given that $y = \frac{1}{3}$, when $x = \frac{1}{2}.$

332

39. $(x+1)\dfrac{dy}{dx} - y = e^x\,(x+1)^3$, given that $y = 0$, when $x = 0$.

40. $(1+x^2)\left(x\dfrac{dy}{dx} - 1\right) = (x^2 - 1)\,y$, given that $y = 1$, when $x = 0$.

41. $x\,(1-x^2)\dfrac{dy}{dx} + (2x^2 - 1)\,y = x^3$, given that $y = 3$, when $x = \frac{3}{5}$.

42. $(1-x^2)\dfrac{dy}{dx} - xy = xy^3$.   43. $x^2 y - x^3\dfrac{dy}{dx} = y^4 \cos x$.

44. $3\dfrac{dy}{dx} + 4y + e^x y^{\frac{5}{2}} = 0$.   45. $\dfrac{dy}{dx} = (x+y)^2$.

46. Show that a differential equation of the form
$$\frac{dy}{dx} = f\,(ax + by)$$
may be solved by means of the substitution $z = ax + by$. Hence solve the differential equation
$$2\,(x+y)\frac{dy}{dx} = 1 - 3x - 3y.$$

47. Solve the differential equation
$$(x+y)\frac{dy}{dx} + (x - y) = 0,$$
given that $y = \sqrt{3}$, when $x = 1$. By writing $x = r\cos\theta$, $y = r\sin\theta$ in the result, show it in the form $r = 2e^{-\left(\theta - \frac{\pi}{3}\right)}$.

48. The normal at a point $P\,(x, y)$ on a curve cuts the x-axis in G, and M is the projection of P on the x-axis ; show that $MG = y\dfrac{dy}{dx}$.

If, for all positions of P on the curve, $MG = 4x$, and if the curve passes through the point $(0, 1)$, find its equation.

49. The tangent and the normal at the point $P\,(x, y)$ on a certain curve meet the x-axis at T and N, respectively. If the mid-point of TN coincides with the origin, prove that the differential equation of the curve is
$$\left(y\frac{dy}{dx} + x\right)^2 = x^2 + y^2.$$

If $u^2 = x^2 + y^2$, show that this equation reduces to $\left(\dfrac{du}{dx}\right)^2 = 1$,

and deduce that any curve having the above property belongs to a system of parabolas.

50. The tangent at the point P on a curve cuts the x-axis in T. If, for all positions of P on the curve, the mid-point of PT lies on the line $y = x$, show that the coordinates of P satisfy the differential equation

$$\frac{dy}{dx} = \frac{y}{2x - y}.$$

If the curve passes through the point $(0, 4)$, find its equation.

51. If I is the intensity of light at a depth x feet below the surface of the sea, then $\dfrac{dI}{dx} = -kI$, where k is a positive constant. State this law in words ; and if I_0 is the light intensity at the surface, express I in terms of x, k, and I_0.

52. In order that a circular disc which rotates with a given angular velocity should have uniform strength, its thickness z should diminish as the distance x from the centre increases, the rate of change being proportional to xz. Express this law as an equation ; show that if the thickness at the centre is z_0, the relation between z and x is of the form $z = z_0 e^{-cx^2}$, where c is a positive constant.

53. Express as a differential equation the law that if the temperature is constant, the atmospheric pressure p at height x above sea-level decreases as x increases, at a rate proportional to p. Deduce that if the pressures at sea-level and at height h are p_0 and p_1, respectively, then $p = p_0 \left(\dfrac{p_1}{p_0}\right)^{\frac{x}{h}}$.

54. Express in symbols the statement* that the rate of cooling of a hot body is proportional to the excess of its temperature (T) over that of its surroundings (T_0). If a liquid at temperature 27° is allowed to cool in a room of temperature 15°, and if after 5 minutes its temperature is 19°, find its temperature after a further 5 minutes.

---

* Newton's Law of Cooling.

55. Compressed gas escapes through a small tap in its container into the free atmosphere, and at time t seconds after the tap is opened, the pressure of the gas is p atmospheres. Express in symbols the law that the rate of decrease of the gas pressure is proportional to the square root of the excess of that pressure over atmospheric pressure. Deduce the gas pressure, in atmospheres, when $t = 20$ seconds, if initially $p = 10$ atmospheres and if $p = 5$ atmospheres after 8 seconds.

56. Find the complete solution of the equation $\dfrac{dp}{dz} = - g\rho$, where $p = k\rho^n$, and g and k are constants. If $p = p_0$, and $\rho = \rho_0$, when $z = 0$, show that if $n \neq 1$ the solution is

$$ gz = \frac{n}{n-1} \left(\frac{p_0}{\rho_0} - \frac{p}{\rho} \right). $$

57. The acceleration a of a particle moving in a straight line is given in terms of the velocity v by the equation

$$ a = - g \left(1 + \frac{v^2}{c^2} \right), $$

where g, c are constants. If $s = 0$, and $v = u$, when $t = 0$, show that when $v = 0$,

$$ s = \frac{c^2}{2g} \log \left(\frac{u^2}{c^2} + 1 \right), \text{ and } t = \frac{c}{g} \tan^{-1} \left(\frac{u}{c} \right). $$

58. The differential equation

$$ L \frac{di}{dt} + Ri = E $$

occurs in electrical theory, L, R, E being positive constants. Find i as a function of t, given that $i = 0$ when $t = 0$. Hence show that as t increases indefinitely, i approaches the value E/R.

59. The potential V of a charged condenser diminishes in accordance with the law $\dfrac{dV}{dt} = - \dfrac{V}{CR}$, where t is time, C the capacity, and R the resistance to earth. If $C = 5 \times 10^{-6}$ units, and if V falls from 150 to 120 units in 50 units of time, calculate the value of R.

60. A curve passes through the point $(c, 0)$, and if $P(x, y)$ is any point on it, the length of the perpendicular to the tangent at P from the foot of the ordinate of P is xy/c. Prove that

$$\left(\frac{dy}{dx}\right)^2 = \frac{c^2 - x^2}{x^2},$$

and find the equation of the curve

61. If a particle starts from rest at distance $2a$ from a fixed point O and moves towards O with an acceleration which varies inversely as the square of the distance of the particle from O, show that, with the usual notation,

$$v\frac{dv}{ds} + \frac{k}{s^2} = 0,$$

where k is a positive constant. Deduce that

$$\frac{v^2}{2k} = \frac{1}{s} - \frac{1}{2a},$$

and that the particle will reach O at time $\pi\sqrt{(a^3/k)}$.

62. A particle starts from rest at a distance a from a fixed point O and moves towards O with acceleration $k\left(s + \dfrac{a^4}{s^3}\right)$, where s is its distance from O, and k is a positive constant. Show that it will reach O at time $\dfrac{\pi}{4\sqrt{k}}$.

Solve the differential equations 63-94 :

63. $\dfrac{d^2y}{dx^2} + 4\dfrac{dy}{dx} + 3y = 0.$ 64. $\dfrac{d^2y}{dx^2} - 2\dfrac{dy}{dx} - 3y = 0.$

65. $\dfrac{d^2y}{dx^2} - 5\dfrac{dy}{dx} + 4y = 0.$ 66. $\dfrac{d^2y}{dx^2} + \dfrac{dy}{dx} - 2y = 0.$

67. $\dfrac{d^2y}{dx^2} + 4y = 0.$ 68. $\dfrac{d^2y}{dx^2} - 10\dfrac{dy}{dx} + 25y = 0.$

69. $\dfrac{d^2y}{dx^2} + 4\dfrac{dy}{dx} + 5y = 0.$ 70. $\dfrac{d^2y}{dx^2} + 2\dfrac{dy}{dx} + 2y = 0.$

71. $4\dfrac{d^2y}{dx^2} + 4\dfrac{dy}{dx} + y = 0.$ 72. $3\dfrac{d^2y}{dx^2} - 7\dfrac{dy}{dx} - 6y = 0.$

73. $2\dfrac{d^2y}{dx^2} - \dfrac{dy}{dx} - 6y = 0.$ 74. $9\dfrac{d^2y}{dx^2} + \dfrac{dy}{dx} = 0.$

75. $\dfrac{d^2y}{dx^2} - 6\dfrac{dy}{dx} + 9y = 0$, given that $y = 0, \dfrac{dy}{dx} = 1$, when $x = 0.$

76. $\dfrac{d^2y}{dx^2} + 6\dfrac{dy}{dx} + 10y = 0$, given that $y = 1, \dfrac{dy}{dx} = 0$, when $x = 0.$

77. $2\dfrac{d^2y}{dx^2} + \dfrac{dy}{dx} = 0$, given that $y = 0, \dfrac{dy}{dx} = 1$, when $x = 0.$

78. $\dfrac{d^2y}{dx^2} + 2\dfrac{dy}{dx} - 3y = 0$, given that $y = -2, \dfrac{dy}{dx} = -6$, when $x = 0.$

79. $2\dfrac{d^2y}{dx^2} + 6\dfrac{dy}{dx} + 17y = 0$, given that $y = \dfrac{5}{2}, \dfrac{dy}{dx} = \dfrac{25}{4}$, when $x = 0.$

80. $\dfrac{d^2y}{dx^2} - \dfrac{dy}{dx} - 2y = e^{-x}.$

81. $\dfrac{d^2y}{dx^2} + 8\dfrac{dy}{dx} + 25y = 26 \cos 3x.$

82. $\dfrac{d^2y}{dx^2} + 4\dfrac{dy}{dx} + 5y = 25x^2 + 3.$

83. $\dfrac{d^2y}{dx^2} - 4\dfrac{dy}{dx} + 4y = e^{2x} + \cos 2x.$

84. $\dfrac{d^2y}{dx^2} + 6\dfrac{dy}{dx} + 10y = 30 \sin 2x.$

85. $\dfrac{d^2y}{dx^2} + 2\dfrac{dy}{dx} - 3y = x - \sin x.$

86. $4\dfrac{d^2y}{dx^2} + 13\dfrac{dy}{dx} + 9y = 7e^{-2x}.$

87. $\dfrac{d^2y}{dx^2} + 5\dfrac{dy}{dx} + 4y = 32x^2.$

88. $\dfrac{d^2y}{dx^2} + 4y = \cos 2x.$

89. $2\dfrac{d^2y}{dx^2} + \dfrac{dy}{dx} = 2x + e^{-\frac{1}{2}x}.$

90. $\dfrac{d^2y}{dx^2} - 3\dfrac{dy}{dx} + 2y = e^{2x}$, given that $y = \dfrac{dy}{dx} = 0$, when $x = 0$.

91. $\dfrac{d^2y}{dx^2} + 2\dfrac{dy}{dx} + 2y = e^{-2x} + \cos x$, given that $y = 1$, $\dfrac{dy}{dx} = 0$, when $x = 0$.

92. $\dfrac{d^2y}{dx^2} - 4\dfrac{dy}{dx} + 3y = 9x + 65 \cos 2x$, given that $y = \dfrac{dy}{dx} = 0$, when $x = 0$.

93. $4\dfrac{d^2y}{dx^2} + y = 4 \sin x$, given that $y = \pi$, $\dfrac{dy}{dx} = 0$, when $x = \pi$.

94. $2\dfrac{d^2y}{dx^2} + 2\dfrac{dy}{dx} + 5y = 5(1-x)^2$, given that $y = \dfrac{8}{25}$, $\dfrac{dy}{dx} = \dfrac{7}{10}$, when $x = 0$.

95. If y is a function of x, and if $x = e^\theta$, prove that

$$x\frac{dy}{dx} = \frac{dy}{d\theta},$$

and $\qquad\qquad\qquad x^2\dfrac{d^2y}{dx^2} = \dfrac{d^2y}{d\theta^2} - \dfrac{dy}{d\theta},$

and use this transformation to solve the differential equations:

(i) $x^2\dfrac{d^2y}{dx^2} + x\dfrac{dy}{dx} - 4y = \log x,$

(ii) $x^2\dfrac{d^2y}{dx^2} + 4x\dfrac{dy}{dx} - 10y = x^2,$

338

(iii) $x^2 \dfrac{d^2y}{dx^2} + 7x \dfrac{dy}{dx} + 9y = \dfrac{1}{x^2}$, given that $y = 2$, $\dfrac{dy}{dx} = -3$
when $x = 1$.

96. Solve the differential equation

$$x^2 \frac{d^2y}{dx^2} + x \frac{dy}{dx} - y = x,$$

and verify your result by first showing that the left-hand side
may be written $x^2 \dfrac{d}{dx}\left(\dfrac{dy}{dx} + \dfrac{y}{x}\right)$.

97. Find the possible values of m so that $y = x^m$ may be a solution
of the differential equation $x^2 \dfrac{d^2y}{dx^2} + x \dfrac{dy}{dx} - n^2 y = 0$, and hence
write down the general solution.

98. Verify that $y = \dfrac{(x+a)^2}{x+b}$ satisfies the differential equation

$$(x+a)^2 (x+b)^2 \frac{d^2y}{dx^2} - 2(a-b)^2 y = 0,$$

and write down the complete primitive.

99. Using the substitution $x = \dfrac{a}{z}$, show that the differential equation

$$x^4 \frac{d^2y}{dx^2} + 2x^3 \frac{dy}{dx} + a^2 (y - 1) = 0$$

reduces to $\dfrac{d^2y}{dz^2} + y = 1$,

and finds its solution, given that $y = \dfrac{dy}{dx} = 0$, when $x = \dfrac{a}{\pi}$.

Solve the simultaneous differential equations **100-111**:

100. $\dfrac{dx}{dt} = 2x + y$, $\dfrac{dy}{dt} = x + 2y$, given that $x = 2, y = 0$, when $t = 0$.

101. $3\dfrac{dx}{dt} + y = 12x$, $\dfrac{dy}{dt} - 2y = 3x$.

102. $\dfrac{dx}{dt} = x - y, \quad \dfrac{dy}{dt} = x + y.$

103. $\dfrac{dx}{dt} = y + e^{-t}, \dfrac{dy}{dt} = 2x + y$, given that $x = y = \tfrac{1}{3}$, when $t = 0$.

104. $\dfrac{dx}{dt} = x + 2y, \dfrac{dy}{dt} = x + e^{-2t}$, given that $x = y = 1$, when $t = 0$.

105. $5\dfrac{dx}{dt} + 3x + 4y + 5 = 0, \quad 5\dfrac{dy}{dt} + 4x - 3y - 35 = 0,$
     given that $x = y = 10$, when $t = 0$.

106. $\dfrac{dx}{dt} = x + y + e^{-2t}, \dfrac{dy}{dt} = 3x - y$, given that $x = \tfrac{3}{4}$, $y = 0$, when $t = 0$.

107. $\dfrac{dx}{dt} - 2x + 2y = e^t, \dfrac{dy}{dt} + 2x + y = \sin t.$

108. $\dfrac{dx}{dt} + x + 2y = 5, \dfrac{dx}{dt} + \dfrac{dy}{dt} + x = 2$, given that $x = 4$, $y = 3$, when $t = 0$.

109. $t\dfrac{dx}{dt} + 2x - y - 3t = 0, \; t\dfrac{dy}{dt} - 12x + 3y - 2t = 0.$

110. $t\dfrac{dx}{dt} - 3x - 2y = t, \; t\dfrac{dy}{dt} + 4x + 3y = 0$, given that $x = \tfrac{1}{2}$, $y = 0$, when $t = 1$.

111. $x + y = t\dfrac{dx}{dt} - 2t^3, \; 5x - 3y = t\dfrac{dy}{dt} - 3t^2.$

112. The coordinates of a point P satisfy the differential equations
$$\frac{d^2x}{dt^2} + 2\frac{dx}{dt} + 2x = 2a,$$
$$\frac{dx}{dt} + y = 2a - x,$$
and it is known that $x = 2a$, $y = a$, when $t = 0$. Prove that the distance of P from the point (a, a) is ae^{-t}.

§34. ARCS, SURFACES, AND CURVATURE.

Lengths of arcs

It will be remembered that in **§ 25** the area of a circle was regarded as the limit to which the area of an inscribed (or circumscribed) n-sided polygon tends as the number of sides (n) increases indefinitely. In exactly the same way we could define the length of the circumference of the circle as the limit to which the perimeter of the inscribed (or circumscribed) polygon tends as the number of sides increases beyond all bound.

The length of an arc of *any* curve may similarly be regarded as the limit to which the perimeter of an open n-sided polygon inscribed in (or circumscribed about) the arc tends as the number of sides (n) increases indefinitely. It follows that if $P(x, y)$ and $Q(x + \delta x, y + \delta y)$ are two neighbouring points on a curve $y = f(x)$ (Fig. 69), although the arc PQ will always exceed the chord PQ in length, the difference between these two lengths will diminish steadily as the point Q approaches the point P along the curve, that is, as δx tends to zero.

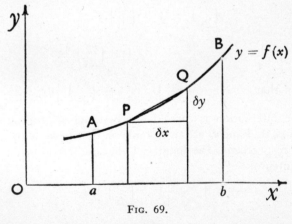

FIG. 69.

Expressed otherwise,

$$\underset{\delta x \longrightarrow 0}{L} \left(\frac{\text{chord } PQ}{\text{arc } PQ}\right) = 1.$$

Let s be the length of the arc AP measured from an arbitrary fixed point A on the curve to the variable point $P(x, y)$. Then s clearly varies with x (the abscissa of P) and is therefore a function of x. Let δs, δy be the increments in s, y, corresponding to the increment δx in x ; then δs is a measure of the length of the arc PQ, where Q is the point $(x + \delta x, y + \delta y)$. By Pythagoras' theorem, we have

$$(\delta x)^2 + (\delta y)^2 = (\text{chord } PQ)^2$$

$$= \left(\frac{\text{chord } PQ}{\delta s}\right)^2 \cdot (\delta s)^2,$$

so that

$$1 + \left(\frac{\delta y}{\delta x}\right)^2 = \left(\frac{\text{chord } PQ}{\text{arc } PQ}\right)^2 \cdot \left(\frac{\delta s}{\delta x}\right)^2.$$

Now let Q approach P along the curve ; then $\delta x \longrightarrow 0$, and

$$\frac{\delta y}{\delta x} \longrightarrow \frac{dy}{dx}, \quad \frac{\text{chord } PQ}{\text{arc } PQ} \longrightarrow 1, \text{ and } \frac{\delta s}{\delta x} \longrightarrow \frac{ds}{dx}.$$

Therefore,

$$\left(\frac{ds}{dx}\right)^2 = 1 + \left(\frac{dy}{dx}\right)^2,$$

that is,

$$\frac{ds}{dx} = \sqrt{\left\{1 + \left(\frac{dy}{dx}\right)^2\right\}}.$$

It follows that

$$s = \int \sqrt{\left\{1 + \left(\frac{dy}{dx}\right)^2\right\}} dx,$$

where the integration is carried out between appropriate limits of x. Thus, if A and B are two points on the curve, with abscissæ a and b, respectively, the length of the arc AB is given by the definite integral

$$\int_a^b \sqrt{\left\{1 + \left(\frac{dy}{dx}\right)^2\right\}} dx.$$

(The reader may verify for himself that if x and y are given in terms of a parameter t, then

$$\dot{s}^2 = \dot{x}^2 + \dot{y}^2,$$

so that $\qquad\qquad s = \int \sqrt{(\dot{x}^2 + \dot{y}^2)}\, dt.)$

For example, let us find the length of the circumference of the circle $x^2 + y^2 = r^2$, that is, a circle with centre the origin and radius r. Considering the upper semi-circle only, we have $y = +\sqrt{(r^2 - x^2)}$.

Then

$$\frac{dy}{dx} = \frac{-x}{\sqrt{(r^2 - x^2)}}, \text{ and } \frac{ds}{dx} = \sqrt{\left(1 + \frac{x^2}{r^2 - x^2}\right)} = \frac{r}{\sqrt{(r^2 - x^2)}}.$$

Therefore, the length of the circumference of the circle

$$= 2\int_{-r}^{r} \frac{r\,dx}{\sqrt{(r^2 - x^2)}} = 2r\left[\sin^{-1}\frac{x}{r}\right]_{-r}^{r}$$

$$= 2r\left(\frac{\pi}{2} + \frac{\pi}{2}\right) = 2\pi r.$$

Surfaces of revolution

We have already seen (**§ 23**) that when the area under a curve $y = f(x)$ between specified points (abscissæ a and b) is revolved about the x-axis a solid is generated, the volume of this solid of revolution having a value given by the definite integral

$$\int_{a}^{b} \pi y^2 dx.$$

In exactly the same way, if an arc of a curve $y = f(x)$ between specified points is revolved about the x-axis, a **surface of revolution** is generated, and it is the purpose of this section to find a formula which will give the value of the area of the surface generated in this way.

If we inscribe in (or circumscribe about) the arc an n-sided open polygon, then when the arc is revolved about the x-axis,

343

each side of the polygon will generate the surface of a frustum of a cone ; and the polygon, regarded as a whole, will generate a surface consisting of n frustums joined end to end. Let the sum of the areas of these n surfaces be denoted by Σ ; then the area of the surface generated by the *arc* in revolving about the x-axis may be regarded as the limit to which Σ tends as the number of sides (n) of the polygon increases indefinitely.

It follows that if $P(x, y)$ and $Q(x + \delta x, y + \delta y)$ are two neighbouring points on a curve $y = f(x)$ (Fig. 69), although the areas, δS and $\delta \Sigma$, of the surfaces generated respectively by the arc PQ and the chord PQ in revolving about the x-axis will always differ, the difference between the areas of these two surfaces will diminish steadily as the point Q approaches the point P along the curve, that is, as δx tends to zero. In other words,

$$\underset{\delta x \,\longrightarrow\, 0}{L} \quad \frac{\delta \Sigma}{\delta S} = 1.$$

Let s be the length of the arc AP of the curve $y = f(x)$ (Fig. 69) measured from an arbitrary fixed point A on the curve to the variable point $P(x, y)$. Let S be the area of the surface generated by revolving the arc AP about the x-axis ; then clearly S varies with x (the abscissa of P) and is therefore a function of x. Let δy, δs, δS be the increments in y, s, S, corresponding to the increment δx in x ; then δs is a measure of the length of the arc PQ, where Q is the point $(x + \delta x, y + \delta y)$, and δS is a measure of the area of the surface generated by revolving the arc PQ about the x-axis.

By the result of Example 16, page 175, we have

$$\delta \Sigma = \pi \,(\text{chord } PQ) \,.\, (y + y + \delta y),$$

so that $\left(\dfrac{\delta \Sigma}{\delta S}\right) . \dfrac{\delta S}{\delta x} = \pi \left(\dfrac{\text{chord } PQ}{\text{arc } PQ}\right) . \dfrac{\delta s}{\delta x}(2y + \delta y).$

Now let Q approach P along the curve ; then $\delta x \rightarrow 0$, and

$$\frac{\delta \Sigma}{\delta S} \rightarrow 1, \quad \frac{\delta S}{\delta x} \rightarrow \frac{dS}{dx}, \quad \frac{\text{chord } PQ}{\text{arc } PQ} \rightarrow 1,$$

$$\frac{\delta s}{\delta x} \rightarrow \frac{ds}{dx}, \text{ and } 2y + \delta y \rightarrow 2y.$$

Therefore
$$\frac{dS}{dx} = 2\pi y \frac{ds}{dx},$$

so that
$$S = \int 2\pi y \frac{ds}{dx}\, dx,$$

where the integration is carried out between appropriate limits of x. Thus, if A and B are two points on the curve, with abscissæ a and b, respectively, the area of the surface generated by revolving the arc AB about the x-axis is given by the definite integral

$$\int_a^b 2\pi y \frac{ds}{dx}\, dx,$$

where $\frac{ds}{dx} = \sqrt{\left\{1 + \left(\frac{dy}{dx}\right)^2\right\}}$.

Similarly, the area of the surface generated by revolving the arc AB about the **y-axis** is given by the definite integral

$$\int_{a'}^{b'} 2\pi x \frac{ds}{dy}\, dy,$$

where $\frac{ds}{dy} = \sqrt{\left\{1 + \left(\frac{dx}{dy}\right)^2\right\}}$, and a', b' are the ordinates of A, B respectively.

By way of illustration, let us find a formula for the surface area of a sphere of radius r. Such a surface will be generated by revolving about the x-axis the upper half of the circle $x^2 + y^2 = r^2$. Thus,

$$y = +\sqrt{(r^2 - x^2)}, \text{ and } \frac{ds}{dx} = \frac{r}{\sqrt{(r^2 - x^2)}} \quad \text{(page 343)}.$$

345

Therefore, the required surface area

$$= \int_{-r}^{r} 2\pi\sqrt{(r^2 - x^2)} \cdot \frac{r}{\sqrt{(r^2 - x^2)}}\, dx$$

$$= 2\pi r \left[x \right]_{-r}^{r} = 4\pi r^2.$$

Examples

1. Find the length of the arc of the curve $8y = 3\,(2x^{\frac{2}{3}} - x^{\frac{4}{3}})$ which lies in the first quadrant ; find also the area of the surface generated by revolving this arc about the x-axis.

When $x = 0$, $y = 0$; when $y = 0$, $x = 0$ or $x^{\frac{2}{3}} = 2$, that is, $x = 2\sqrt{2}$.

Thus, the arc in question extends from $x = 0$ to $x = 2\sqrt{2}$.

Since $y = \frac{3}{8}(2x^{\frac{2}{3}} - x^{\frac{4}{3}})$,

$$\frac{dy}{dx} = \frac{1}{2}x^{-\frac{1}{3}} - \frac{1}{2}x^{\frac{1}{3}},$$

and $\dfrac{ds}{dx} = \sqrt{\left\{ 1 + \frac{1}{4}(x^{-\frac{1}{3}} - x^{\frac{1}{3}})^2 \right\}} = \frac{1}{2}\sqrt{(4 + x^{-\frac{2}{3}} - 2 + x^{\frac{2}{3}})}$,

$$= \frac{1}{2}\sqrt{(x^{-\frac{2}{3}} + 2 + x^{\frac{2}{3}})} = \frac{1}{2}(x^{-\frac{1}{3}} + x^{\frac{1}{3}}).$$

Therefore, the length of the arc

$$= \frac{1}{2}\int_{0}^{2\sqrt{2}} (x^{-\frac{1}{3}} + x^{\frac{1}{3}})\, dx = \frac{1}{2}\left[\frac{3}{2}x^{\frac{2}{3}} + \frac{3}{4}x^{\frac{4}{3}} \right]_{0}^{2\sqrt{2}}$$

$$= \frac{1}{2}(\frac{3}{2}.2 + \frac{3}{4}.4) = 3 \text{ units.}$$

The area of the surface of revolution

$$= \int_{0}^{2\sqrt{2}} 2\pi\, y\, \frac{ds}{dx}\, dx = 2\pi \int_{0}^{2\sqrt{2}} \frac{3}{8}(2x^{\frac{2}{3}} - x^{\frac{4}{3}}) \cdot \frac{1}{2}(x^{-\frac{1}{3}} + x^{\frac{1}{3}})\, dx,$$

$$= \frac{3\pi}{8} \int_{0}^{2\sqrt{2}} (2x^{\frac{1}{3}} - x + 2x - x^{\frac{5}{3}})\, dx = \frac{3\pi}{8} \int_{0}^{2\sqrt{2}} (2x^{\frac{1}{3}} + x - x^{\frac{5}{3}})\, dx,$$

$$= \frac{3\pi}{8} \left[\frac{3}{2}x^{\frac{4}{3}} + \frac{1}{2}x^2 - \frac{3}{8}x^{\frac{8}{3}} \right]_{0}^{2\sqrt{2}}$$

$$= \frac{3\pi}{8}\left(\frac{3}{2}\cdot 4 + \frac{1}{2}\cdot 8 - \frac{3}{8}\cdot 16\right) = \frac{3\pi}{8}(6+4-6)$$

$$= \frac{3\pi}{2} \text{ square units.}$$

2. Find the length of the perimeter of the loop of the curve
$12y^2 = x(x-4)^2$; find also the area of the surface of revolution of the loop about the x-axis.

The curve has a form similar to that shown in Fig. 59, and cuts the x-axis where $x = 0$ and $x = 4$.

We have $y = \dfrac{1}{2\sqrt{3}}(4-x)\sqrt{x}$, where the form $(4-x)$ is

used instead of $(x-4)$ in order that y will be positive in the range $0 < x < 4$ (which is the range in which we are interested).

Therefore, $\dfrac{dy}{dx} = \dfrac{1}{2\sqrt{3}}(2x^{-\frac{1}{2}} - \tfrac{3}{2}x^{\frac{1}{2}}) = \dfrac{4-3x}{4\sqrt{3}\cdot\sqrt{x}}$,

and $\left(\dfrac{ds}{dx}\right)^2 = \dfrac{1}{48x}(48x+16-24x+9x^2)$,

$$= \frac{1}{48x}(16+24x+9x^2) = \frac{1}{48x}(4+3x)^2.$$

Thus, the perimeter of the loop

$$= 2\int_0^4 \frac{4+3x}{4\sqrt{3}\cdot\sqrt{x}}dx = \frac{1}{2\sqrt{3}}\int_0^4\left(\frac{4}{\sqrt{x}}+3\sqrt{x}\right)dx,$$

$$= \frac{1}{2\sqrt{3}}\left[8x^{\frac{1}{2}}+2x^{\frac{3}{2}}\right]_0^4 = \frac{1}{2\sqrt{3}}(16+16),$$

$$= \frac{16}{\sqrt{3}} = \frac{16\sqrt{3}}{3} \text{ units.}$$

The area of the surface of revolution

$$= \int_0^4 2\pi y\,\frac{ds}{dx}dx,$$

$$= 2\pi\int_0^4 \frac{1}{2\sqrt{3}}(4-x)\sqrt{x}\cdot\frac{1}{4\sqrt{3}}\frac{4+3x}{\sqrt{x}}dx,$$

$$= \frac{\pi}{12} \int_0^4 (16 + 8x - 3x^2)\, dx,$$

$$= \frac{\pi}{12} \left[16x + 4x^2 - x^3 \right]_0^4 = \frac{16\pi}{3} \text{ square units.}$$

3. Find the length of one arch of the cycloid whose freedom equations are

$$x = a\,(\theta - \sin \theta), \quad y = a\,(1 - \cos \theta),$$

and find also the area of the surface generated by revolving this arch about the x-axis.

We have, $y = 0$ at the ends of an arch,
so that $\cos \theta = 1$, and $\theta = 0$, 2π, etc.
Differentiating, we obtain $\dot{x} = a\,(1 - \cos \theta)$, $\dot{y} = a \sin \theta$,

so that $\dot{s}^2 = a^2\,(2 - 2 \cos \theta) = 4a^2 \sin^2 \dfrac{\theta}{2}$.

Thus, the total length of an arch $= \displaystyle\int_0^{2\pi} 2a \sin \frac{\theta}{2}\, d\theta$

$$= \left[-4a \cos \frac{\theta}{2} \right]_0^{2\pi} = 8a \text{ units.}$$

The formula for the area of a surface of revolution may be expressed in several equivalent forms—

$$\int 2\pi y \frac{ds}{dx}\, dx, \text{ or } \int 2\pi y\, ds, \text{ or } \int 2\pi y \frac{ds}{dt}\, dt.$$

This last form is appropriate for a curve defined by freedom equations. Thus,

the area of the required surface

$$= \int_0^{2\pi} 2\pi a\,(1 - \cos \theta) \,.\, 2a \sin \frac{\theta}{2}\, d\theta$$

$$= 4\pi a^2 \int_0^{2\pi} 2\left(1 - \cos^2 \frac{\theta}{2}\right) \sin \frac{\theta}{2}\, d\theta$$

$$= 8\pi a^2 \left[-2 \cos \frac{\theta}{2} + \frac{2}{3} \cos^3 \frac{\theta}{2} \right]_0^{2\pi} = \frac{64\pi a^2}{3} \text{ square units.}$$

Curvature

We have already (§ 5) defined the gradient of a curve at a point on it as the gradient of the tangent at that point. The direction of this tangent may be taken as the " direction of the curve " at the point in question. This direction usually changes from point to point on the curve, so that the tangent rotates as we move along the curve from a selected initial point.

If $P(x, y)$ and $Q(x + \delta x, y + \delta y)$ are neighbouring points on a curve $y = f(x)$, such that (Fig. 70) the tangents at P and Q

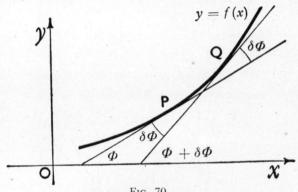

FIG. 70.

make angles Φ and $\Phi + \delta\Phi$, respectively, with the positive direction of the x-axis, then the greater the angle $\delta\Phi$, the greater the change of direction from P to Q. The angle $\delta\Phi$ may be taken as a measure of the total change of direction of the curve from P to Q, or of the **total curvature** of the arc PQ. Also, if s is the length of the arc measured from some fixed point to P, and if δs is the length of the arc PQ, the ratio $\delta\Phi/\delta s$ is taken as a measure of the **average curvature** of the arc PQ. And the limit, $\dfrac{d\Phi}{ds}$, to which this ratio approaches as the point Q tends to the point P is defined to be the **curvature** of the curve at P. Thus, we have,

the total curvature of the arc PQ $= \delta\Phi$,

the average curvature of the arc PQ $= \delta\Phi/\delta s$,

the curvature of the curve at the point $P = \dfrac{d\Phi}{ds}$.

In the particular case of a circle of centre C and radius R, the two radii, CP and CQ, will be inclined at an angle $\delta\Phi$, and, from elementary trigonometry, $\delta s = R \cdot \delta\Phi$, so that

$$\frac{\delta\Phi}{\delta s} = \frac{1}{R},$$

and

$$\frac{d\Phi}{ds} = \frac{1}{R} = \text{a constant.}$$

In considering the curvature at a point P on any other curve, we may imagine (Fig. 71) a circle passing through P with

(*a*) the same tangent at P as the given curve ;

(*b*) the same curvature at P as the given curve.

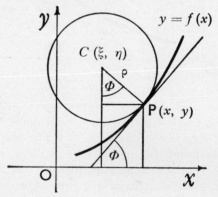

FIG. 71.

This circle is called the **circle of curvature** at P, its radius (ρ) is called the **radius of curvature** at P, and its centre (C) is called the **centre of curvature** at P. Thus,

$$\text{the radius of curvature} = \rho = \frac{ds}{d\Phi},$$

and the coordinates of C (ξ, η) are given by

$$\xi = x - \rho \sin \Phi, \quad \eta = y + \rho \cos \Phi.$$

350

The curvature, and therefore the radius of curvature also, usually varies from point to point along the curve : it is only in the case of the circle that the curvature and the radius of curvature are constant for all points.

We shall now derive a formula for finding the radius of curvature, ρ, of a given curve. If the equation of the curve is $y = f(x)$, then

$$\tan \Phi = \frac{dy}{dx},$$

so that
$$\sec^2 \Phi \cdot \frac{d\Phi}{ds} = \frac{d}{ds}\left(\frac{dy}{dx}\right) = \frac{d^2y}{dx^2} \cdot \frac{dx}{ds}.$$

But
$$\sec^2 \Phi = 1 + \tan^2 \Phi = 1 + \left(\frac{dy}{dx}\right)^2,$$

and
$$\frac{ds}{dx} = \sqrt{\left\{1 + \left(\frac{dy}{dx}\right)^2\right\}}, \text{ see page 342.}$$

Hence,

the curvature at $P = \dfrac{d\Phi}{ds} = \dfrac{\dfrac{d^2y}{dx^2}}{\left\{1 + \left(\dfrac{dy}{dx}\right)^2\right\}^{\frac{3}{2}}};$

and the radius of curvature at $P = \rho = \dfrac{1}{\dfrac{d\Phi}{ds}}$

$$= \frac{\left\{1 + \left(\dfrac{dy}{dx}\right)^2\right\}^{\frac{3}{2}}}{\dfrac{d^2y}{dx^2}} \quad \text{or} \quad \frac{\left(1 + {y'}^2\right)^{\frac{3}{2}}}{y''} \quad . \quad . \quad (1)$$

The square root involved in these formulæ raises questions of sign. We may ignore this difficulty, however, because we shall be interested merely in numerical values. If, however, we always consider the positive root, then ρ will have the same sign as $\dfrac{d^2y}{dx^2}$, and will therefore be positive or negative according as the curve is concave upwards or concave downwards in the immediate vicinity of the point P.

At once, we may derive two useful results from formula (1):

(a) At a point of inflexion, $\dfrac{d^2y}{dx^2} = 0$, and therefore at such a point, ρ is infinite and the circle of curvature becomes a straight line.

(b) If $\dfrac{dy}{dx}$ is small (as frequently happens in practical applications, such as in the theory of the bending of beams), then the formula (1) gives

$$\rho \doteqdot \dfrac{1}{\dfrac{d^2y}{dx^2}}.$$

If the given curve is defined by freedom equations

$$x = f(t), \quad y = F(t),$$

where t is a parameter, then formula (1) is transformed to

$$\rho = \dfrac{(\dot{x}^2 + \dot{y}^2)^{\frac{3}{2}}}{\dot{x}\ddot{y} - \ddot{x}\dot{y}} \quad . \quad . \quad . \quad . \quad . \quad (2)$$

where the " points " indicate differentiation with respect to t. For

$$\dfrac{dy}{dx} = \dfrac{\dot{y}}{\dot{x}}, \quad 1 + \left(\dfrac{dy}{dx}\right)^2 = \dfrac{\dot{x}^2 + \dot{y}^2}{\dot{x}^2},$$

and

$$\dfrac{d^2y}{dx^2} = \dfrac{d}{dt}\left(\dfrac{\dot{y}}{\dot{x}}\right) \cdot \dfrac{dt}{dx} = \dfrac{\dot{x}\ddot{y} - \ddot{x}\dot{y}}{\dot{x}^3};$$

hence

$$\rho = \dfrac{\left\{1 + \left(\dfrac{dy}{dx}\right)^2\right\}^{\frac{3}{2}}}{\dfrac{d^2y}{dx^2}} = \dfrac{(\dot{x}^2 + \dot{y}^2)^{\frac{3}{2}}}{\dot{x}^3} \cdot \dfrac{\dot{x}^3}{\dot{x}\ddot{y} - \ddot{x}\dot{y}}$$

$$= \frac{(\dot{x}^2 + \dot{y}^2)^{\frac{3}{2}}}{\dot{x}\ddot{y} - \ddot{x}\dot{y}} \, .$$

Examples (continued)

4. Find the radius of curvature at the vertex of the parabola $y^2 = 4ax$.
   The vertex is the origin.

   Since $y^2 = 4ax$,

   we have $yy' = 2a$, or $y' = \dfrac{2a}{y}$;

   and $(y')^2 + yy'' = 0$, or $y'' = -\dfrac{4a^2}{y^3}$.

   Thus, $\rho = \dfrac{(1 + y'^2)^{\frac{3}{2}}}{y''} = \dfrac{(y^2 + 4a^2)^{\frac{3}{2}}}{y^3} \cdot \left(-\dfrac{y^3}{4a^2} \right)$

   $\qquad = -\dfrac{(y^2 + 4a^2)^{\frac{3}{2}}}{4a^2}$,

   $\qquad = 2a$ (numerically), when $y = 0$.

5. Find the radius of curvature at any point of the curve defined by the freedom equations
   $$x = 2 \cos \theta + \cos 2\theta,$$
   $$y = 2 \sin \theta + \sin 2\theta.$$

   We have $\dot{x} = -2 \sin \theta - 2 \sin 2\theta$; $\dot{y} = 2 \cos \theta + 2 \cos 2\theta$.
   $\qquad\qquad \ddot{x} = -2 \cos \theta - 4 \cos 2\theta$; $\ddot{y} = -2 \sin \theta - 4 \sin 2\theta$.

   Hence $\dot{x}^2 + \dot{y}^2 = 8 + 8 \cos \theta \cos 2\theta + 8 \sin \theta \sin 2\theta$

   $$= 16 \cos^2 \frac{\theta}{2} \, ;$$

   $$\dot{x}\ddot{y} - \ddot{x}\dot{y} = 12 + 12 \cos \theta \cos 2\theta + 12 \sin \theta \sin 2\theta$$

   $$= 24 \cos^2 \frac{\theta}{2} \, ;$$

   and $$\rho = \frac{64 \cos^3 \dfrac{\theta}{2}}{24 \cos^2 \dfrac{\theta}{2}} = \frac{8}{3} \cos \frac{\theta}{2} \, .$$

353

Alternatively, we may proceed as follows.

We have $\dot{x} = -2 \sin \theta - 2 \sin 2\theta = -4 \sin \dfrac{3\theta}{2} \cos \dfrac{\theta}{2}$;

$$\dot{y} = 2 \cos \theta + 2 \cos 2\theta = 4 \cos \dfrac{3\theta}{2} \cos \dfrac{\theta}{2}.$$

Hence $y' = \dfrac{dy}{dx} = \dfrac{dy}{d\theta} \cdot \dfrac{d\theta}{dx} = \dfrac{\dot{y}}{\dot{x}} = -\cot \dfrac{3\theta}{2}$,

and $1 + y'^2 = 1 + \cot^2 \dfrac{3\theta}{2} = \operatorname{cosec}^2 \dfrac{3\theta}{2}.$

Also $y'' = \dfrac{d^2 y}{dx^2} = \dfrac{d}{d\theta} \left(\dfrac{dy}{dx} \right) \cdot \dfrac{d\theta}{dx} = \dfrac{3}{2} \operatorname{cosec}^2 \dfrac{3\theta}{2} \cdot \dfrac{-\operatorname{cosec} \dfrac{3\theta}{2}}{4 \cos \dfrac{\theta}{2}}$

$$= -\frac{3}{8} \frac{\operatorname{cosec}^3 \dfrac{3\theta}{2}}{\cos \dfrac{\theta}{2}}$$

Therefore $\rho = \dfrac{(1 + y'^2)^{\frac{3}{2}}}{y''} = \operatorname{cosec}^3 \dfrac{3\theta}{2} \cdot \dfrac{-8 \cos \dfrac{\theta}{2}}{3 \operatorname{cosec}^3 \dfrac{3\theta}{2}}$

$$= \frac{8}{3} \cos \frac{\theta}{2} \text{ (numerically).}$$

This procedure has the advantage that it renders formula (2), page 352, unnecessary, but it must be used with care. The value of y' having been found in terms of θ, it must be remembered that the value of y'' is got by differentiating **with respect to** x, and not with respect to θ.

6. Find the radius of curvature and also the coordinates of the centre of curvature at any point P on the curve

$$x = a \sec^2 t, \quad y = 2a \tan t.$$

Deduce that as P varies, the locus of Q is the curve $27ay^2 = 4 (x - 3a)^3$.

We have $\dot{x} = 2a \sec^3 t \sin t$; $\dot{y} = 2a \sec^2 t.$

               $\ddot{x} = 2a \sec^2 t + 6a \sec^4 t \sin^2 t$; $\ddot{y} = 4a \sec^3 t \sin t.$

Hence $\dot{x}^2 + \dot{y}^2 = 4a^2 \sec^4 t (\tan^2 t + 1) = 4a^2 \sec^6 t$;

$$\dot{x}\ddot{y} - \dddot{x}\dot{y} = 8a^2 \sec^6 t \sin^2 t - 4a^2 \sec^4 t - 12a^2 \sec^6 t \sin^2 t$$
$$= -4a^2 \sec^4 t (1 + \tan^2 t) = -4a^2 \sec^6 t ;$$

and
$$\rho = \frac{8a^3 \sec^9 t}{-4a^2 \sec^6 t} = -2a \sec^3 t.$$

For Q (ξ, η), the centre of curvature,

$$\xi = x - \rho \sin \Phi$$
$$= a \sec^2 t + \frac{2a \sec^3 t \cdot 2a \sec^2 t}{2a \sec^3 t}$$
$$= 3a \sec^2 t ;$$

and $\eta = y + \rho \cos \Phi = 2a \tan t - \dfrac{2a \sec^3 t \cdot 2a \sec^3 t \cdot \sin t}{2a \sec^3 t}$

$$= 2a \tan t (1 - \sec^2 t) = -2a \tan^3 t.$$

Eliminating t, we have

$$\frac{\eta^2}{4a^2} = \tan^6 t = (\sec^2 t - 1)^3 = \left(\frac{\xi}{3a} - 1\right)^3,$$

or $$27a\eta^2 = 4 (\xi - 3a)^3.$$

This relation holds for all values of ξ, η ; the equation of the locus of Q is therefore found by substituting x, y, for ξ, η, respectively, thus—

$$27ay^2 = 4 (x - 3a)^3.$$

The locus of the centre of curvature of a curve is known as the **evolute** of that curve.

Find the lengths of the arcs of the following curves (Examples 7-14) for the ranges indicated :

7. $ay^2 = x^3$, from $x = 0$ to $x = a/4$.
8. $y = \frac{1}{2}a (e^{\frac{x}{a}} + e^{-\frac{x}{a}})$, from $x = 0$ to $x = a$.
9. $y = \log (\sin x + \cos x)$, from $x = 0$ to $x = \dfrac{\pi}{2}$.
10. $y = \log x$, from $x = 1$ to $x = \sqrt{3}$.
11. $y^2 = 4ax$, from $x = 0$ to $x = a$.
12. $x = e^t \cos t$, $y = e^t \sin t$, from $t = 0$ to $t = 1$.
13. $x = c \sec \Phi$, $y = c \log (\sec \Phi + \tan \Phi)$, from $\Phi = 0$ to $\Phi = \dfrac{\pi}{4}$.
14. $x = 2\theta - \sin 2\theta$, $y = 8 \sin \theta$, from $\theta = 0$ to $\theta = \pi$.

Show that the following curves (Examples 15-18) are closed, and find their total perimeters :

15. $x^{\frac{2}{3}} + y^{\frac{2}{3}} = a^{\frac{2}{3}}$.

16. $16y^2 = x^2 (2 - x^2)$.

17. $x = 3\cos t - \cos^3 t$, $y = \sin^3 t$.

18. $x = a \cos t (1 + \cos t)$, $y = a \sin t (1 + \cos t)$.

Find the lengths of the arcs of the following curves (Examples 19-25) for the ranges indicated, and find also the areas of the surfaces generated by revolving these arcs about the x-axis :

19. $6xy = x^4 + 3$, from $x = 1$ to $x = 2$.

20. $30x^3 y = 3x^8 + 5$, from $x = 1$ to $x = 2$.

21. $y = (x - 1) . \sqrt{\left(\dfrac{x}{3} \right)}$, from $x = 0$ to $x = 1$.

22. $x = \cos \theta + \sin \theta$, $y = \frac{1}{4}\cos 2\theta$, from $\theta = -\dfrac{\pi}{4}$ to $\theta = \dfrac{\pi}{4}$.

23. $x = t - \frac{1}{3}t^3$, $y = t^2$, from $t = -\sqrt{3}$ to $t = \sqrt{3}$.

24. $x = \theta \sin \theta + \cos \theta$, $y = \sin \theta - \theta \cos \theta$, from $\theta = 0$ to $\theta = \dfrac{\pi}{2}$.

25. $x = a (\sin^3 t + \cos^3 t)$, $y = a (\sin^3 t - \cos^3 t)$, from $t = \dfrac{\pi}{4}$ to $t = \dfrac{\pi}{2}$.

Find the perimeters of the loops of the following curves (Examples 26-30), and also the areas of the surfaces generated by revolving these loops about the x-axis :

26. $9y^2 = x (3 - x)^2$.

27. $12y^2 = (x + 1)(3 - x)^2$.

28. $6y^2 = x^2 (2 - x)$.

29. $x = 3t^2$, $y = 3t - t^3$.

30. $x = a \cos^3 t$, $y = a \sin^3 t$.

31. Find the length of the arc cut off from the parabola $y^2 = 8x$, by the straight line $y = 4 (x - 1)$.

32. If A is the point where the curve $x = e^t \sin t$, $y = e^t \cos t$ crosses the y-axis, and if P is any other point on the curve, prove that the arc $AP = \sqrt{2} (OP - OA)$, where O is the origin.

33. Sketch the arc of the curve whose freedom equations are $x = ae^{-t} \cos t$, $y = ae^{-t} \sin t$, for values of t from 0 to 2π. Show

that the x-axis divides this arc into two lengths in the ratio $e^{\pi} : 1$, and that if the two parts are revolved about the x-axis, the areas of the two surfaces generated are in the ratio $e^{2\pi} : 1$.

34. Find the total perimeter of the curve whose freedom equations are $x = a \cos t \ (1 + \sin t)$, $y = a \sin t \ (1 + \sin t)$, and also the area of the surface generated by the revolution of the curve about the y-axis.

35. A dome-shaped roof is in the form of a surface of revolution obtained by revolving a parabola about its own axis, which is vertical. If the base of the dome is a circle of radius r, and the height is $\frac{2}{3}r$, find the surface area of the dome.

Find the radius of curvature of each of the following curves (Examples 36-45), at the points indicated :

36. $3y = x^3$, at the point (x, y).
37. $y^2 = 4ax$, at the point (x, y).
38. $x^2 - y^2 = 4$, at the point $(2, 0)$.
39. $y = \frac{1}{2}a \ (e^{\frac{x}{a}} + e^{-\frac{x}{a}})$, at the point $(0, a)$.
40. $xy^2 = 1 + x$, at the point $(-1, 0)$.
41. $x = a \cos^3 t$, $y = a \sin^3 t$, at the point whose parameter is t.
42. $x = 2\theta - \sin \theta$, $y = 2 - \cos \theta$, at the point $(2\pi, 3)$.
43. $x = a \sin \theta$, $y = b \cos 2\theta$, at the point where $\theta = \dfrac{\pi}{3}$.
44. $x = a \sin \theta - b \sin \left(\dfrac{a\theta}{b}\right)$, $y = a \cos \theta - b \cos \left(\dfrac{a\theta}{b}\right)$, at the point whose parameter is θ.
45. $x = a \sec \Phi$, $y = b \tan \Phi$, at the point whose parameter is Φ.

46. Find the coordinates of the point of the curve $y = e^x$ at which the curvature is a maximum.

47. Show that the radius of curvature at the point $P \ (a \cos \theta, b \sin \theta)$ of the ellipse $\dfrac{x^2}{a^2} + \dfrac{y^2}{b^2} = 1$ is numerically equal to OR^3/ab, where O is the origin, and R is the point $(-a \sin \theta, b \cos \theta)$.

48. Show that for the curve $x = e^t \cos 2t$, $y = e^t \sin 2t$, the radius of curvature is given by $\rho = \dfrac{\sqrt{5}}{2} . e^t$. Show also that for this curve, $\dfrac{dy}{dx} = \dfrac{2x + y}{x - 2y}$, find $\dfrac{d^2y}{dx^2}$, and hence verify the above value of ρ.

49. Find the radius of curvature at the point whose parameter is θ on the cycloid $x = a\,(\theta - \sin\theta)$, $y = a\,(1 - \cos\theta)$. Find also the coordinates of the corresponding centre of curvature.

50. Prove that the centre of curvature at the point whose parameter is t on the curve $x = 2\cos\,t - \cos\,2t$, $y = 2\sin\,t - \sin\,2t$, has coordinates $[\frac{1}{3}\,(2\cos\,t + \cos\,2t),\ \frac{1}{3}\,(2\sin\,t + \sin\,2t)]$.

51. For the curve whose freedom equations are $x = a\,(9t^2 - 2t^4)$, $y = 8at^3$, prove that the length of the curve in the first quadrant is equal to the radius of curvature at the point where x is a maximum.

52. Show that the curve $x = a\,(5\cos\theta - \cos\,5\theta)$, $y = a\,(5\sin\theta - \sin\,5\theta)$ is a closed curve of total perimeter $40a$. Show also that the freedom equations of its evolute are $3x = 2a\,(5\cos\theta + \cos\,5\theta)$, $3y = 2a\,(5\sin\theta + \sin\,5\theta)$.

§ 35. SIMPLE APPLICATIONS OF
INTEGRATION.

In the paragraphs which follow, we shall be referring to certain simple problems in the field of Applied Mathematics for which the powerful methods of the Integral Calculus are available. It is not possible to explain fully the various technical terms employed, but an attempt has been made to ensure that the reader who does not already possess the necessary background of knowledge is not left completely in the dark.

Before proceeding further, the reader is advised to re-read § 21, in which was developed the idea that under certain circumstances the limit of a sum can be expressed as a definite integral. It will be recalled that in the consideration of the area under the curve $y = f(x)$ between $x = a$ and $x = b$, a small rectangular strip of height y and width δx was regarded as a typical element of this area, and the sum of these rectangular areas was denoted by

$$\sum_{x=a}^{x=b} y \, \delta x.$$

The required area does not equal $\Sigma y \, \delta x$, for to each such rectangle should be added a small, almost triangular area (see Fig. 31, page 116). Provided, however, that δx is small, it is true to say that the required area equals $\Sigma y \, \delta x$, *approximately*. The exact value of the area is obtained by finding the limit to which the sum $\Sigma y \, \delta x$ tends, as δx tends to zero. Since the

area is given *exactly* by $\int_a^b y \, dx$, we may write

$$\lim_{\delta x \to 0} \sum_{x=a}^{x=b} y \, \delta x = \int_a^b y \, dx.$$

This is a result of which we shall make considerable use in this chapter, and despite the formidable array of symbols, it expresses a really very simple idea. In effect, it means that if, in circumstances similar to those outlined above, we find that some quantity in which we are interested—not necessarily an area—may be expressed *approximately* by a sum $\Sigma\, y\, \delta x$, it will be given *exactly* by $\int y\, dx$, where the data of the problem will indicate the range of integration. Similarly, quantities given approximately by $\Sigma\, x\, \delta m$, $\Sigma\, p\, \delta v$, etc., will be given exactly by $\int x\, dm$, $\int p\, dv$, etc.

Mean values

The object of this paragraph is to find an expression for the mean value of the ordinate y of a curve $y = f(x)$ in a given range, say, from $x = a$ to $x = b$. Clearly, an infinite number of ordinates exist in this range, and therefore the methods of elementary arithmetic cannot be applied. We may, however, proceed as follows.

Let the range from $x = a$ to $x = b$ be divided into a large number, n, of equal sections, each of length δx, and let mid-

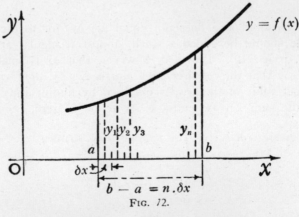

FIG. 12.

360

ordinates of length y_1, y_2, y_3, ..., y_n, be erected on each section (Fig. 72).

Then, provided that n is large enough—that is, that δx is small enough—the mean value of y from $x = a$ to $x = b$ is given approximately by

$$\frac{1}{n}(y_1 + y_2 + y_3 + \dots + y_n),$$

or

$$\frac{y_1\,\delta x + y_2\,\delta x + y_3\,\delta x + \dots + y_n\,\delta x}{n\,\delta x},$$

or

$$\frac{\Sigma\,y\,\delta x}{b - a}, \text{ since } \delta x = \frac{b - a}{n}.$$

Therefore, the mean value of y in the given range will be given exactly by $\dfrac{1}{b - a}\displaystyle\int y\,dx$, where the integration is effected from $x = a$ to $x = b$. That is,

the mean value of y in the range from $x = a$ to $x = b$

$$= \frac{1}{b - a}\int_a^b y\,dx.$$

Since the definite integral in this last expression represents the area under the curve $y = f(x)$ from $x = a$ to $x = b$, and $(b - a)$ is the length of the base on which this area stands, the **mean value** of the ordinate y (or of the function $f(x)$), or the **mean height** of the curve $y = f(x)$ in the range from $x = a$ to $x = b$, is found by dividing the area by the length of the base and is therefore the height of the rectangle of equal area, standing on the same base. Expressed more concisely,

$$\text{the mean ordinate} = \frac{\text{the area under the curve}}{\text{the length of the base}}.$$

By way of illustration, let us find the mean value of the function $I \sin \omega x$ between $x = 0$ and $x = \dfrac{\pi}{\omega}$.

The area under the curve between the given limits

$$= I \int_0^{\frac{\pi}{\omega}} \sin \omega x \, dx = \frac{I}{\omega} \Big[- \cos \omega x \Big]_0^{\pi/\omega}$$

$$= \frac{2I}{\omega}.$$

The length of the base on which this area stands

$$= \frac{\pi}{\omega}.$$

Hence, the mean value of the function in the given range

$$= \frac{\text{area}}{\text{length of base}} = \frac{2I/\omega}{\pi/\omega} = \frac{2I}{\pi}.$$

The function $I \sin \omega x$ is a periodic function (see page 232) of period $2\pi/\omega$, and therefore we have found the mean value of the function over a half period, or half cycle. Had we investigated the mean value over a complete cycle, we should have obtained the value zero. This is because the graph of the function over a complete cycle consists of two equal parts, one above the x-axis (for which, ordinates are positive), and one below the x-axis (for which, ordinates are negative).

Periodic functions are of particular interest in the theory of alternating currents. For such functions, the difficulty of sign is removed by the introduction of the **root mean square** value, found by taking the square *root* of the *mean* value of the *square* of the function over the given range. Thus, the root mean square (or R.M.S.) value of the function $I \sin \omega x$ in the range from $x = 0$ to $x = \dfrac{2\pi}{\omega}$ is obtained by finding the square root of

$$\frac{\omega}{2\pi} \int_0^{2\pi/\omega} I^2 \sin^2 \omega x \, dx = \frac{I^2 \omega}{4\pi} \int_0^{2\pi/\omega} (1 - \cos 2\omega x) \, dx$$

$$= \frac{I^2 \omega}{4\pi} \left[x - \frac{1}{2\omega} \sin 2\omega x \right]_0^{2\pi/\omega}$$

$$= \frac{I^2 \omega}{4\pi} \cdot \frac{2\pi}{\omega} = \frac{I^2}{2}.$$

Hence, the R.M.S. value $\quad = \dfrac{I}{\sqrt{2}}$,

a result of particular interest to students of electricity, for it implies that an alternating current of maximum value I has the same heating effect as a direct current of $\dfrac{I}{\sqrt{2}}$.

Centres of gravity

If a number of particles of masses m_1, m_2, m_3, ..., are situated at points (x_1, y_1), (x_2, y_2), (x_3, y_3), ..., respectively, in the plane of the coordinate axes, then for certain purposes, the system of particles behaves as if the total mass of the system were concentrated at a point known as the **centre of mass,** or **centre of inertia,** of the system. The coordinates of this point are conventionally denoted $(\bar{x}, \bar{y})$, and are given by the equations

$$\bar{x} = \frac{m_1x_1 + m_2x_2 + m_3x_3 + \ldots}{m_1 + m_2 + m_3 + \ldots} = \frac{\Sigma mx}{\Sigma m},$$

$$\bar{y} = \frac{m_1y_1 + m_2y_2 + m_3y_3 + \ldots}{m_1 + m_2 + m_3 + \ldots} = \frac{\Sigma my}{\Sigma m}.$$

If we are concerned with a continuous body of matter instead of separate particles, we may regard the whole body as broken up into small elements of mass δm, and the position of the centre of mass is then given approximately by the formulae

$$\bar{x} = \frac{\Sigma x \delta m}{\Sigma \delta m}, \quad \bar{y} = \frac{\Sigma y \delta m}{\Sigma \delta m},$$

and exactly, by the formulae

$$\bar{x} = \frac{\int x\,dm}{\int dm}, \qquad \bar{y} = \frac{\int y\,dm}{\int dm},$$

the integration being extended throughout the total mass. The denominator of these formulæ is clearly the total mass of the body.

Since the weight of each element of the body is proportional to the mass of the element, the **centre of gravity** of the body coincides with its centre of mass ; the above formulæ may therefore be regarded as giving the coordinates of the centre of gravity of the body.

Examples

1. Find the centre of gravity of a hemisphere of radius *r*.

   Clearly, by symmetry, the centre of gravity must lie on the radius of symmetry. Let this radius be taken as OX (Fig. 73), where O is the centre of the hemisphere.

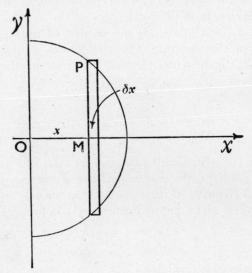

FIG. 73.

Consider an elemental cylinder, distant x from O, and of thickness δx. The base-radius of this cylinder is MP, and

$$MP = \sqrt{(OP^2 - OM^2)} = \sqrt{(r^2 - x^2)}.$$

The volume of the cylinder is therefore $\pi (r^2 - x^2) \, \delta x$, and its mass is $\rho \pi (r^2 - x^2) \, \delta x$, where ρ is the mass per unit volume. (This item corresponds to δm in the formulæ of page 363.)

The volume of the hemisphere is $\frac{2}{3}\pi r^3$, and its mass is therefore $\rho \cdot \frac{2}{3}\pi r^3$; hence

$$\bar{x} = \frac{\int x\,dm}{\int dm} = \frac{\rho\pi \int_0^r x\,(r^2 - x^2)\,dx}{\rho \cdot \frac{2}{3}\pi r^3}$$

$$= \frac{3}{2r^3}\left[\frac{r^2 x^2}{2} - \frac{x^4}{4}\right]_0^r = \frac{3}{8}\,r.$$

That is, the centre of gravity of a hemisphere of radius r lies on the radius of symmetry, distant $\frac{3}{8}r$ from the centre.

If the body whose centre of gravity we have to locate consists of a uniformly thin lamina of surface area S, or of a uniformly thin linear strip of length s, the formulæ of page 363 reduce to

$$\bar{x} = \frac{\int x\,dS}{\int dS}, \text{ and } \bar{x} = \frac{\int x\,ds}{\int ds},$$

respectively, with corresponding formulæ for y. The first denominator clearly denotes the total surface area of the lamina ; the second denominator represents the total length of the strip.

These formulæ are often used to find the centre of gravity of an *area*, or of an *arc*. Strictly, the point found in this way should be called the **centroid,*** or **mean centre,** since only a three-dimensional entity can have mass. But the centroid of an area (or of an arc) coincides with the centre of gravity of a thin lamina (or rod) of equal dimensions, and therefore the term " centre of gravity " is often somewhat loosely used when the terms " centroid " or " mean centre " would be more appropriate.

2. Find formulæ for the coordinates of the centre of gravity of
    (i) the area under the curve $y = f(x)$ from $x = a$ to $x = b$;
    (ii) the arc of the curve $y = f(x)$ from $x = a$ to $x = b$.

---

* The reader is no doubt familiar with the " centroid " of a triangle, the point of intersection of the medians of the triangle.

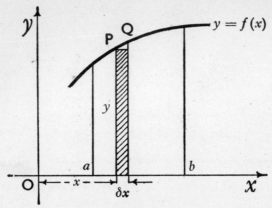

FIG. 74.

(i) Consider the small rectangle shaded in Fig. 74. Its area is $y\delta x$, and every element of this strip may be regarded as distant x from OY. Hence

$$\bar{x} = \frac{\int x\,dS}{\int dS} = \frac{\int_a^b xy\,dx}{\int_a^b y\,dx}.$$

The elements of this strip are not, however, all equidistant from OX; we therefore adopt the procedure we should employ if we were dealing with a plane lamina, and regard the area of the strip as if it were " concentrated " at the centre of gravity of the strip. that is, at a distance $\frac{1}{2}y$ from OX. Hence

$$\bar{y} = \frac{\int_a^b \frac{1}{2}y^2\,dx}{\int_a^b y\,dx}.$$

(ii) Consider the elemental arc PQ, of length δs. It is distant x from OY, and y from OX. Therefore

$$\bar{x} = \frac{\int x\,ds}{\int ds} = \frac{\int_a^b x\frac{ds}{dx}\,dx}{\int_a^b \frac{ds}{dx}\,dx},$$

366

$$\bar{y} = \frac{\int_a^b y \dfrac{ds}{dx}\, dx}{\int_a^b \dfrac{ds}{dx}\, dx}.$$

Formulæ (i) and (ii) should be regarded as standard formulæ to be committed to memory.

3. Find the centre of gravity of the area included between one half-cycle of the curve $y = I \sin \omega x$ and the x-axis.

The given curve cuts the x-axis where $x = 0,\ \dfrac{\pi}{\omega},\ \dfrac{2\pi}{\omega},\ \dots$.

Clearly, by symmetry, the centre of gravity of the area under the curve from $x = 0$ to $x = \dfrac{\pi}{\omega}$ lies on the line $x = \dfrac{\pi}{2\omega}$.

Also

$$\bar{y} = \frac{\int \tfrac{1}{2} y^2 dx}{\int y\, dx}.$$

We have $\displaystyle \int \tfrac{1}{2} y^2 dx = \int_0^{\pi/\omega} \frac{I^2}{2} \sin^2 \omega x\ dx = \frac{I^2}{4} \int_0^{\pi/\omega} (1 - \cos 2\omega x)\, dx$

$$= \frac{I^2}{4} \left[x - \frac{1}{2\omega} \sin 2\omega x \right]_0^{\pi/\omega} = \frac{I^2}{4} \cdot \frac{\pi}{\omega}\ ;$$

and $\displaystyle \int y\, dx = \int_0^{\pi/\omega} I \sin \omega x\, dx = I \left[-\frac{1}{\omega} \cos \omega x \right]_0^{\pi/\omega}$

$$= \frac{2I}{\omega}.$$

Hence $\displaystyle \bar{y} = \left(\frac{I^2}{4} \cdot \frac{\pi}{\omega} \right) \div \frac{2I}{\omega} = \frac{\pi}{8} \cdot I.$

4. Prove that if a plane area revolve about an axis in its plane but not intersecting it, the volume of revolution generated is equal to the product of the area and the length of the path of its centre of gravity.*

---

* This result, and that of the example which follows, are known as the **Theorems of Pappus.** They were first enunciated by Pappus of Alexandria in the third century A.D., and then later discovered independently by the Swiss mathematician, Guldin, in the seventeenth century.

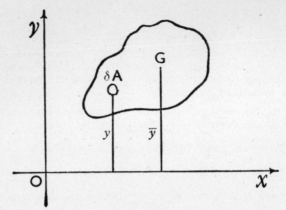

FIG. 75.

Let A be a closed plane area (Fig. 75), and let OX be a fixed straight line in its plane which does not intersect the area. Let δA be a small element of the area A, distant y from OX, and let G, the centre of gravity of the area, be distant $\bar{y}$ from OX.

Then
$$\bar{y} = \frac{\int y\,dA}{\int dA} = \frac{1}{A}\int y\,dA, \quad \cdot \quad \cdot \quad \cdot \quad (1)$$

where the integration is taken over the whole area.

The volume generated by the element δA when the area A revolves about OX is $2\pi y \delta A$.

Therefore, the total volume generated $= 2\pi \int y\,dA$

$$= 2\pi \bar{y} \cdot A, \text{ by (1)}.$$

But the path traced out by G is a circle of radius $\bar{y}$, and therefore has length $2\pi\bar{y}$; hence the required result follows.

5. Prove that if the arc of a plane curve revolves about an axis lying in its plane but not intersecting it, the area of the surface of revolution generated is equal to the product of the length of the arc and the length of the path of its centre of gravity.

The argument, which is substantially that of the previous example, is left as an exercise for the reader.

Moments of inertia

For a system of particles of masses m_1, m_2, m_3, ..., whose perpendicular distances from a fixed axis are r_1, r_2, r_3, ... respectively, the **moment of inertia** of the system about the given axis is defined to be

$$m_1r_1^2 + m_2r_2^2 + m_3r_3^2 + ...,$$

or, more concisely, Σmr^2,* and is conventionally denoted by the symbol I.

If the body consists of a continuous distribution of matter instead of a system of separate particles, then by considering an element of mass δm, distant r from an axis, the moment of inertia of the body about the axis is given approximately by $\Sigma r^2 \delta m$, and exactly by

$$I = \int r^2 dm,$$

where the integration is taken throughout the entire body.

If I be the moment of inertia of a body of mass M about a given axis, and if k be the distance from that axis at which a single particle of mass M must be situated in order to have the same second moment, then

$$I = Mk^2, \text{ and } k = \sqrt{\frac{I}{M}}.$$

This length, k, is called the **radius of gyration** of the body about the given axis. It follows that

$$k^2 = \frac{\int r^2 dm}{\int dm},$$

[**Note.**—Newton's first law of motion implies the principle that a body has no innate tendency to change its state of rest or of uniform motion in a straight line. This " unwillingness " to have its state of rest or of uniform linear motion altered is

---

* The quantity Σmr^2 is sometimes spoken of as the **second moment** of the system about the axis, the quantity Σmr being the **first moment**.

known as the body's **inertia**. The mass of a body may be taken as a measure of its inertia, as far as purely translational motion is concerned. If, however, the body rotates about an axis, it might be anticipated that its shape and its dimensions would also have to be considered in determining its inertia. This is indeed so, and I may be taken as a measure of the inertia of the body, provided that the motion is purely rotational. That is why I is called the " moment of inertia " of the body about the given axis of rotation.]

Examples (continued)

6. Find the moment of inertia of a thin straight rod AB, of length l and mass M, about an axis perpendicular to the bar

   (i) passing through one end,

   (ii) passing through its centre.

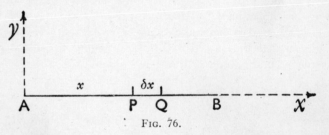

FIG. 76.

Consider an element of the rod, of length δx and distant x from A (Fig. 76), A being the end through which passes the axis of rotation.

If m is the line-density of the rod, the mass of the element is $m . \delta x$, and the second moment of this element about the axis through A is $mx^2\delta x$. Therefore

$$I_A = \int_0^l mx^2dx = \frac{ml^3}{3},$$

$$= \frac{1}{3}Ml^2, \text{ since } m = \frac{M}{l}.$$

370

Similarly, if the axis of rotation (that is, the y-axis) passes through C, the mid-point of AB,

$$I_C = \int_{-l/2}^{l/2} mx^2 dx = \frac{m}{3} \cdot \frac{l^3}{4} = \frac{1}{12} Ml^2.$$

7. Find the moment of inertia and the radius of gyration of a uniform circular disc, of mass M and radius a, about an axis passing normally through O, the centre of the disc.

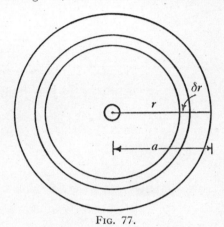

FIG. 77.

Consider (Fig. 77) the element of the disc contained between two concentric circles of radii r and $r + \delta r$.

If m is the superficial density, the mass of the element may be taken as $m \cdot 2\pi r \delta r$, and the second moment of this element about a vertical axis through O as $m \cdot 2\pi r^3 \delta r$, every " particle " of this element being at distance r from the axis.

Therefore $\quad I_O = 2\pi m \int_0^a r^3 dr = \tfrac{1}{2} m\pi a^4,$

$$= \tfrac{1}{2} Ma^2, \text{ since } m = \frac{M}{\pi a^2}.$$

But if k is the radius of gyration of the disc about the axis through O,

$$Mk^2 = I_O = \tfrac{1}{2} Ma^2 \text{ ;}$$

hence $\qquad\qquad k = \frac{a}{\sqrt{2}}.$

371

8. **Find** the moment of inertia of a solid right cone of height h, semi-vertical angle α, and mass M, about its axis of symmetry.

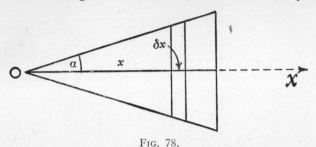

FIG. 78.

Consider (Fig. 78) an element of the cone contained between two planes distant x and $x + \delta x$ from the vertex O.

If m is the mass per unit volume, the mass of this element may be taken as $m \cdot \pi (x \tan \alpha)^2 \, \delta x$, and the second moment of this element about OX as $m\pi (x \tan \alpha)^2 \, \delta x \cdot \frac{1}{2} (x \tan \alpha)^2$, because of the result established in Example **7**. Hence

$$I_{OX} = \tfrac{1}{2} m\pi \tan^4 \alpha \int_0^h x^4 dx = \tfrac{1}{10} m\pi \tan^4 \alpha \, h^5,$$

$$= \tfrac{3}{10} M h^2 \tan^2 \alpha, \text{ since } m = \frac{M}{\frac{1}{3}\pi h^3 \tan^2 \alpha}.$$

The task of finding moments of inertia is greatly simplified by the following theorems, the proofs of which may be found in any standard textbook on mechanics.   see Borchardt p 370

(i) The moment of inertia of a body about any axis is equal to the moment of inertia of the body about a parallel axis through the centre of gravity plus the product of the mass of the body and the square of the distance between the two axes.

(ii) The sum of the moments of inertia of a thin plane lamina about two perpendicular axes in its plane is equal to the moment of inertia of the lamina about an axis perpendicular to these two axes through their point of intersection.

These two theorems may be expressed symbolically as follows :

(i) $I = I_G + Ma^2$, where a is the distance between the two axes.

(ii) $I_{OX} + I_{OY} = I_{OZ}$, where OX, OY, OZ are three mutually perpendicular axes, OX and OY lying in the plane of the lamina.

For example, it has already been established (Example 7) that for a circular disc, centre O and radius a,

$$I_O = \tfrac{1}{2} Ma^2.$$

If we denote the moment of inertia of the disc about a diameter by I_d, then, by theorem (ii),

$$I_d + I_d = I_O = \tfrac{1}{2} Ma^2 ;$$

hence $\qquad\qquad I_d = \tfrac{1}{4} Ma^2.$

If we denote the moment of inertia of the disc about a tangent by I_T, then, by theorem (i),

$$I_T = I_d + Ma^2 = \tfrac{5}{4} Ma^2.$$

The reader should note carefully that theorem (i) applies to any object, whereas theorem (ii) applies only to a thin lamina.

Centres of pressure

If a plane surface is wholly in contact with a non-viscous fluid then each point of the surface is subjected to a pressure which is perpendicular to the plane of the lamina and proportional to the depth of the point below the free horizontal surface of the fluid.* These individual pressures therefore constitute a system of parallel forces which like all such systems will have a resultant acting at some particular point of the surface. This resultant is the **total fluid pressure,** and the point at which it acts is called the **centre of pressure.**

In order to determine formulæ for the total fluid pressure and the position of the centre of pressure, let us consider a plane lamina of area A, immersed in a fluid of density ρ in such a way

---

* Throughout this section, we disregard completely the pressure of the atmosphere.

that the plane of the lamina makes an angle θ with the free horizontal surface of the fluid. Let us choose rectangular coordinate axes in the plane of the lamina such that one of the axes also lies in the free surface of the fluid (Fig. 79), and with such axes of reference let the coordinates of C, the centre of pressure, be (ξ, η).

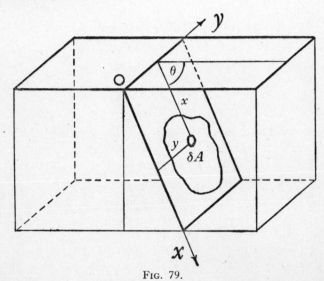

FIG. 79.

[The additional lines are inserted in order to improve the perspective of the figure, and bring out more clearly the horizontal and vertical planes.]

Consider a small element of the lamina, of area δA, situated at the point (x, y), and therefore at a depth of $x \sin \theta$.

The fluid pressure on $\delta A = \rho \, . \, x \sin \theta \, . \, \delta A$.

Hence the total fluid pressure on the lamina is given approximately by $\Sigma \rho x \sin \theta \; \delta A$, and exactly by $\rho \sin \theta \int x \, dA$, where the integration is taken over the whole area. That is,

$$\text{the total fluid pressure} = \rho \sin \theta \int x \, dA \qquad . \quad (1)$$

Let us now take moments about the coordinate axes.

The moment about OY of the fluid pressure on δA

$$= \rho \, x \sin \theta \, \delta A \cdot x = \rho \sin \theta \cdot x^2 \, \delta A.$$

The moment about OY of the total fluid pressure acting at C

$$= \xi \cdot \rho \sin \theta \int x dA.$$

Hence $\xi \cdot \rho \sin \theta \int x dA = \rho \sin \theta \int x^2 dA,$

so that
$$\xi = \frac{\displaystyle\int x^2 dA}{\displaystyle\int x dA}.$$

Similarly
$$\eta = \frac{\displaystyle\int xy dA}{\displaystyle\int x dA}.$$

It will be observed that the coordinates of C, the centre of pressure, are independent of the value of θ and therefore of the angle at which the plane lamina is inclined.

Since dA is two-dimensional, the above formulæ will normally yield " double " integrals, which are beyond the scope of this book. We shall, however, confine our attention to areas which have at least one axis of symmetry ; with such areas, the integrals obtained will be readily evaluated. Also, with such areas, it will usually be possible, from considerations of symmetry, to fix a line in the plane of the lamina on which the centre of pressure must lie. The problem will then reduce to that of finding merely the depth of the centre of pressure, which, as we have seen, may be derived from the formula

$$\xi = \frac{\int x^2 dA}{\int x dA} \qquad . \qquad . \qquad . \qquad . \quad (2)$$

If the centre of gravity, G, of the lamina has coordinates $(\bar{x}, \bar{y})$, then

$$A\bar{x} = \int x dA.$$

It follows that

the total fluid pressure $= \rho \sin \theta . \int x dA$

$= A . \rho \bar{x} \sin \theta$

= (the area of the lamina) × (the pressure at the centre of gravity) . . . (3)

Again, if the radius of gyration of the lamina about the y-axis is k, then

$$Ak^2 = \int x^2 dA.$$

It therefore follows that

$$\xi = \frac{\int x^2 dA}{\int x dA} = \frac{Ak^2}{A\bar{x}} = \frac{k^2}{\bar{x}}, \quad . \quad . \quad (4)$$

a formula which is useful in that it sometimes enables us to avoid the evaluation of awkward integrals.

Despite the generality of the results numbered (1) to (4), the reader will probably find it just as easy to treat each exercise from first principles. All that he need remember is that the pressure at depth d below the surface of a fluid of density ρ is given by ρd, and that the centre of pressure of a plane area is that point at which the resultant fluid pressure acts.

Examples (continued)

9. Find the position of the centre of pressure of a square lamina of side a which is immersed in a liquid with its plane vertical and with one side lying in the surface of the liquid.

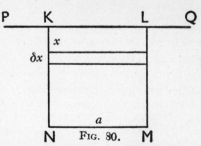

Fig. 80.

Consider (Fig. 80) an element of the lamina contained between two horizontal planes distant x and $x + \delta x$ from the free surface PQ. Then the area of the elemental strip $= a\delta x$,

and

the pressure on this strip $= \rho . ax\delta x$,

where ρ is the density of the liquid.

Therefore,

the total pressure on the lamina $= \rho a \int_0^a xdx = \tfrac{1}{2}\rho a^3$.

The centre of pressure, C, clearly lies on the straight line joining the mid-points of KL, NM; let it lie at a distance ξ from KL. Then

the moment of the pressure on the elemental strip about PQ

$$= (\rho a \, x \, \delta x) . x = \rho a \, x^2 \, \delta x \; ;$$

and the moment of the resultant pressure at C about PQ

$$= \tfrac{1}{2}\rho a^3 . \xi.$$

Hence $\qquad\qquad\qquad \xi . \tfrac{1}{2}\rho a^3 = \rho a \int_0^a x^2 dx = \tfrac{1}{3}\rho a^4,$

that is $\qquad\qquad\qquad\qquad \xi = \tfrac{2}{3}a.$

10. If, in the previous example, the square lamina is lowered until its upper edge is distant h from PQ, find the new position of the centre of pressure.

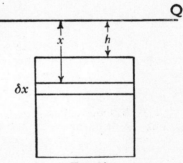

Fig. 81 is self-explanatory.

FIG. 81.

The arguments are exactly as in Example 9, but the range of integration is from h to $a + h$, instead of from 0 to a. Thus,

$$\xi . \rho a \int_h^{a+h} xdx = \rho a \int_h^{a+h} x^2 dx,$$

so that, $\qquad \xi = \tfrac{2}{3} . \dfrac{a^3 + 3a^2h + 3ah^2}{a^2 + 2ah} = \tfrac{2}{3} . \dfrac{a^2 + 3ah + 3h^2}{a + 2h} .$

11. A circular lamina, radius 2 feet, is immersed in a liquid with its plane vertical and its centre at a depth 3 feet below the surface. Find the position of the centre of pressure.

Consider, as usual, an element of the lamina contained between two horizontal planes distant x and $x + \delta x$ from PQ (Fig. 82).

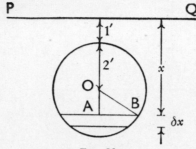

FIG. 82.

The length of this elemental strip
$$= 2AB = 2\sqrt{(OB^2 - OA^2)}$$
$$= 2\sqrt{\{4 - (x - 3)^2\}},$$

and without proceeding further we realise that some of the integrals we shall have to evaluate will not be easy (though within the capabilities of the reader who has developed good manipulative skill). However, remembering that

$$\xi = \frac{k^2}{\bar{x}},$$

where k is the radius of gyration of the lamina about PQ, and $\bar{x}$ is the depth of the centre of gravity of the lamina, we have, at once, $\bar{x} = 3$.

Also, the moment of inertia of a circle, radius a, about a diameter is $\frac{1}{4}Ma^2$ (see page 373), in this case, equal to M, since $a = 2$.

Hence, by the theorem of parallel axes (page 372),
$$Mk^2 = M + Mh^2, \text{ where } h = 3,$$
$$= 10M.$$

Therefore $\xi = \dfrac{10}{3} = 3\tfrac{1}{3}$ feet.

378

12. A lamina in the form of an equilateral triangle of side a is immersed in a liquid of density ρ so that its plane is inclined at an angle of 60° to the horizontal, and one of its sides lies in the surface of the liquid. Find the total pressure on the lamina and the position of its centre of pressure.

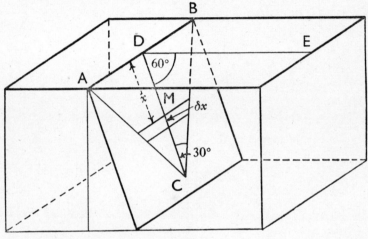

FIG. 83.

In Fig. 83, ABE represents the horizontal surface of the liquid, and ABC the triangular lamina ; so that angle $CDE = 60°$.

Consider an element of the lamina contained between two horizontal lines in the plane of the lamina distant x and $x + \delta x$ from AB. Then

$$DC = BC \cos 30° = \frac{\sqrt{3}}{2}a,$$

and

$$MC = DC - DM = \frac{\sqrt{3}}{2}a - x.$$

Therefore, the area of the elemental strip

$$= (2MC \tan 30°) . \delta x$$

$$= \frac{2}{\sqrt{3}}\left(\frac{\sqrt{3}}{2}a - x\right)\delta x ;$$

379

and, since this strip is at depth $x \sin 60°$ below the surface,

the pressure on this strip $= \dfrac{2}{\sqrt{3}} \left(\dfrac{\sqrt{3}}{2} a - x \right) \delta x \cdot \rho x \sin 60°$

$$= \rho \left(\dfrac{\sqrt{3}}{2} ax - x^2 \right) \delta x.$$

Hence, the total fluid pressure on the lamina

$$= \rho \int_0^{\frac{\sqrt{3}}{2} a} \left(\dfrac{\sqrt{3}}{2} ax - x^2 \right) dx$$

$$= \rho \left(\dfrac{\sqrt{3}}{2} a \cdot \dfrac{3}{8} a^2 - \dfrac{\sqrt{3}}{8} a^3 \right)$$

$$= \dfrac{\sqrt{3}}{16} \rho \, a^3.$$

Taking moments about AB, we have

$$\xi \cdot \dfrac{\sqrt{3}}{16} \rho a^3 = \rho \int_0^{\frac{\sqrt{3}}{2} a} \left(\dfrac{\sqrt{3}}{2} ax^2 - x^3 \right) dx$$

$$= \rho \left(\dfrac{\sqrt{3}}{2} a \cdot \dfrac{\sqrt{3}}{8} a^3 - \dfrac{9}{64} a^4 \right)$$

$$= \dfrac{3}{64} \rho a^4.$$

Hence $\qquad\qquad \xi = \dfrac{\sqrt{3}}{4} a,$

so that the centre of pressure is at the mid-point of the median DC.

Find the mean values of the following functions (Examples 13-20) for the ranges indicated :

13. x^2, from $x = 1$ to $x = 4$.

14. $(x - 2)^{1/2}$, from $x = 6$ to $x = 11$.

15. $\log x$, from $x = 1$ to $x = 2$.

16. $\tan x$, from $x = 0$ to $x = \dfrac{\pi}{4}$.

17. $\dfrac{x}{1 + x^3}$, from $x = \frac{1}{2}$ to $x = 1$.

18. $\sin^4 x$, from $x = 0$ to $x = 2\pi$.

19. $\dfrac{x}{\sqrt{(2ax - x^2)}}$, from $x = 0$ to $x = 2a$.

20. $x^4 \sqrt{(a^2 - x^2)}$, from $x = 0$ to $x = a$.

21. Find the mean value of the product
$$I_1 \sin(\omega t + a_1) . I_2 \sin(\omega t + a_2)$$
over a complete period, I_1, I_2, a_1, a_2, ω being constants.

22. A particle moves in a straight line, the velocity-time equation of the motion being $3v = 2(1 + t)^{3/2}$, where v is in inches per second, and t in seconds. Find the average velocity during the first eight seconds.

23. A gas of pressure p pounds per square inch and volume v cubic inches expands in accordance with the law $pv^{5/4} = 750$, the initial and final volumes being 16 and 81 cubic inches. Find the mean pressure during the expansion.

24. Find the length of the mean ordinate of the upper half of the ellipse $\dfrac{x^2}{a^2} + \dfrac{y^2}{b^2} = 1$.

25. Find the mean value of the function $p + q \sin(x + a)$ over a period, p, q, a being constants. Find also the corresponding root-mean-square value.

26. Find the root-mean-square value of
$$I_1 \sin(\omega t + a_1) + I_2 \sin(2\omega t + a_2)$$
over a complete period, I_1, I_2, a_1, a_2, ω being constants.

27. Find the centre of gravity of a solid right cone of height h and semi-vertical angle a.

28. Find the centre of gravity of the area included between the curve $y = \dfrac{1}{1 + x^2}$ and the x-axis.

29. Find the centre of gravity of the finite area between the parabola $y^2 = 4ax$ and the straight line $x = a$.

30. Find the centre of gravity of a semi-circular plate of radius r.

31. Find the centre of gravity of the loop of the curve $y^2 = x(4 - x)^2$.

32. Find the centre of gravity of the loop of the curve $y^2 = x^3(1 - x)^2$.

33. Find the centre of gravity of the spherical cap cut from a solid sphere of radius r by a plane distant c from the centre.

34. Find the centre of gravity of the area of that part of the ellipse $\dfrac{x^2}{a^2} + \dfrac{y^2}{b^2} = 1$ which lies in the first quadrant.

35. Find the centre of gravity of the area under one arch of the cycloid $x = a(\theta - \sin\theta)$, $y = a(1 - \cos\theta)$.

36. Find the centre of gravity of a circular sector of radius r and central angle 2α. Find also the centre of gravity of its circular arc.
37. Find the centre of gravity of a hemispherical shell of radius r.
38. Use the theorems of Pappus in order to find the centre of gravity of (i) a semicircle of radius r,
    (ii) a semicircular arc of radius r.
39. Find, using the theorems of Pappus, (i) the volume, (ii) the surface area of the anchor ring generated by the revolution of a circle of radius b about a line in its own plane at a distance a from its centre, $(a > b)$.
40. Trace the curve $xy^2 = 4(2 - x)$. Find (i) the area between this curve and the y-axis, and (ii) the volume generated by revolving this area about the y-axis. Hence, using the first theorem of Pappus, deduce the position of the mean centre of the area (i).
41. Find the moment of inertia of a rectangular lamina of mass M, length $2a$, and breadth $2b$, about
    (i) an edge of length $2b$,
    (ii) a parallel axis through the centre of gravity,
    (iii) an axis through the centre of gravity perpendicular to the plane of the rectangle.
42. Find the moment of inertia of a rectangular solid of mass M, and edges of length a, b, c, about
    (i) an axis through the centre of gravity perpendicular to the face ab,
    (ii) a parallel axis through the centroid of the face ac.
43. Find the moment of inertia of a piece of uniform thin wire, of mass M, bent into the form of a circle of radius r, about
    (i) an axis through the centre perpendicular to the plane of the circle,
    (ii) a diameter.
44. Find the moment of inertia of a solid sphere of mass M and radius r, about
    (i) a diameter,   (ii) a tangent.
    Find also the moment of inertia of a solid hemisphere about a diameter in its plane face.
45. Find the moment of inertia of a lamina in the shape of an isosceles triangle of mass M, length of base b, and vertical height h, about
    (i) its base,
    (ii) a parallel axis through the vertex,
    (iii) the perpendicular bisector of the base,
    (iv) an axis through the vertex perpendicular to the plane of the triangle.

46. Find the moment of inertia of a rectangular lamina of mass M, length a, and breadth b, about a diagonal.

47. Find the moment of inertia of a solid cylinder of mass M, length l, and radius r, about

      (i) its axis of symmetry,

      (ii) a diameter through its centre of gravity.

      (iii) a diameter through one end.

48. Find the moment of inertia of a lamina in the shape of a circular ring of external and internal radii R and r, respectively, about an axis through the centre perpendicular to the plane of the ring. Deduce the moment of inertia of a hollow cylinder of external and internal radii R and r, respectively, about its axis of symmetry.

49. A triangle ABC is immersed vertically in a liquid with the base BC horizontal and below A, which is at a depth d. If the altitude of the triangle has length h, find the depth of the centre of pressure below the surface. What does the result become if A is at the surface ?

50. If the triangle of Example **49** is immersed with the base BC in the surface of the liquid and with A vertically below, find the position of the centre of pressure.

51. A trapezium $PQRS$, in which PQ is parallel to SR, and PS is perpendicular to PQ, is immersed in a liquid with its plane vertical and with PQ in the surface of the liquid. If $PQ = a$, $SR = 2a$, $PS = h$, find the resultant fluid pressure on the trapezium and the depth of the centre of pressure.

52. A plane lamina in the shape of a parabolic sector is immersed vertically in a liquid with its vertex in the surface and with its double ordinate horizontal at a depth h. Find the depth of its centre of pressure.

53. A plane lamina in the shape of a parabolic sector is immersed in a liquid with its axis vertical and with its vertex at a depth h. Find the position of its centre of pressure.

54. A semicircle of radius r is immersed in a liquid with its diameter vertical and with one extremity of the diameter in the surface of the liquid. Find the position of its centre of pressure.

55. Find the depth of the centre of pressure of an equilateral triangle of side 12 feet immersed in a liquid and with one side vertical.

56. A square door, hinged along its lower edge which is horizontal, is made in the vertical side of a water tank. Find the force which must be applied to the upper edge of the door in order to keep it

shut against the pressure of the water, if the side of the door is 2 feet long and the depth of the upper edge below the surface of the water is 6 feet. (1 cubic foot of water weighs $62\frac{1}{2}$ lb.)

57. A horizontal circular pipe, 1 foot in diameter, is fixed in the vertical side of a water tank with its upper edge $1\frac{1}{2}$ feet below the surface of the water. The end of the pipe is closed by a vertical flap hinged at the top and kept shut by the pressure of the water. Find, in pounds per square inch, the air pressure required in the pipe, in excess of atmospheric pressure, in order to open the flap. (1 cubic foot of water weighs $62\frac{1}{2}$ lb.)

58. A plane lamina is totally immersed in a water tank with its plane vertical. More water is added until the surface has been raised an amount h. Prove that, ignoring atmospheric pressure, the centre of pressure of the lamina is thereby raised by an amount

$$\frac{h\,(\xi - \bar{x})}{\bar{x} + h},$$

where ξ, $\bar{x}$ are the original depths of the centre of pressure and centre of gravity, respectively.

FURTHER MISCELLANEOUS EXAMPLES

1. Find the limits of the following functions:

   (i) $\dfrac{x-2}{\sqrt{x}-\sqrt{2}}$, as $x \to 2$;

   (ii) $\dfrac{x^2+2x}{x^2-x-6}$, as $x \to -2$;

   (iii) $\dfrac{2x-5}{x^2-5x+3}$, as $x \to \infty$;

   (iv) $\dfrac{x^{1/2}-1}{x^{1/3}-1}$, as $x \to 1$;

   (v) $\dfrac{x^3+x+2}{x^3-x^2-3x-1}$, as $x \to -1$;

   (vi) $\dfrac{27x^3-36x-16}{27x^3+27x^2-4}$, as $x \to -\frac{2}{3}$.

2. Find the limits of the following functions:

   (i) $\dfrac{\operatorname{cosec} x - \cot x}{x}$, as $x \to 0$;

   (ii) $\dfrac{\sin^2 \theta + \sin^2 2\theta}{1 - \cos 3\theta}$, as $\theta \to 0$;

   (iii) $n \sin \dfrac{x}{n}$, as $n \to \infty$;

   (iv) $\dfrac{\tan 3x}{\tan x}$, as $x \to \dfrac{\pi}{2}$;

   (v) $\dfrac{\tan 2ax - 2 \tan ax}{x^2 \sin x}$, as $x \to 0$;

   (vi) $\dfrac{\tan 2\theta + \tan 3\theta}{\tan \theta + \tan 2\theta}$, as $\theta \to \dfrac{\pi}{2}$.

3. Find the limits of the following functions:

   (i) $\dfrac{x^2}{a - \sqrt{(a^2 + x^2)}}$, as $x \to 0$;

   (ii) $\dfrac{\sqrt{(1+x)} - \sqrt{(1-x)}}{\sqrt{(2+x)} - \sqrt{(2-x)}}$, as $x \to 0$;

   (iii) $\dfrac{\sqrt{(1+x^2)} - \sqrt{(1-x^2)}}{\sqrt{(1+x)} - \sqrt{(1-x)}}$, as $x \to 0$;

385

(iv) $\dfrac{\sqrt{(1 + x^2)} - \sqrt{(1 + x)}}{\sqrt{(1 - x^2)} - \sqrt{(1 - x)}}$, as $x \longrightarrow 1$;

(v) $\sqrt{x}\{\sqrt{(x + 1)} - \sqrt{x}\}$, as $x \longrightarrow \infty$;

(vi) $\dfrac{\sqrt{x} - \sqrt{a} + \sqrt{(x - a)}}{\sqrt{(x^2 - a^2)}}$, as $x \longrightarrow a$.

4. Find the limits of the following functions :

(i) $\dfrac{\cos^2 \pi x}{e^{2x} - 2ex}$, as $x \longrightarrow \tfrac{1}{2}$;

(ii) $\dfrac{1 - \cos\left(\dfrac{\pi}{6} - \theta\right)}{(2 \sin \theta - 1)^2}$, as $\theta \longrightarrow \dfrac{\pi}{6}$;

(iii) $\dfrac{e^x - e^{\frac{1}{x}}}{\dfrac{1}{x} e^{-x} - xe^{-\frac{1}{x}}}$, as $x \longrightarrow 1$;

(iv) $\dfrac{\tan^{-1}(m \tan \theta) - \tan^{-1} \theta}{m \tan \theta - \theta}$, as $\theta \longrightarrow 0$;

(v) $\dfrac{m^x - n^x}{x}$, as $x \longrightarrow 0$;

(vi) $\dfrac{(2^x - 1)(2 \sin x - \sin 2x)^2}{x^2 \sin x \, (\cos x - \cos 2x)^2}$, as $x \longrightarrow 0$.

5. Find the limits of the following functions :

(i) $\dfrac{x\,(1 + e^{-x})}{1 - e^{-x}}$, as $x \longrightarrow 0$;

(ii) $\dfrac{(1 + 2x)^{1/2} - (1 + 3x)^{1/3}}{\sec x - 1}$, as $x \longrightarrow 0$;

(iii) $\dfrac{2 - x \tan x - 2 \cos x}{x^2\,(1 - \cos 3x)}$, as $x \longrightarrow 0$;

(iv) $\dfrac{\cos 2x + x \tan 2x - 1}{x^2 \sin^2 x}$, as $x \longrightarrow 0$;

(v) $\dfrac{2^x - x \log 2 - 1}{x^2}$, as $x \longrightarrow 0$;

(vi) $\dfrac{\log(1 + x) + \tan^{-1} x + \tfrac{1}{2}x^2 - 2x}{(1 - \cos x)^2}$, as $x \longrightarrow 0$;

(vii) $\dfrac{\cos x \cosh x - 1}{\cos x + \cosh x - 2}$, as $x \longrightarrow 0$;

(viii) $\dfrac{1}{x^4}\left(\log \dfrac{\tan x}{x} + x \cot x - 1\right)$, as $x \longrightarrow 0$;

(ix) $\dfrac{1}{x^5}\left\{e^x \sin x + \log (1 - x) - \dfrac{1}{2}\cdot\dfrac{x^2}{\sqrt{(1 + x^2)}}\right\}$, as $x \longrightarrow 0$;

(x) $\dfrac{3 \sin (x^2) + 2 \cos (x^2) - 2 \cos^2 x - 5 \sin^2 x}{\sqrt{(1 + x^3)} + \sqrt{(1 - x^3)} - 2}$, as $x \longrightarrow 0$.

6. Express the following limits as definite integrals, and hence find their values :

(i) $\dfrac{1}{n + 1} + \dfrac{1}{n + 2} + \dfrac{1}{n + 3} + \ldots + \dfrac{1}{n + n}$, as $n \longrightarrow \infty$;

(ii) $\dfrac{1}{n}\left(\sin \dfrac{a}{n} + \sin \dfrac{2a}{n} + \sin \dfrac{3a}{n} + \ldots + \sin \dfrac{na}{n}\right)$, as $n \longrightarrow \infty$;

(iii) $\dfrac{1^k + 2^k + 3^k + \ldots + n^k}{n^{k+1}}$, as $n \longrightarrow \infty$;

(iv) $n\left(\dfrac{1}{1^2 + n^2} + \dfrac{1}{2^2 + n^2} + \dfrac{1}{3^2 + n^2} + \ldots + \dfrac{1}{n^2 + n^2}\right)$,

$$\text{as } n \longrightarrow \infty \text{ ;}$$

(v) $\dfrac{1}{\sqrt{n}}\left\{\dfrac{1}{\sqrt{(1 + n)}} + \dfrac{1}{\sqrt{(2 + n)}} + \dfrac{1}{\sqrt{(3 + n)}} + \ldots + \right.$

$$\left. \dfrac{1}{\sqrt{(n + n)}}\right\}, \text{ as } n \longrightarrow \infty \text{ ;}$$

(vi) $\dfrac{1}{n^2}\left(\cos \dfrac{\pi}{2n} + 2 \cos \dfrac{2\pi}{2n} + 3 \cos \dfrac{3\pi}{2n} + \ldots + n \cos \dfrac{n\pi}{2n}\right)$,

$$\text{as } n \longrightarrow \infty.$$

7. Prove that $\underset{x \longrightarrow \infty}{\mathcal{L}}\ xe^{-x} = 0$, and, by means of the substitution $y = e^{-x}$, deduce that $\underset{y \longrightarrow 0}{\mathcal{L}}\ y \log y = 0$. Use this latter result to find the limit of $\left(\dfrac{1}{x}\right)^{\sin x}$, as x tends to zero.

8. *TP, TQ* are two tangents to a circle. Show that as the point Q approaches the point P, the ratio of the area included between those tangents and the arc PQ of the circle to that of the minor segment of the circle cut off by the chord PQ tends to the limit $\frac{1}{2}$.

9. A pyramid of height $3a$, standing on a square base of side a, is divided into n slices of equal thickness by planes parallel to the base. If each slice is regarded as a square lamina with the larger face of the slice as base, show that the sum of the volumes of the laminæ so formed is

$$\tfrac{1}{2}a^3 \left(1 + \frac{1}{n}\right)\left(2 + \frac{1}{n}\right),$$

and deduce the volume of the pyramid.

10. Three intersecting edges of a tetrahedron are mutually perpendicular and have lengths a, b, c. By supposing the tetrahedron divided into n slices of equal thickness by planes perpendicular to one of these edges, show that the volume of the tetrahedron has a value between

$$\frac{abc}{2n^3}\{1^2 + 2^2 + 3^2 + \ldots + (n-1)^2\}$$

and

$$\frac{abc}{2n^3}(1^2 + 2^2 + 3^2 + \ldots + n^2),$$

and deduce the exact value.

11. A sphere of radius r is divided into two parts by a plane distant $r/2$ from the centre. The smaller part is then divided into n slices of equal thickness by planes parallel to the circular face, and each slice is regarded as a right circular cylinder with the smaller face of the slice as base. Show that the sum of the volumes of the cylinders so formed is

$$\frac{1}{48}\pi r^3 \left(1 - \frac{1}{n}\right)\left(10 + \frac{1}{n}\right),$$

and deduce a formula for the volume of a spherical cap of height $r/2$.

Differentiate the functions of x shown in Examples 12-35 :

12. $x^3 (5 - 3x^2)^{1/3}$.

13. $\dfrac{(x^2 - 1)^2}{x^2 + 1}$.

14. $\log \sqrt{\left(\dfrac{x^2 - a^2}{x^2 + a^2}\right)}$.

15. $\log \dfrac{\cos x - \sin x}{\cos x + \sin x}$.

16. $e^{-x^2} \sin 2x$.

17. $e^{-x} (x \sin x + x \cos x + \cos x)$.

18. $xe^{-\frac{1}{2}x^2} \cos x$.

19. $\{x + b + \sqrt{(x^2 + 2bx + c)}\}^n$.

20. $x \sqrt{\left(\dfrac{4 - x}{4 + x}\right)}$.

21. $x \sqrt{\left(\dfrac{x^2 - a^2}{x^2 + a^2}\right)}$.

22. $\dfrac{\sqrt{(x^2 + a^2)} + x}{\sqrt{(x^2 + a^2)} - x}$.

23. $\dfrac{(2x + 1)(x + 3)^{1/2}}{(1 - 2x)(3 - x)^{1/2}}$.

24. $(x - a)^2 \sqrt{\left(\dfrac{x}{2a - x}\right)}$.

25. $\log \dfrac{x^{\frac{1}{3}} - x^{-\frac{1}{3}}}{x^{\frac{1}{3}} + x^{-\frac{1}{3}}}$.

26. $\left(\dfrac{\sin^2 x}{a + b \cos^2 x}\right)^3$.

27. $\dfrac{\sin x}{\sqrt{(a \cos^2 x + b \sin^2 x)}}$.

28. $\cos^{-1} \left(\dfrac{1 + 2 \cos x}{2 + \cos x}\right)$.

29. $\tan^{-1} \left(\dfrac{3 \sin x}{4 + 5 \cos x}\right)$.

389

30. $\dfrac{x \sin^{-1} x}{\sqrt{(1 - x^2)}}.$

31. $\tan^{-1} \left(\dfrac{1}{x^2} - 1\right)^{1/2}.$

32. $\dfrac{1}{6} \log \dfrac{x - 1}{x + 1} + \dfrac{\sqrt{2}}{3} \tan^{-1} \dfrac{x}{\sqrt{2}}.$

33. $\sqrt{(1 + x^2)} \tan^{-1} x - \log \{x + \sqrt{(1 + x^2)}\}.$

34. $\sqrt{2} \sec x + \log \dfrac{\sqrt{2} - \sec x}{\sqrt{2} + \sec x}.$

35. $\dfrac{1}{\sqrt{3}} \tan^{-1} \dfrac{2x - 1}{\sqrt{3}} - \dfrac{1}{6} \log \dfrac{x^3 + 1}{(x + 1)^3}.$

36. If $1 + y^2 = (2x - x^2)^{n/2}$, prove that
$$2 (2x - x^2) y \frac{dy}{dx} = n (1 - x)(1 + y^2).$$

37. If $x = y \log xy$, prove that $\dfrac{dy}{dx} = \dfrac{y (x - y)}{x (x + y)}.$

38. If $y = e^{x^2/2y^2}$, prove that $\dfrac{dy}{dx} = \dfrac{xy}{x^2 + y^2}.$

39. Using logarithmic differentiation, prove that if $x^a y^b = (x + y)^{a + b}$ then $\dfrac{dy}{dx} = \dfrac{y}{x}$, provided $ay \neq bx$.

40. If $y = \dfrac{\sin ax}{1 + x}$, prove that
$$\frac{d^2y}{dx^2} + \frac{2}{1 + x} \frac{dy}{dx} + a^2 y = 0.$$

41. If $y = (\sin^{-1} x)^2$, prove that
$$(1 - x^2) \frac{d^2y}{dx^2} - x \frac{dy}{dx} = 2.$$

42. If $y = \sin (m \sin^{-1} x)$, prove that
$$(1 - x^2) \frac{d^2y}{dx^2} = x \frac{dy}{dx} - m^2 y.$$

Calculus—II

43. If $y = x \tan \dfrac{x}{3}$, prove that

$$\frac{d^2y}{dx^2} - \frac{2y}{3x}\frac{dy}{dx} = \frac{2}{3}.$$

44. If $y = \tan^{-1}(m \tan x)$, prove that

$$\frac{d^2y}{dx^2} = \left\{ \left(\frac{1}{m} - m\right) \sin 2y \right\} \frac{dy}{dx}.$$

45. If $x^2 + xy + y^2 = a^2$, prove that

$$(x + 2y)^3 \frac{d^2y}{dx^2} + 6a^2 = 0.$$

46. If $x - y = \log(x + y)$, prove that

$$\frac{d^2y}{dx^2} = \frac{4(x + y)}{(x + y + 1)^3}.$$

47. If $\sin x + \sin y = 1$, prove that

$$\frac{dy}{dx} = -\frac{\cos x}{\sqrt{(2 \sin x - \sin^2 x)}},$$

and find also $\dfrac{d^2y}{dx^2}$ in terms of x.

48. If $y = 3x - \tan^{-1}x$, find $\dfrac{d^2y}{dx^2}$ and $\dfrac{d^2x}{dy^2}$ in terms of x.

49. If $y = 2x - 3x \cos x + \frac{1}{3}\sin 3x$, show that for small values of x, $\dfrac{d^2y}{dx^2}$ is approximately equal to $11x^3$.

50. If $\dfrac{dy}{dx} = \dfrac{1}{x^2\sqrt{(2x^2 - 3)}}$, and $ux^2 = 1$, find $\dfrac{d^2y}{du^2}$ in terms of u.

51. If $x = r \cos\theta$, $y = r \sin\theta$, where r and θ are functions of t, prove that

$$\frac{d^2x}{dt^2}\cos\theta + \frac{d^2y}{dt^2}\sin\theta = \frac{d^2r}{dt^2} - r\left(\frac{d\theta}{dt}\right)^2.$$

52. If $x = t^2 + 2t$, $y = 2t + 2\log 2t$, prove that

$$2\frac{d^2y}{dx^2}\left(1 + \frac{dy}{dx}\right) + \left(\frac{dy}{dx}\right)^3 = 0.$$

391

53. If $x = \sin t$, $y = \sinh mt$, where m is a constant, prove that
$$\frac{1 - x^2}{y}\frac{d^2y}{dx^2} - \frac{x}{y}\frac{dy}{dx}$$ is constant.

54. Find the nth derivatives of the following functions :

    (i) $\log (1 - x)$,   (ii) $\dfrac{1 + x}{1 - x}$,

    (iii) $\dfrac{x}{1 + x}$,   (iv) $\dfrac{x}{x^2 - 1}$,

    (v) $x^2 \log x$,   (vi) $x^{n-1} \log x$,

    (vii) $\log \dfrac{2x + 3}{x^2}$,   (viii) $e^{\sqrt{3}x} \cos x$,

    (ix) $e^{-\frac{1}{2}x} \sin \left(\dfrac{\sqrt{3x}}{2} \right)$,   (x) $e^{4x} \sin 3x$.

55. If $y = e^{x \cos \frac{\pi}{n}} \cos \left(x \sin \dfrac{\pi}{n} \right)$, prove that
$$\frac{d^n y}{dx^n} + y = 0.$$

56. Show that the nth derivative of $xe^x \cos x$ is zero when
$$n \{ 1 + \tan (x + \tfrac{1}{4} n\pi) \} + 2x = 0.$$

57. Find the nth derivative of $\cos ax$, and show that if $y = \cos x \cos 2x$, then
$$2 \frac{d^n y}{dx^n} = 3^n + (-1)^n,$$
when $x = \tfrac{1}{2}n\pi$.

58. Find the differential equations of which the following equations are the complete primitives, A and B being arbitrary constants in each case :

    (i) $y = Ax + Bx \log x$;

    (ii) $xy = A \sin x + B \cos x$;

    (iii) $y = e^x (A \log x + B)$;

    (iv) $y = A \cos \sqrt{x} + B \sin \sqrt{x}$;

    (v) $y = A \cos \dfrac{a}{x} + B \sin \dfrac{a}{x}$;

    (vi) $ye^{3x} = A \cos 2x + B \sin 2x$;

    (vii) $y\sqrt{x} = A \sin (B + m\sqrt{x})$;

(viii) $y = x \, (A \sin \log x + B \cos \log x + \log x)$;

(ix) $xy = A e^{-3x} \cos (2x + B)$;

(x) $y = A \sqrt{x} \cos (\log B \sqrt{x})$.

59. Show that the tangent to the curve $y^3 = x^3 + 3ax^2$ at the point at which $x = -\frac{8}{3}a$ has gradient unity, and does not meet the curve again.

60. Show that the straight line joining the points on the curve $x^2 + 4xy - y^2 + 4x - 4y = 0$ at which the gradient is zero has the equation $x + 2y + 2 = 0$.

61. Find the points on the ellipse $x^2 - xy + y^2 = 27$ at which the tangent is (i) parallel to the x-axis, (ii) parallel to the y-axis, (iii) at right angles to the radius from the origin.

62. If the tangent at any point P on the curve

$$y = \sqrt{(a^2 - x^2)} + a \log \frac{a - \sqrt{(a^2 - x^2)}}{x}$$

meets the y-axis in T, show that PT is of constant length.

63. Prove that the curves
$$3x^2 - y^2 + 4x + 1 = 0 \quad \text{and} \quad (36 - 7y)^3 = 8(1 - x^2)^2$$
intersect orthogonally at the point $(-3, 4)$.

64. Prove that for the curve $x^4 + 12\,xy + y^4 = 14$, the value of $\frac{d^2y}{dx^2}$ is zero at the points of intersection of the curve with the hyperbola $xy = 1$.

65. Show that for any curve the length of the perpendicular from the foot of the ordinate to the tangent at the point (x, y) is

$y \left/ \left\{ 1 + \left(\frac{dy}{dx} \right)^2 \right\}^{1/2} \right.$, and prove that this quantity is constant

for the curve $y = \frac{1}{2}a \, (e^{x/a} + e^{-x/a})$.

66. Find the point on the curve given by the freedom equations $x = a \sin^2 t$, $y = a \cos^3 t$, at which the tangent is parallel to the line $4y - 3x = 0$.

67. The freedom equations of a curve are
$$x = \frac{2t}{t^2 + 1}, \quad y = \frac{t + 1}{t^2 + 1}.$$

Find the equation of the tangent at the point (0, 1) and show that this tangent does not meet the curve in any other point.

68. Show that the equation of the tangent at the point t on the curve $x \cos t = 1 - \sin t$, $y \sin t = 1 - \cos t$, is
$$(1 + \sin t)\, x + (1 + \cos t)\, y = \sin t + \cos t.$$

69. Show that the equation of the normal at the point θ on the curve
$$x = \theta \cos \theta + (\tfrac{1}{2}\, \theta^2 - 1) \sin \theta,$$
$$y = \theta \sin \theta - (\tfrac{1}{2}\, \theta^2 - 1) \cos \theta,$$
is $x \cos \theta + y \sin \theta = \theta$.

70. Show that the curves
$$y = a \log \left(k \sec \frac{x}{a} \right), \quad y = a \log \left(k' \operatorname{cosec} \frac{x}{a} \right)$$
intersect at right angles.

71. Show that the length of the perpendicular from the origin to the tangent at the point t on the curve whose freedom equations are
$$x = t \cos t - \sin t, \quad y = t \sin t + \cos t$$
is t.

72. If $y = \dfrac{1 + nx + \tfrac{1}{2}n\,(n-1)\,x^2}{(1+x)^n}$, find the value of $\dfrac{dy}{dx}$, and deduce that if n is negative and x is positive, then
$$(1+x)^n < 1 + nx + \tfrac{1}{2}n\,(n-1)\,x^2.$$

73. Show that the concavity of the curve $y = \dfrac{x^2 - 2}{x(x-1)}$ changes direction between $x = 4$ and $x = 5$.

74. Show that the curve $x^3 + y^3 = 3a^2 x$ is concave down at all points above the x-axis.

75. If $z = \dfrac{k \sinh x}{\sinh y - \sinh x}$, and if x and y are subject to small errors δx, δy, respectively, show that the corresponding error δz in z is given approximately by
$$\frac{\delta z}{z} = \frac{\sinh x}{\sinh y - \sinh x} (\coth x\, \delta x - \coth y\, \delta y).$$

76. If a wire of length s is stretched fairly tightly between two points in the same horizontal plane, and if the sag at the middle is denoted by v, then

$$2vs = 2v \sqrt{(a^2 + 4v^2)} + a^2 \log \frac{2v + \sqrt{(a^2 + 4v^2)}}{a}.$$

If v is increased by δv, find the corresponding increase δs in s.

77. Show that the curves
$$(x + y)^3 = axy, \quad x^2 - xy + y^2 = b (x - y)$$
are orthogonal for all values of a and b.

78. Two rods AB, AC of equal length l inches are inclined at an angle θ. If θ increases at the rate of 20 degrees per second find the rate at which the length BC is increasing when $\theta = 60°$.

79. If $y = e^{-\frac{1}{4}x} \cos 2x$, and if x increases from $45°$ to $50°$, find the approximate change in the value of y.

80. The interior of a vessel containing water is of the form obtained by rotating about the y-axis the portion of the parabola $9y = 8x^2$ from $y = 0$ to $y = 4$, the unit on each axis being 1 foot. When the vessel is full, an orifice is opened at the base. If when the depth of water is y feet, the rate of outflow is $\frac{1}{4}\sqrt{y}$ cubic feet per second, find how long the vessel takes to empty.

81. A right circular cylinder, originally of height 100 inches and base-radius 40 inches, is being compressed along its axis so that its height is diminishing at the uniform rate of 3 inches per second. If the volume remains constant, find the rate of change of (i) the base-radius, and (ii) the curved surface after 12 seconds.

82. In a circle whose radius is r feet, OA, OB are perpendicular radii, and AT is the tangent at A. A point P moves with uniform velocity 5 feet per second along the chord AB from A to B. If OP produced meets AT in Q, and if $AP = x$ feet, $AQ = y$ feet, show that $y = rx/(r\sqrt{2} - x)$, and find the velocity of Q along AT at the instant when $AQ = r$ feet.

83. A rope APB of length 25 feet passes over a pulley P which is 4 feet above a straight horizontal track on which the ends A, B move, the rope being kept taut. If A and B are on opposite sides of D, the foot of the perpendicular from P to the track, and if B moves away from D with uniform speed 2 feet per second, find the speed of A when $DB = 3$ feet.

84. The jib PQ of a crane is a feet in length. It is pivoted at P and is raised by a chain attached to the end Q and passing over a pulley R which is a feet directly above P. The chain is wound in at a steady rate of $a/4$ feet per second. Find the angular velocity and the angular acceleration of the jib about P when angle $QPR = \pi/3$.

85. A triangular plate ABC, such that $AB = AC$, the base $BC = 24$ inches, and the altitude $AD = 56$ inches, is suspended by the vertex A and lowered into a tank of water. If, when the base of the plate is immersed to a depth of 35 inches, the unwetted area of either side is decreasing at the rate of 40 square inches per second, find the rate of descent of the plate at that instant.

86. A, B are the points on the line $x = -a$ at distance $8a$ from the origin. A rod PQ, of length $8a$, always passes through O while P moves along the line AB. If, at time t, the rod makes an angle θ with OX, show that the ratio of the velocities of Q and P is $\sqrt{(64 \cos^4 \theta - 16 \cos^3 \theta + 1)}$. If $a = 2$ inches, and if the rod rotates with constant angular velocity 3 radians per second, find the acceleration of P at the instant when $\theta = \pi/4$.

87. A solid right circular cone of base-radius r feet and height h feet stands on the bottom of a cylindrical tank of radius a feet, and water pours into the tank at the steady rate of v cubic feet per minute. Show that, when the depth of water in the tank is $\frac{1}{3}h$ feet, the water level is rising at the rate of $\dfrac{9v}{\pi (9a^2 - 4r^2)}$ feet per minute, and find, for that same instant, the rate at which the volume of the submerged part of the cone is increasing.

88. A point P moves with uniform speed $6\frac{1}{2}$ feet per second along the diagonal BD of a rectangle $ABCD$ whose dimensions are $AB = 50$ feet, $BC = 120$ feet. If AP produced meets BC in Q, find the velocity and acceleration of Q along BC at the instant when $BQ = QC$.

89. A rope attached to a weight which rests on the ground, passes vertically upwards, over a small pulley 24 feet above the ground, then vertically downwards, and is kept taut by a man who holds the end, which is 4 feet above the ground. If the man carries the end of the rope away in a horizontal straight line at a steady rate of 5 feet per second, find the velocity and acceleration of the weight (i) after 3 seconds, (ii) when the weight is 10 feet from the ground.

90. One end A of a string AB is tied to a bead which slides on OX, the positive part of the x-axis. The string passes over a pulley of radius 3 inches, whose centre is at the origin, and hangs down vertically on the other side of the pulley. If C is the highest point of the pulley, show that when $OA = x$ inches, the length of string

from C to A is $3 \sin^{-1} \left(\dfrac{3}{x}\right) + \sqrt{(x^2 - 9)}$ inches. If the end B of the string is pulled downwards with uniform speed 2 inches per second, find, for the instant when $x = 5$ inches, (i) the velocity, and (ii) the acceleration of A along the x-axis, and (iii) the rate of change of the length of the arc of contact of string and pulley.

91. One end A of a straight rod AB, 20 feet long, moves along the x-axis with uniform velocity 5 feet per second. The rod is supported by a peg at the point C $(0, 3)$, the unit of length being the foot. Find for the instant at which $OA = 4$ feet, (i) the vertical velocity, and (ii) the vertical acceleration of the end B. Find also whether, at the instant when $OA = 2\sqrt{10}$ feet, the end B is moving towards or away from the y-axis.

92. A ladder PQ, 20 feet long, rests with one end P on the ground, and the other end Q projecting over a vertical wall, 12 feet high. If the end P is pushed along the ground towards the wall with uniform speed 2 feet per second, find (i) the angular velocity, and (ii) the angular acceleration of PQ about P at the instant when P is 5 feet from the wall.

93. A straight rod APB of length 10 units passes through a fixed point P $(3, 4)$, and the end A is on the x-axis to the left of the origin. This end is now moved along the x-axis in the direction OX at a uniform rate of 1 unit per second. Find, for the instant when A is at the origin, (i) the angular velocity, and (ii) the angular acceleration of the rod about A, and also the magnitude and direction of the velocity of the end B.

94. Sketch the curves whose equations are:

(i) $y = 1 + \dfrac{1}{3x - 5}$; (ii) $y = \dfrac{(2x + 1)^2}{2x - 1}$;

(iii) $y = \left(1 + \dfrac{1}{x}\right)^2$; (iv) $y = \dfrac{x(x - 2)}{(x - 1)(x - 3)}$;

(v) $y = \dfrac{x}{x^2 + 3}$; (vi) $y = \dfrac{(1 + x)^2}{x(2 - x)}$;

(vii) $y = \dfrac{(x + 1)^2}{x^2 + 1}$; (viii) $y = \dfrac{3x - x^3}{x^2 + 1}$;

(ix) $y = \dfrac{27(x - 1)^2}{x^3}$; (x) $y = \dfrac{(x - 2)^2}{(x + 1)^3}$;

(xi) $y = \dfrac{(x-1)^2 (x+2)}{(x-2)^3}$; (xii) $y = \dfrac{8 (x^2 - 1)}{x^4 + 8}$.

95. Sketch the curves whose equations are :

(i) $y = \sin x + \frac{1}{3} \sin 3x$; (ii) $y = \sin x \sin 2x$;

(iii) $y = \sin^2 \left(x - \dfrac{\pi}{3} \right) \cos 2x$;

(iv) $y = \sec x + \operatorname{cosec} x$; (v) $y = \dfrac{\sin^3 x}{\sin 3x}$;

(vi) $y = x + \sin x, \left(-\dfrac{\pi}{2} \leqq x \leqq \dfrac{\pi}{2} \right)$;

(vii) $y = e^{-x} (\cos x + \sin x)$, $(0 \leqq x \leqq 2\pi)$;

(viii) $y = x e^{-2/x^2}$.

96. Sketch the curves whose equations are :

(i) $9y^2 = x (3 - x)^2$; (ii) $6y^2 = x (2x - 9)^2$;
(iii) $y^2 = x^2 (6 - x^2)$; (iv) $y^2 = x^3 (2 - x)$;
(v) $y^2 = (1 - x^2)^3$; (vi) $y^2 = x^5 (3 - x)$;
(vii) $64y^2 = (8 + x^2)^2 (4 - x^2)$;

(viii) $y^4 = x^4 (1 - x)$; (ix) $y^2 = \dfrac{1 - x}{1 + x}$;

(x) $y^2 = \dfrac{x^2 (x - 1)}{x + 1}$.

97. Sketch the curves whose freedom equations are :

(i) $x = 2 \tan \theta, \ y = 2 \sin^2 \theta$;

(ii) $x = \cos \theta + \sin \theta, \ y = \frac{1}{4} \cos 2\theta, \left(-\dfrac{\pi}{4} \leqq \theta \leqq \dfrac{\pi}{4} \right)$;

(iii) $x = 2 \cos t - \cos 2t, \ y = 2 \sin t - \sin 2t$;
(iv) $x = \cos t (1 + \cos t), \ y = \sin t (1 + \cos t)$;
(v) $x = \sin^3 t + \cos^3 t, \ y = \sin^3 t - \cos^3 t$;
(vi) $x + 1 = 3 \sin \theta + \sin 3\theta, \ y - 1 = 3 \cos \theta - \cos 3\theta$.

98. Find the turning values of the following functions :

(i) $\dfrac{x^2 + 4}{(x + 2)^2}$; (ii) $\dfrac{2x^2 - 3x + 6}{x^2 + x + 2}$;

398

(iii) $\dfrac{3x - 5}{(x^2 - 4x + 5)^{3/2}}$;   (iv) $\dfrac{(5 - x)\sqrt{(2x - x^2)}}{(3 - x)^2}$.

99. Show that the curve $y = \cos x \,(1 + \sin x)$ has a horizontal inflexion where $x = \dfrac{3\pi}{2}$, and determine the shape of the curve near this point.

100. Sketch the shape of the curve $y = \tan^{-1} x + \log \sqrt{\left(\dfrac{1 + x}{1 - x}\right)}$ near its point of inflexion.

101. Show that the line joining the origin to the point where the curve $y = \dfrac{5x^2 - 6x}{x^2 - 4}$ crosses its horizontal asymptote touches the curve at the origin.

102. If the inflexional tangents to the curve $yx^3 = 4 - 6x^2$ meet it again in the points P_1, P_2, show that the equation of the straight line P_1P_2 is $4y = 27x$.

103. Prove that if a is a positive constant, while x is a variable taking only positive values, the function $\dfrac{(x + a)^2}{x}$ has the minimum value $4a$.

104. Prove that the curves
$$y = \frac{x^2 - x + 1}{1 - x}, \quad y = \left(\frac{x - 1}{x^2 + x - 1}\right)^{1/2}.$$
have a common turning point, and that the other turning points lie on the same ordinate at a distance $\left(3 + \dfrac{1}{\sqrt{5}}\right)$ units apart.

105. If $xy^3 = c^4$, show that the maximum value of $x^2 + y^2$ is $\dfrac{4}{3} c^2\, 3^{1/4}$.

106. Prove that if $y = \dfrac{x^2}{(x - 1)(x + p)}$, the turning values of y when $p = 3$ are the same as when $p = \tfrac{1}{3}$.

107. If the equation $ax^2 + 2\,hxy + by^2 = 1$ is transformed by the substitutions $x = r \cos \theta$, $y = r \sin \theta$, show that the turning values of r occur when $\theta = \tfrac{1}{2} \tan^{-1} \left(\dfrac{2h}{a - b}\right)$.

399

108. A pointer oscillates so that its angular deviation θ, in radians, is given in terms of the time t, in seconds, since the beginning of the motion, by the equation

$$\theta = 2\, e^{-\frac{t}{5}} \sin\frac{\pi t}{3}.$$

Draw a rough graph to illustrate the movement, and find

    (i) the maximum amplitude of the oscillation,

    (ii) the time-interval between successive maxima.

109. The power in an electric circuit is given by $EI \cos \Phi$, where $I = \dfrac{E}{(R^2 + \omega^2 L^2)^{1/2}}$, and $\Phi = \tan^{-1}\dfrac{\omega L}{R}$. If L, E, ω are constants, find the value of R which makes the power a maximum.

110. The strength of a current sent through a resistance R by a battery consisting of a fixed number (n) of cells, each of voltage E and internal resistance r, arranged with sets of x cells in series and $\dfrac{n}{x}$ such sets in parallel, is given by $\dfrac{nxE}{nR + rx^2}$ amperes. How many cells must be in series in order to give the maximum current ?

111. A segment of a circle of radius $\sqrt{6}$ units is cut off by a chord at unit distance from the centre of the circle. Find the area of the greatest rectangle that can be inscribed in the segment.

112. If the radii of the circular faces of a frustum of a cone are r and $2r$, and the slant height is l, show that the volume of the frustum is $\dfrac{7}{3}\pi r^2 \sqrt{(l^2 - r^2)}$, and find the maximum volume that the frustum can have if the slant height is constant.

113. A variable straight line through the point $P\,(1, 2)$ cuts the positive parts OX, OY of the co-ordinate axes in A, B, respectively. If the angle $PAO = \theta$ radians, express the perimeter of the triangle OAB in terms of θ, and show that it is a minimum when $\theta = \tan^{-1}\dfrac{4}{3}$.

114. A flagstaff, 18 feet long, stands on the top of a tower, 32 feet high. If the flagstaff subtends an angle θ at a point on the ground x feet from the foot of the tower, show that θ is a maximum when $x = 40$ feet.

115. Find the area of the largest rectangle which can be inscribed in the ellipse $\dfrac{x^2}{a^2} + \dfrac{y^2}{b^2} = 1$.

116. Two passages are at right angles to one another, one being 4 feet wide, and the other 5 feet wide. Is it possible for a ladder 13 feet long to pass horizontally from one passage to the other ?

117. Find the length of the shortest beam that can be used to brace a vertical wall, if the beam rests on another wall that is b feet in height and a feet distant from the first wall.

118. A buoy, composed of two equal cones having a common base, is to be constructed from two circular sheets of radius R. Find the dimensions of the cones if the buoy has the greatest possible volume.

119. The speed of signalling in a submarine cable is proportional to $x^2 \log \left(\dfrac{1}{x}\right)$, where x is the ratio of the radius of the core to that of the insulating cover. Show that the speed is a maximum when the radius of the covering is $\sqrt{e}$ times that of the core.

120. Show that the radius of curvature of the catenary $y = a \cosh \left(\dfrac{x}{a}\right)$ at the point (x, y) is y^2/a.

121. Find the radius of curvature at the point with abscissa $a/2$ on the curve
$$x = \frac{at}{1 + t^3}, \; y = \frac{at^2}{1 + t^3}.$$

122. Find the radius of curvature of the curves :
  (i) $x^2 y = x - y$, where $x = 1$;
  (ii) $xy^2 = 1 - x$, where $x = 1$;
  (iii) $\quad y = c \log \left(\sec \dfrac{x}{c}\right)$, where $x = 0$.

123. Show that the radius of curvature at any point on the curve
$$x^{2/3} + y^{2/3} = a^{2/3}$$
is $3 (axy)^{1/3}$

124. Find the curvature of the curve $y^2 = 4 x^2 (1 - x^2)$ at one of its turning points.

401   14

125. Find the radius of curvature of the curve
$$x = a \sin 2\theta \, (1 + \cos 2\theta), \quad y = a \cos 2\theta \, (1 - \cos 2\theta).$$
Sketch the shape of the curve near the origin, and show that the curve has the same curvature there as the parabola $x^2 = 8ay$.

126. Show that for the curve $y = \sinh x$,
$$\rho^2 = \frac{(2 - t)^3}{t \, (1 - t)^2},$$
where $t = \tanh^2 x$, and deduce that ρ has a minimum value $3\sqrt{3}$ when $y = 1$.

127. A circle of radius b rolls without slipping on the outside of a fixed circle of radius a. Show that the locus of a point fixed on the circumference of the rolling circle can be represented by the freedom equations
$$x = (a + b) \cos \theta - b \cos \{(a + b) \, \theta / b\},$$
$$y = (a + b) \sin \theta - b \sin \{(a + b) \, \theta / b\}.$$
For the special case in which $a = 3b$, show that the curve consists of three arches, each of length $32a/9$, and make a rough sketch of the curve. Find also the radius of curvature of the curve at the mid-point of an arch.

128. Prove that the radius of curvature at any point P on the curve $3x = \sec^2 t$, $3y = 2\tan t$, is numerically equal to twice the length of the part of the normal at P intercepted between P and the y-axis. Show also that the constraint equation of the evolute of this curve is $9y^2 = 4 \, (x - 1)^3$.

129. Find the evolutes of the following curves :
    (i) the parabola $y^2 = 4 \, ax$,
    (ii) the ellipse $\dfrac{x^2}{a^2} + \dfrac{y^2}{b^2} = 1$,
    (iii) the rectangular hyperbola $xy = c^2$.

130. Establish the following expansions in ascending powers of x as far as the terms indicated :
    (i) $\log \sqrt{(1 + x^2)} = \frac{1}{2}x^2 - \frac{1}{4}x^4 + \frac{1}{6}x^6 - \frac{1}{8}x^8 + \ldots$;
    (ii) $e^x \log (1 + x) = x + \frac{1}{2}x^2 + \frac{1}{3}x^3 + \frac{3}{40}x^5 + \ldots$;
    (iii) $\sin x . \tan^{-1} x = x^2 - \frac{1}{2}x^4 + \ldots$;
    (iv) $x + (1 - x) \log (1 - x) = \dfrac{x^2}{1.2} + \dfrac{x^3}{2.3} + \dfrac{x^4}{3.4} + \ldots$;

$\checkmark$ (v) $\quad x \tan^{-1} x - \log \sqrt{(1 + x^2)} = \dfrac{x^2}{1.2} - \dfrac{x^4}{3.4} + \dfrac{x^6}{5.6} - \cdots$;

(vi) $\quad x \cot x = 1 - \dfrac{x^2}{3} - \dfrac{x^4}{45} + \cdots$;

(vii) $\quad \sin x . \tan x = x^2 + \frac{1}{6} x^4 + \frac{31}{360} x^6 + \cdots$;

(viii) $\quad e^{1 - \cos x} = 1 + \dfrac{x^2}{2} + \dfrac{x^4}{12} + \dfrac{x^6}{720} + \cdots$;

(ix) $\quad e^{x \cos x} = 1 + x + \frac{1}{2} x^2 - \frac{1}{3} x^3 - \frac{11}{24} x^4 + \cdots$;

(x) $\quad \cos x \left(\dfrac{x}{\sin x} \right)^2 = 1 - \frac{1}{6} x^2 - \frac{7}{120} x^4 + \cdots$;

(xi) $\quad \log (6 + x - x^2) = \log 6 + \frac{1}{6} x - \frac{13}{72} x^2 + \frac{19}{648} x^3 - \cdots$;

(xii) $\quad \sec^2 x = 1 + x^2 + \frac{2}{3} x^4 + \cdots$;

(xiii) $\quad \log (1 + \cos x) = \log 2 - \dfrac{x^2}{4} - \dfrac{x^4}{96} + \cdots$;

(xiv) $\quad \log \{ x + \sqrt{(1 + x^2)} \} = x - \dfrac{1}{2} \cdot \dfrac{x^3}{3} + \dfrac{1 . 3}{2 . 4} \cdot \dfrac{x^5}{5} - \dfrac{1 . 3 . 5}{2 . 4 . 6} \cdot \dfrac{x^7}{7} + \cdots$;

(xv) $\quad \dfrac{1}{3} e^x + \dfrac{2}{3} e^{-\frac{1}{2}x} \cos \left(\dfrac{\sqrt{3} x}{2} \right) = 1 + \dfrac{x^3}{3!} + \dfrac{x^6}{6!} + \dfrac{x^9}{9!} + \cdots$.

131. Calculate, correct to four decimal places, the values of :
  (i) $\sin 5°$;   (ii) $\cos 12°$;
  $\checkmark$(iii) $\log 1 \cdot 1$;   (iv) $\tan 45° \, 30'$;
  (v) $\tan 31°$;   (vi) $\cos 59° \, 30'$;
  (vii) $\sin 46'$;
  (viii) $\tan^{-1} 0 \cdot 2$, to the nearest degree.

132. In the expansion of $\log \dfrac{1 + x}{1 - x}$, substitute $\dfrac{1}{2n + 1}$ for x and deduce that

$$\log (n + 1) = \log n + 2 \left\{ \dfrac{1}{2n + 1} + \dfrac{1}{3(2n + 1)^3} + \dfrac{1}{5(2n + 1)^5} + \cdots \right\}.$$

Hence find the value of $\log 2$ to four significant figures.

133. Prove that, if $|y| > 1$,
$$2 \log y - \log (y + 1) - \log (y - 1) = \frac{1}{y^2} + \frac{1}{2y^4} + \frac{1}{3y^6} + \cdots .$$

134. Establish the expansion
$$\tan^{-1} (x + h) = \tan^{-1} x + \frac{h}{1 + x^2} - \frac{xh^2}{(1 + x^2)^2} + \frac{(3x^2 - 1) h^3}{3(1 + x^2)^3} \\ - \cdots ,$$
and deduce the expansion for $\tan^{-1} (1 + x)$ in ascending powers of x, as far as the term in x^3.

135. Find an expression for the nth term in the expansion in ascending powers of x of each of the expressions :
(i) $e^x (1 + 3x + x^2)$,   (ii) $(1 + x)e^{-x} - (1 - x)e^x$.

136. Prove that
$$\log (1 + \sin x) = x - \frac{x^2}{2} + \frac{x^3}{6} - \frac{x^4}{12} + \frac{x^5}{24} - \cdots ,$$
and deduce similar expansions for

(i) $\log \sqrt{\left(\dfrac{1 + \sin x}{1 - \sin x} \right)}$,   (ii) $\log (\sec x)$.

137. Establish the expansion
$$\frac{x}{\sin x} = 1 + \tfrac{1}{6} x^2 + \tfrac{7}{360} x^4 + \cdots ,$$
and deduce that
$$\log (x \operatorname{cosec} x) = \frac{x^2}{6} + \frac{x^4}{180} + \cdots .$$

138. Find expansions in ascending powers of x for $\cosh x$ and $\sinh x$, and prove that if eighth and higher powers of x may be neglected
$$\cos x \cosh x = 1 - \tfrac{1}{6}x^4.$$

139. Prove that $\log \tan (x + h)$ is approximately equal to
$$\log \tan x + \frac{2h}{\sin 2x},$$
when h is small. Given that $\log \tan 60° = 0 \cdot 54931$, estimate the value of $\log \tan 60° \, 2'$.

140. By integrating the function $\dfrac{1}{1 - x^4}$, show that
$$1 + \frac{1}{5} \cdot \frac{1}{3^2} + \frac{1}{9} \cdot \frac{1}{3^4} + \cdots = \frac{\sqrt{3}}{4} \log (2 + \sqrt{3}) + \frac{\pi\sqrt{3}}{12} .$$

141. Show that

$$\log (1 + x + x^2) = \int \frac{dx}{1 - x} - 3 \int \frac{x^2\, dx}{1 - x^3} + C,$$

and deduce the series in ascending powers of x for $\log (1 + x + x^2)$ as far as the term in x^6.

142. By expanding the integrand in a series of ascending powers of x and integrating term by term, evaluate, correct to four decimal places, the definite integral

$$\int_0^1 \left(1 - \frac{x^2}{10}\right)^{\frac{1}{3}} dx.$$

143. Find, by integrating the series for $(1 - x^2)^{-1/2}$, the expansion in ascending powers of x for $\sin^{-1} x$, and hence show that

$$\frac{\theta}{\sin \theta} = 1 + \frac{1}{2} \cdot \frac{\sin^2\theta}{3} + \frac{1 \cdot 3}{2 \cdot 4} \cdot \frac{\sin^4\theta}{5} + \frac{1 \cdot 3 \cdot 5}{2 \cdot 4 \cdot 6} \cdot \frac{\sin^6\theta}{7} + \cdots.$$

Deduce a convergent arithmetical series for π, and evaluate π correct to three decimal places.

144. If $y = e^{\tan^{-1}x}$, show that $\dfrac{dy}{dx} = \dfrac{y}{1 + x^2}$. By means of this equation, calculate the values of y', y'', y''', for $x = 0$, and deduce that up to the term in x^3,

$$e^{\tan^{-1}x} = 1 + x + \tfrac{1}{2}x^2 - \tfrac{1}{6}x^3.$$

145. If $y = \sinh x \sin x$, show that $\dfrac{d^4y}{dx^4} = -4y$, and deduce a series, in ascending powers of x, for y, quoting the general term.

146. Establish **Machin's** formula

$$\frac{\pi}{4} = 4 \tan^{-1}\frac{1}{5} - \tan^{-1}\frac{1}{239},$$

and use this result to compute the value of π correct to six decimal places.

Evaluate the integrals shown in Examples 147—206 :

147. $\displaystyle\int (x + 3)\, \sqrt{(x + 1)}\, dx.$

148. $\displaystyle\int_1^3 \frac{(x^2 + 1)(x + 2)}{(x + 1)^2}\, dx.$

149. $\displaystyle\int \frac{\cos^3 x\, dx}{\sqrt{(\sin x)}}.$

150. $\displaystyle\int_0^{2\pi} (1 - \sin \theta)^3\, d\theta.$

151. $\displaystyle\int \frac{4 + x}{4 + x^2}\, dx.$

152. $\displaystyle\int_1^{3/2} \frac{x + 1}{\sqrt{(x^2 + 2x - 3)}}\, dx$

ELEMENTARY

153. $\int \sec^2 x \csc^2 x \, dx.$

154. $\int_0^{\frac{\pi}{4}} (2 \sin \theta \cos \theta)^4 d\theta.$

155. $\int_0^\pi \cos mx \cos nx \, dx.*$

156. $\int_0^\pi \cos^2 mx \cos^2 nx \, dx.*$

157. $\int \frac{(2x-1)\,dx}{x^2(x-1)^2}.$

158. $\int_1^4 \frac{8\,dx}{x(x^2+4)^2}.$

159. $\int \frac{dx}{x^3-1}.$

160. $\int_0^1 \frac{(x+4)\,dx}{(x+1)(x^2+3)}.$

161. $\int \frac{(2x-1)\,dx}{(x-2)(x^2-4x+5)}.$

162. $\int_0^1 \frac{x^2\,dx}{(x-2)^2(x^2+2)}.$

163. $\int \frac{2x^2+5x-6}{2x^2+x-1}\,dx.$

164. $\int_1^3 \frac{(x^2-1)\,dx}{x^2-2x+5}.$

165. $\int \frac{dx}{\sqrt{(2x^2-6x-9)}}.$

166. $\int_1^2 \frac{(3-2x)\,dx}{\sqrt{(3+2x-x^2)}}.$

167. $\int \frac{(5+x)\,dx}{\sqrt{(9+8x-x^2)}}.$

168. $\int_0^a \frac{x^{3/2}\,dx}{(a-x)^{1/2}}.$

169. $\int \frac{x\,dx}{\sqrt{(x^2+2x+4)}}.$

170. $\int_0^1 \frac{\sqrt{(1+x)}-\sqrt{(1-x)}}{\sqrt{(1+x)}+\sqrt{(1-x)}}\,dx.$

171. $\int \frac{x^3\,dx}{\sqrt{(x^2+a^2)}}.$

172. $\int_a^{2a} \frac{dx}{x^2(x^2+a^2)^{3/2}}.$

173. $\int_0^\infty \frac{x^2\,dx}{(1+x)^7}.$

174. $\int_0^1 \sqrt{\left(\frac{1-x}{1+x}\right)}\,dx.$

175. $\int_2^5 \sqrt{\{(x-2)(5-x)\}}\,dx.$

176. $\int \frac{dx}{x\sqrt{\{(2x-1)(x+1)\}}}.$

177. $\int_0^a x\sqrt{(ax-x^2)}\,dx.$

178. $\int_0^1 \frac{dx}{(1+x^2)\sqrt{(1-x^2)}}.$

*Where m and n are positive integers.

406

179. $\displaystyle\int_2^3 \frac{x\,dx}{(1-x^2)\,\sqrt{(x^4-1)}}$.

180. $\displaystyle\int \frac{\sqrt{(\tan x)}\,dx}{\sin x \cos x}$.

181. $\displaystyle\int_0^{\frac{\pi}{2}} \frac{\cos x\,dx}{1+\cos x}$.

182. $\displaystyle\int \frac{2\sin x}{\cos x + \sin x}\,dx$.

183. $\displaystyle\int_0^{\pi} \frac{dx}{11-5\cos x}$.

184. $\displaystyle\int \frac{\sin^2 x}{\cos^6 x}\,dx$.

185. $\displaystyle\int_0^{\pi/2} \frac{dx}{(1+\sin x)^2}$.

186. $\displaystyle\int \frac{\cos^2\theta\,d\theta}{\sin\theta\,(\sin^3\theta + \cos^3\theta)}$.

187. $\displaystyle\int_0^{\pi} \frac{\sin x + \cos x}{2+\cos x}\,dx$.

188. $\displaystyle\int \frac{dx}{2\sin x + 3}$.

189. $\displaystyle\int_{\pi/2}^{\pi} \frac{dx}{1-\cos x + 2\sin x}$.

190. $\displaystyle\int \frac{dx}{\sin x \cos^3 x}$.

191. $\displaystyle\int_0^1 x^2\,e^{-2x}\,dx$.

192. $\displaystyle\int x^2 \sin x \cos x\,dx$.

193. $\displaystyle\int_1^2 (x^2+2)\log x\,dx$.

194. $\displaystyle\int (1-3x^2)\sin^{-1} x\,dx$.

195. $\displaystyle\int_0^{\infty} e^{-2t}\sin 3t\,dt$.

196. $\displaystyle\int \tan^{-1}(\tfrac{1}{2}x)\,dx$.

197. $\displaystyle\int_0^1 \frac{\tan^{-1}x}{(1+x)^2}\,dx$.

198. $\displaystyle\int \log(1-x^2)\,dx$.

199. $\displaystyle\int_0^{\frac{\pi}{2}} x \sin^3 x \cos^2 x\,dx$.

200. $\displaystyle\int \frac{dx}{x \log x}$.

201. $\displaystyle\int \frac{dx}{x\,(\log x)^n}$.

202. $\displaystyle\int_0^{\frac{\pi}{2}} \sin^2 2\theta \sin^3\theta\,d\theta$.

203. $\displaystyle\int_0^{\frac{\pi}{2}} \sin^2\theta\,(1-\cos 4\theta)\,d\theta$.

204. $\displaystyle\int x\,(1-x^2)^{1/2} \sin^{-1} x\,dx$.

205. $\displaystyle\int (x^2+a^2)^{3/2}\,dx$.

206. $\displaystyle\int x^2\,(x^2-a^2)^{1/2}\,dx$.

407

207. Integrate $\dfrac{1}{x\sqrt{\{(x-2)(3x+2)\}}}$, using the substitution $x = \dfrac{2(1+u^2)}{1-3u^2}$.

208. Integrate $\dfrac{1}{\{2x+\sqrt{(x^2-1)}\}\sqrt{(x^2-1)}}$, using the substitution $u = x + \sqrt{(x^2-1)}$.

209. If $(a+b)\tan\Phi = (a-b)\tan\frac{1}{2}\theta$,

show that $\dfrac{d\Phi}{d\theta} = \dfrac{1}{2}\cdot\dfrac{a^2-b^2}{a^2+b^2+2ab\cos\theta}$,

and hence evaluate the definite integral

$$\int_0^{\pi/2}\frac{d\theta}{a^2+b^2+2ab\cos\theta}.$$

210. Show that, for $0 < a \leq \dfrac{\pi}{2}$,

$$\int_0^{a\sin\alpha}\sqrt{(a^2-x^2)}\,dx = \tfrac{1}{2}a^2(a+\sin\alpha\cos\alpha),$$

and verify the result geometrically.

211. Show, using the result of Example 79, page 296, that

$$\int_0^{\frac{\pi}{2}}(\pi x - 2x^2)\cos^2 x\,dx = \int_0^{\frac{\pi}{2}}\left(\frac{\pi}{2}x - x^2\right)dx = \frac{\pi^3}{48}.$$

212. Prove that

$$\int_a^b f(x)\,dx = \int_a^b f(a+b-x)\,dx,$$

and hence prove that

$$\int_{\pi/6}^{\pi/3}\frac{dx}{1+\tan x} = \frac{\pi}{12}.$$

213. Prove that, if n is a positive integer,

$$\int_0^{\frac{\pi}{2}}\frac{\sin(2n+1)x}{\sin x}\,dx = \int_0^{\frac{\pi}{2}}\frac{\sin(2n-1)x}{\sin x}\,dx,$$

and find the common value.

214. If $I_n = \int \dfrac{dx}{(x^2 + 1)^n}$, prove that

$$I_n = \frac{2n - 3}{2n - 2} I_{n-1} + \frac{x}{(2n - 2)(x^2 + 1)^{n-1}},$$

and evaluate

$$\int_0^1 \frac{dx}{(x^2 + 1)^5}.$$

215. If $I_n = \int_0^a \dfrac{x^n \, dx}{\sqrt{(a^2 - x^2)}}$, show that

$$I_n = \frac{n - 1}{n} \, a^2 \, I_{n-2},$$

and find the values of I_5 and I_6.

216. If $I_n = \int x^k (\log x)^n \, dx$, prove that

$$I_n = \frac{x^{k+1}}{k + 1} (\log x)^n - \frac{n}{k + 1} I_{n-1},$$

and evaluate

$$\int x^2 (\log x)^2 \, dx.$$

217. Find a reduction formula for $\int x^n e^{ax} \, dx$, and hence evaluate

$$\int_0^\infty (2x^2 + 4x - 3) \, e^{-2x} \, dx.$$

218. Using nine equidistant ordinates, and working to four decimal places, find by Simpson's Rule an approximation to the definite integral $\int_1^5 \dfrac{x\,dx}{x + 1}$. Show by integration that the exact value is $4 - \log 3$, and hence find an approximation to the value of e.

219. Show that the area bounded by the curve $y = 1 - \sin 4x$, the x-axis, and the ordinates $x = \dfrac{\pi}{12}$, $x = \dfrac{\pi}{3}$, is given by Simpson's Rule, using seven equidistant ordinates, as approximately $(14 - \sqrt{3})\dfrac{\pi}{72}$. Equating this to the exact area, found by

409

integration, show that

$$\pi \doteqdot \frac{18}{4 + \sqrt{3}}.$$

220. Find by means of Simpson's Rule, using seven equidistant ordinates and working to three decimal places, an approximate value to the definite integral $\int_0^{0\cdot6} \sqrt{(1 - x^3)}\, dx$. Expand the integrand in ascending powers of x by means of the binomial theorem, and by integrating the first three terms obtain another approximation to the value of the integral.

221. Calculate by Simpson's Rule the value of the definite integral $\int_{12}^{18} \sqrt{(x^2 - 128)}\, dx$, using seven equidistant ordinates. Compare your result with the exact value found by integration.

222. If $\dfrac{d^2y}{dx^2} = \dfrac{x}{1 + \sqrt{(1 - x)}}$, and if $y = \dfrac{dy}{dx} = 0$ when $x = 1$, prove that $30y = (1 - x)^2 \{ 15 - 8(1 - x)^{1/2} \}$.

223. If $\dfrac{d^2y}{dx^2} = \dfrac{x^2 + 1}{(x^2 - 1)^2}$, and if $y = 0$ when $x = \pm \sqrt{2}$, prove that $x^2 = 1 + e^{-2y}$.

224. If $\dfrac{d^2y}{dx^2} = \dfrac{x^2 + 6}{(x + 2)^2 (2x - 1)}$, and if $y = 2\log 3$ and $\dfrac{dy}{dx} = \dfrac{2}{3}$ when $x = 1$, find y in terms of x.

225. If, for a certain curve, $\dfrac{d^2y}{dx^2} = \dfrac{6}{(9 - x^2)^{3/2}}$, and if the curve passes through the points $(3, 0)$, $(0, -2)$, find the equation of the curve and show that it is an ellipse.

226. If $\dfrac{dV}{dy} = a^2 \sin^4 \theta$ and $y = a\,\dfrac{\cos^3 \theta}{\sin \theta}$, find $\dfrac{dV}{d\theta}$ in terms of θ, and show that

$$V = \frac{a^3}{16}(- 4\theta + \tfrac{1}{2} \sin 2\theta + \sin 4\theta - \tfrac{1}{6} \sin 6\theta),$$

provided that $V = 0$ when $\theta = 0$.

410

227. Find the following areas :

    (i) Enclosed by the curve $y^2 = (1 - x^2)^3$;

    (ii) Enclosed by the curve $y^2 = x^8 (1 - x^2)$;

    (iii) Enclosed by the curve $a^4 y^2 + b^2 x^4 = a^2 b^2 x^4$;

    (iv) Between the curve $x = a \tan \theta, y = a \sin^2 \theta$, the x-axis, and the ordinate $x = a$;

    (v) The loop of the curve $a (x^2 - y^2) = x^3$;

    (vi) Bounded by the curves $y = \sin x, \ y = \cos (x + a)$, between two consecutive points of intersection ;

    (vii) Above the x-axis, bounded by the curve $y = x (1 + 2x) e^{-x}$ and the x-axis ;

    (viii) Between the curve $(1 + x) y^2 = 1 - x$ and its asymptote.

228. Show that the areas of the successive segments intercepted between the x-axis and the curve $y = e^{-x} \sin 2x$ form a geometric progression of common ratio $- e^{-\pi/2}$.

229. Find the volume obtained by revolving about the x-axis the part of the curve $y^2 (a^2 + x^2) = x^2 (a^2 - x^2)$ between $x = 0, \ x = a$.

230. The curve $y = c \cosh \dfrac{x}{c}$ is rotated about the x-axis. Find the volume of the reel-shaped solid generated by the area under the curve from $x = - c$ to $x = c$.

231. The ellipse $(y - 4)^2 = 4 (1 - x^2)$ is revolved round the x-axis so as to make a ring-shaped solid. Show that the volume of the solid is $16\pi^2$.

232. Find the volume of the solid formed by revolving the ellipse $\dfrac{x^2}{a^2} + \dfrac{y^2}{b^2} = 1$ about (i) the y-axis, (ii) the tangent at either extremity of the major axis.

233. A semi-circular lamina of radius b is made to rotate about a line in its plane parallel to its bounding diameter, on the convex side of the arc, and at distance a, where $a > b$, from the centre of the semicircle. Find the volume swept out by the lamina.

234. Find the areas indicated below, and also the volumes generated when these areas are revolved about the x-axis :

    (i) The loop of the curve $9y^2 = x (3 - x)^2$;

    (ii) Enclosed by the curve $y^2 = x^3 (2 - x)$:

411

(iii) Under the curve $y = x \cos x$ from $x = 0$ to $x = \frac{1}{2}\pi$;

(iv) Enclosed by the curve $a^2 y^2 = x^2 (a^2 - x^2)$;

(v) Enclosed by the curve $64 y^2 = (8 + x^2)^2 (4 - x^2)$;

(vi) In the first quadrant, between the curve $y = \sin x$ and the line $\pi y = 2x$.

235. From the point P (h, k) on the curve $y^2 = x^3$, perpendiculars PM and PN are drawn to OX and OY. Show that the rectangle $OMPN$ is divided by the curve into two parts whose areas are in the ratio $2 : 3$. If the area OMP is revolved round the x-axis, and the area ONP round the y-axis, find the value of h for which the volumes generated are equal.

236. The finite area bounded by the curve $y = x^2 (3a - x)$ and the x-axis is revolved round that axis ; find the volume generated. The finite area bounded by the same curve and the tangent parallel to the x-axis is revolved round that tangent. Show that the volume generated is measured by the definite integral

$$\pi \int_{-a}^{2a} (x - 2a)^4 (x + a)^2 \, dx,$$

and by transforming, but not evaluating, this integral, show that the two volumes are equal.

237. Find the area enclosed by the curve $y^2 = x^3 (4 - x)$, and find also the volume swept out when that area revolves about the x-axis. Hence show that the ordinate of the centroid of the area in the first quadrant is $\dfrac{6 \cdot 4}{\pi}$.

238. A quadrant AB of a circle of radius a is revolved round the chord AB. Find (i) the volume, (ii) the surface-area of the spindle-shaped solid so formed.

239. Find the volume of the solid of revolution obtained by revolving about the y-axis the area bounded by the arc of the curve $y = x^2 (3 - x)$ from $x = 0$ to $x = 3$, and the x-axis.

240. If the length s of the arc of the curve

$$x = c \log t, \ y = \tfrac{1}{2} c (t + t^{-1})$$

is measured from the point at which $t = 1$, show that the gradient at any point on the curve is proportional to the value of s there. Find also the area of the curved surface generated when the arc of the curve from $t = 1$ to $t = 2$ revolves about the x-axis.

241. Find a formula for the length of an arc measured from the lowest point of

    (i) the catenary $y = \frac{1}{2}a\,(e^{x/a} + e^{-x/a})$,

    (ii) the parabola $y = a + \dfrac{x^2}{2a}$.

Compare the numerical results when $a = 100$, $x = 10$.

242. Show that the arc of the curve
$$x = \tfrac{1}{2}a\,(3\cos t - \cos 3t), \quad y = \tfrac{1}{2}a\,(3\sin t + \sin 3t),$$
for which $0 \leq t \leq \pi$, touches the lines $x \pm y = 0$, and that the length of the arc between the points of contact is $3a$.

243. Find the perimeter of the loop of the curve $12\,y^2 = (x + 2)\,(x - 2)^2$, and find also the area of the surface of revolution of the loop about the x-axis.

244. Prove that the total length of the curve
$$x = 4a\,(\sin\theta - \cos\theta), \quad y = a\cos 2\theta$$
is $8\pi a$. Find also the area of the surface generated by rotating the curve about the y-axis.

245. If A is the minimum turning point of the curve $30\,x^3 y = 3x^8 + 5$ and P is the point with abscissa 2, show that the arc AP is approximately $3\frac{1}{4}$ units in length, and find also the area of the surface generated by revolving this arc about the y-axis.

246. Show that the length in the first quadrant of the curve
$$x = \tfrac{1}{2}\log\frac{t^2 + 4}{t^2 + 1}, \quad y = \tan^{-1} t - \tfrac{1}{2}\tan^{-1}(\tfrac{1}{2}t)$$

is $3\displaystyle\int_0^\infty \frac{dt}{(t^2 + 4)\sqrt{(t^2 + 1)}}$, and evaluate this integral.

247. Prove that the length of the arc
$$x = e^t\,(2t - 1), \quad y = 2e^t\,(t^2 - t + 1)$$
between the points where $t = 0$ and $t = 1$ is $3\,(e - 1)$.

248. Show that the curve
$$x = a\sin t\,(1 + \sin t), \quad y = a\cos t\,(1 + \sin t)$$
is closed, and find its total perimeter. Find also the area of the surface generated by the revolution of the curve about the x-axis.

249. For the curve $x = 6t^2$, $y = 4t^3 - 3t$, find
   (i) the area of the loop,
   (ii) the perimeter of the loop,
   (iii) the area of the curved surface generated by revolving the loop about the x-axis.

250. If P and Q are the points on the curve $4y = x^2 - 2 \log x$ whose abscissae are $1/e$ and e, respectively, prove that
   (i) the area bounded by the arc PQ, the x-axis, and the ordinates of P and Q is $\frac{1}{8} \sinh 3 - \frac{1}{e}$;
   (ii) the length of the arc PQ is $1 + \frac{1}{2} \sinh 2$;
   (iii) the area of the curved surface generated by the revolution of the arc PQ about the x-axis is $\frac{\pi}{8} \left(\sinh 4 - \frac{4}{e^2} \right)$.

251. If $P(x, y)$ is a point on the curve $y = \frac{1}{2} \tan x - \frac{1}{4}x - \frac{1}{4} \sin x \cos x$, where $0 < x < \frac{\pi}{2}$, and if s is the length of the arc OP, where O is the origin, show that
$$s + y = \tan x.$$
If the arc OP makes a complete revolution about the x-axis, show that the area of the surface generated is
$$2\pi \int_0^s \tan x \, ds - \pi s^2,$$
and deduce the surface area when $x = \frac{1}{4}\pi$.

252. The arc-length of a certain curve passing through the origin is given by the formula
$$3s^2 = x(x + 1)^2.$$
Find the equation of the curve.

253. If, for a certain curve, $s^2 = 4ax$, show that
$$\frac{dy}{dx} = \sqrt{\left(\frac{a - x}{x} \right)},$$
and deduce freedom equations for the curve in the form
$$x = a \sin^2 \theta, \quad y = a(\theta + \sin \theta \cos \theta),$$
the origin being on the curve.

254. Find the mean distance of points on the circumference of a circle of radius r from a fixed point A on the circumference.

$$s_1 = s_4 \quad \text{and} \quad s_2 = s_3$$

$$\therefore E = \frac{3Q_4 - iQ_2}{3Q_1} = \frac{T_3 - T_1}{T_3} = 1 - \frac{T_1}{T_3}$$

T_3 is highest heat added in cycle, T_1 lowest, similar to atmos. temperature.

(1) Gas is compressed in cylinder adiabatically, const. temp T_1. If cylinder is perfectly heat insulated all work done is converted in heat causing temp to rise to T_3.

(2) Gas expands at const. temp.

Carnot Cycle

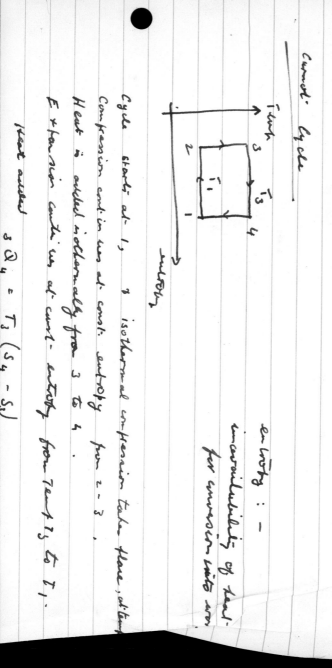

temp

3 → $\bar{T}_3$

2 → $\bar{T}_1$

1

4

entropy

entropy : —

unavailability of heat —
for conversion into work

Cycle starts at 1, 2 isothermal compression takes place, at temp
Compression ends in two at const. entropy from 2 - 3.

Heat is added isothermally from 3 to 4.

Extension continues at const. entropy from Temp 3 to T_1.

Heat added

$$\delta Q_4 = T_3 (S_4 - S_3)$$

$$h = 2a \cos 30$$
$$= 2a \frac{\sqrt{3}}{2}$$

$$I = \frac{1}{24} M (12 h^2 + b^2)$$
$$= \frac{1}{24} M \left(12 (\sqrt{3} a)^2 + 4a^2 \right)$$
$$= M \cdot \frac{40 a^2}{24}$$

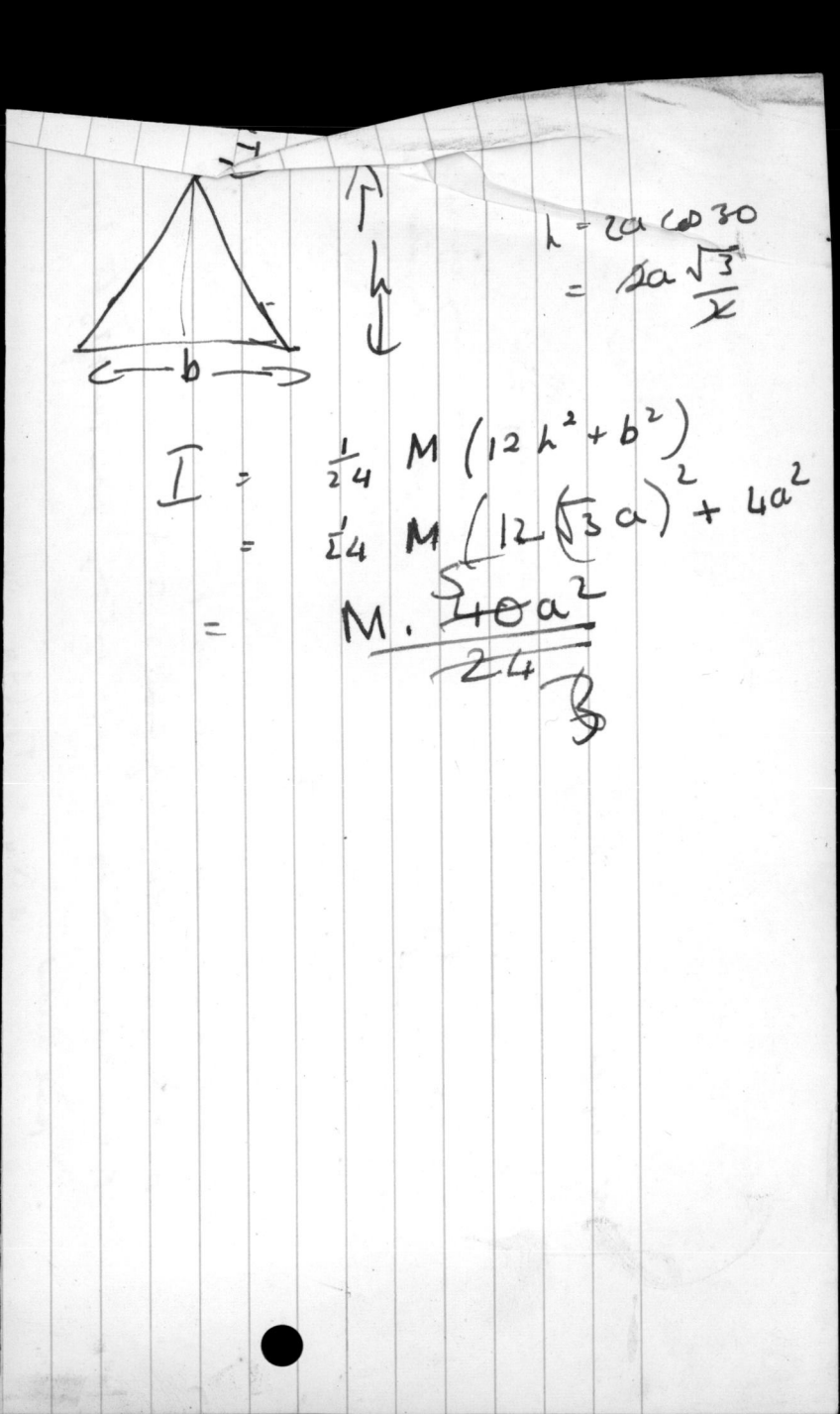

255. Find, correct to two decimal places, (i) the mean value, (ii) the root-mean-square value of the alternating current given by
$$i = 5 \sin \omega t + \sin 3\omega t$$
over the range $t = 0$ to $t = \dfrac{\pi}{\omega}$.

256. Calculate the mean value and the root-mean-square value, m, of $x \sin x$ in the range $0 \leqq x \leqq \pi$. If $\bar{y}$ is the ordinate of the centroid of the area between the curve $y = x \sin x$ and the x-axis from $x = 0$ to $x = \pi$, show, without evaluating $\bar{y}$, that $\bar{y} = \frac{1}{2}m^2$.

257. Find the centroid of the area under the curve
$$y = \frac{x^3 + 1}{x^2}$$
from $x = 1$ to $x = 2$.

258. Show that the centroid of the area under the curve $y = x \sin x$ from $x = 0$ to $x = \dfrac{\pi}{2}$ is approximately 1·14 units distant from the y-axis.

259. Find the centre of gravity of the area enclosed in the first quadrant by the curve $a^4y^2 + b^2x^4 = a^2b^2x^2$.

260. For the portion of the curve
$$x = a \sin^3 \theta, \quad y = a \cos^3 \theta,$$
contained within the first quadrant, find the centre of gravity of (i) the arc, (ii) the area enclosed.

261. Find the centre of gravity of the solid formed by revolving about the x-axis the area under the curve $y = e^x$ from $x = 0$ to $x = 2$.

262. Find the centre of gravity of a conical shell of height h and semi-vertical angle a.

263. Two circles of radius r and $\frac{2}{3}r$ touch internally. Find the centroid of the crescent-shaped area between the two circles.

264. A quadrant of a circle of radius r is revolved about the tangent at one extremity. Find the centre of gravity of the surface generated in this way.

265. Find the moment of inertia of a uniform rod of mass M and length $2l$ about an axis distant d beyond one end and perpendicular to the line of the rod.

266. The base BC of a triangle ABC, has length a and the altitude from A to BC has length h. Find the second moment of the area of the triangle about an axis through its centroid parallel to BC.

267. A solid of mass M is formed by revolving the area under the curve $xy^2 = 1$ between $x = 1$ and $x = 4$, about the x-axis. Find its moment of inertia about this axis.

268. The area under the curve $y = \sin \dfrac{\pi x}{a}$ from $x = 0$ to $x = a$ is revolved about the x-axis. Find the radius of gyration about the axis of revolution of the solid generated in this way.

269. A body is moved along a straight track OX by a force F pounds weight acting in the direction of motion. If $F = F_0 \dfrac{a + x^2}{1 + x^2}$, where x feet is the distance of the body from O, and a and F_0 are constants, find the work done in foot pounds from $x = 0$ to $x = l$. If F has that same value, but its line of action makes an angle θ with the track, where $\theta = \cos^{-1} \dfrac{1}{1 + x^2}$, find the work done.

270. A vertical dock-gate is approximately a segment of a parabola whose axis is vertical and whose vertex is downwards. If the breadth of the gate at the top is 90 feet, and the greatest depth is 30 feet, show that when the dock is full the resultant thrust of the water on the gate is approximately 600 tons. Find also the depth of the centre of pressure.

271. Solve the differential equations :

$\quad$ (i) $e^{x+2y} = (1 + e^x) \dfrac{dy}{dx}$;

$\quad$ (ii) $2xy \dfrac{dy}{dx} = 4x^2 + y^2$;

$\quad$ (iii) $\cos x \dfrac{dy}{dx} - 2y \sin x = 1 + \sec x$;

$\quad$ (iv) $(x^2 - y^2) \dfrac{dy}{dx} = 2\,xy$;

$\quad$ (v) $\dfrac{dy}{dx} = e^{x-y} + 3x^2 e^{-y}$;

416

(vi) $(4x + 3y)\dfrac{dy}{dx} + 4y = 3x$;

(vii) $x\dfrac{dy}{dx} + y = xy\left(1 - \dfrac{dy}{dx}\right)$;

(viii) $(x^2 + 1)\left(\dfrac{dy}{dx} - x\right) = 3xy$;

(ix) $x^2\dfrac{dy}{dx} + (x^2 + 2x)\,y = 1$;

(x) $\dfrac{dy}{dx} + 2xy = x^3$.

272. Solve the differential equations :

(i) $y\,(1 - x)\dfrac{dy}{dx} - xy = x$, given that $y = 0$ when $x = 0$;

(ii) $x^2\dfrac{dy}{dx} - 2xy + y^2 = 0$, given that $y = -1$ when $x = 1$;

(iii) $(x - 1)\dfrac{dy}{dx} = e^{-2x} - 2y$, given that $y = 0$ when $x = \frac{1}{2}$;

(iv) $(xy + 2x + y + 2)\dfrac{dy}{dx} = xy + x + 2y + 2$, given that $y = 3$ when $x = 3$;

(v) $(x^2 - 1)\dfrac{dy}{dx} - xy = x^3 - x$, given that $y = 3$ when $x = -2$;

(vi) $(1 - x^2)\dfrac{dy}{dx} + xy - 1 = 0$, given that $y = -1$ when $x = 0$;

(vii) $3xy\dfrac{dy}{dx} - y^2 = x^2$, given that $y = 1$ when $x = \sqrt{2}$;

(viii) $x\left(\dfrac{dy}{dx} + 1\right) = y\left(1 - \dfrac{dy}{dx}\right)$, given that $y = 0$ when $x = 1$;

(ix) $(x^2 - x^2y)\dfrac{dy}{dx} + y^2 - xy^2 = 0$, given that $y = -2$ when $x = 2$;

(x) $\dfrac{dy}{dx} + \dfrac{2y}{1 - x^2} = \dfrac{1 - x}{(1 + x)^3}$, given that $y = \tfrac{1}{9}$ when $x = \tfrac{1}{2}$.

273. Solve the differential equations :

(i) $\sin x \dfrac{dy}{dx} = y \cos x + y^2 \sin x$;

(ii) $2x^2 \dfrac{dy}{dx} = y(3y^2 + x)$;

(iii) $(x^2 + 1)\dfrac{dy}{dx} + 4xy^{1/2} = xy$;

(iv) $(x^2 + x)\dfrac{dy}{dx} + 2y = 2x^2 y^{3/2}$.

274. Solve the differential equations :

(i) $2\dfrac{d^2y}{dx^2} = 1 + \left(\dfrac{dy}{dx}\right)^2$, given that $y = 0$, $\dfrac{dy}{dx} = 1$, when $x = \dfrac{\pi}{2}$;

(ii) $\dfrac{d^2y}{dx^2} = \left\{1 + \left(\dfrac{dy}{dx}\right)^2\right\}^{3/2}$, given that $y = 1$, $\dfrac{dy}{dx} = 0$, when $x = 0$;

(iii) $(1 - x^2)\dfrac{d^2y}{dx^2} - x\dfrac{dy}{dx} = 0$, given that $y = \dfrac{\pi}{6}$ when $x = \tfrac{1}{2}$, and $y = \dfrac{\pi}{2}$ when $x = 1$;

(iv) $(1 + x^2)\dfrac{d^2y}{dx^2} - x\dfrac{dy}{dx} = (1 + x^2)^{3/2}$, given that $y = \tfrac{1}{3}$, $\dfrac{dy}{dx} = 0$, when $x = 0$.

275. Prove that the equation $(x^2 - 1)\dfrac{dy}{dx} - xy + x = 0$ is transformed by means of the substitutions
$$y = u + 1, \quad x = \sqrt{(1 + t^2)},$$
into $\dfrac{d}{dt}\left(\dfrac{u}{t}\right) = 0$. Hence find the value of y when $x = 4$, given that $y = 2$ when $x = 2$.

276. The tangent at a point P on a curve meets the x-axis in A, and B is the projection of P on the x-axis. If the curve is such that for every point on it $OB = 2OA$, where O is the origin, show that the curve belongs to a family of parabolas which pass through the origin and have the y-axis as a common axis.

277. The tangent at any point P (x, y) of a curve meets the x-axis in Q. If $OP = OQ$, where O is the origin, show that

$$\frac{dy}{dx} = \frac{y}{x - \sqrt{(x^2 + y^2)}},$$

and deduce, using the substitution $u^2 = x^2 + y^2$, that the curves having this property are parabolas which have the x-axis as common axis.

278. The normal at the point P (x, y) on a curve meets the x-axis in G and $OG = k \cdot OP$, where O is the origin and k is a constant. Show that the differential equation of the curve is

$$x + y\frac{dy}{dx} = k\sqrt{(x^2 + y^2)}.$$

If the curve passes through the point $(0, k)$, find its equation.

279. The linear velocity v of a particle moving in a resisting medium decreases at a rate proportional to v. If initially the velocity is v_0, find the velocity at time t, and prove that the particle never attains a greater distance than v_0/k from the starting point, where k is a positive constant.

280. The angular velocity, ω radians per second, of a rotating fly-wheel decreases from a value ω_0 at a rate proportional to ω^2. Find the angular velocity after t seconds, and the angle through which any given radius of the wheel has turned in that time.

281. A particle moves under a force directed towards a fixed point O and proportional to the square of its displacement from O. If the particle is momentarily at rest when $x = a$, show that its velocity is proportional to $\sqrt{(a^3 - x^3)}$.

282. When a particle is projected vertically upwards from the earth's surface, its distance x from the centre of the earth is connected with its upward speed v by the equation

$$v\frac{dv}{dx} = -g\frac{a^2}{x^2},$$

419

where a is the earth's radius, and g is the acceleration due to gravity at the earth's surface. If v_0 is the speed of projection, show that the height h above the surface to which the particle will ascend is given by

$$h = \frac{av_0{}^2}{2ga - v_0{}^2}.$$

283. A falling raindrop is acted upon by its own weight mg, and a resisting force $mg\, v^2/V^2$, where V is a constant and v is the velocity of the drop at time t. Show that, if the raindrop starts from rest,

$$v = V \tanh \frac{gt}{V}.$$

284. Find the two curves which pass through the point $(4, 1)$ and which satisfy the differential equation

$$\left(\frac{dy}{dx}\right)^2 - \frac{dy}{dx} + \frac{y}{x}\left(1 - \frac{y}{x}\right) = 0.$$

285. The tangent and normal at P, a point on a certain curve, meet the x-axis at T and N, respectively. If, for every position of P on the curve, $OT \cdot ON = OP^2$, where O is the origin, prove that the differential equation of the curve is

$$x\left(\frac{dy}{dx}\right)^2 - 2y\frac{dy}{dx} - x = 0.$$

If the curve passes through the point $(3, 4)$, prove that its equation is

$$2y = x^2 - 1, \quad \text{or} \quad 18y = 81 - x^2.$$

286. The motion of a car which starts from rest on a rough level road is subject to the condition $\dfrac{d^2x}{dt^2} = a - b\left(\dfrac{dx}{dt}\right)^2$, where a, b are positive constants, x being the total distance travelled up to time t. Show that the car has a limiting speed V, and find V in terms of a and b; then show that at time t the speed and distance travelled are respectively

$$V \tanh\left(\frac{at}{V}\right) \quad \text{and} \quad \frac{V^2}{a} \log \cosh\left(\frac{at}{V}\right).$$

287. Solve the differential equations :

(i) $\dfrac{d^2y}{dx^2} + 4\dfrac{dy}{dx} + 3y = 7e^{4x}$;

(ii) $\dfrac{d^2y}{dx^2} - 2\dfrac{dy}{dx} - 3y = 3e^{2x} - 12$;

(iii) $\dfrac{d^2y}{dx^2} - 6\dfrac{dy}{dx} + 9y = 2 \sin 3x$;

(iv) $\dfrac{d^2y}{dx^2} + 4\dfrac{dy}{dx} + 5y = e^{-2x}$;

(v) $\dfrac{d^2y}{dx^2} - 2\dfrac{dy}{dx} + 2y = e^x + e^{-x}$;

(vi) $9\dfrac{d^2y}{dx^2} - 6\dfrac{dy}{dx} + y = x + 25 \sin x$;

(vii) $2\dfrac{d^2y}{dx^2} - \dfrac{dy}{dx} - 6y = 7e^{2x} - 10 \cos 2x$;

(viii) $\dfrac{d^2y}{dx^2} - y = ae^x + be^{-x}$;

(ix) $\dfrac{d^2y}{dx^2} + 4\dfrac{dy}{dx} + 20y = 25xe^x$;

(x) $\dfrac{d^3y}{dx^3} + \dfrac{d^2y}{dx^2} - \dfrac{dy}{dx} - y = 0$.

288. Solve the differential equations :

(i) $\dfrac{d^2y}{dx^2} + y = a \cos x + b \sin x$, given that $y = 0$,

$\dfrac{dy}{dx} = -\tfrac{1}{2}b$, when $x = 0$;

(ii) $\dfrac{d^2y}{dx^2} + 2\dfrac{dy}{dx} + y = 2e^{-x} + \cos x - 2 \sin x$, given that

$y = 1$, $\dfrac{dy}{dx} = \tfrac{3}{2}$, when $x = 0$;

(iii) $\dfrac{d^2y}{dx^2} - 10\dfrac{dy}{dx} + 9y = 9(3x^2 - 7) + 10 \sin 3x$, given that

$y = \dfrac{2}{27}$, $\dfrac{dy}{dx} = 0$, when $x = 0$;

(iv) $6\dfrac{d^2y}{dx^2} - 5\dfrac{dy}{dx} - 6y = (x + 1)^2$, given that $y = 0$,

$\dfrac{dy}{dx} = -\dfrac{1}{27}$, when $x = 0$;

(v) $\dfrac{d^2y}{dx^2} + 4\dfrac{dy}{dx} + 5y = 32 \sin x + 65 \sin 2x,$ given that

$y = -10, \dfrac{dy}{dx} = 0,$ when $x = 0$;

(vi) $\dfrac{d^2y}{dx^2} + 4y = 4x - 8 - 3 \cos x,$ given that $y = -3,$ when

$x = 0,$ and $y = \dfrac{\pi}{3} - \dfrac{5}{2}$ when $x = \dfrac{\pi}{3}$;

(vii) $\dfrac{d^2y}{dx^2} + 5\dfrac{dy}{dx} - 6y = e^x + e^{2x},$ given that $y = 0, \dfrac{dy}{dx} = \dfrac{15}{56},$

when $x = 0$;

(viii) $\dfrac{d^2y}{dx^2} - \dfrac{dy}{dx} - 2y = 3e^{2x} + 10 \sin x,$ given that $y = 2,$

$\dfrac{dy}{dx} = 0,$ when $x = 0$;

(ix) $\dfrac{d^2y}{dx^2} + 4\dfrac{dy}{dx} + 4y = e^{2x} + e^{-2x},$ given that $y = 0, \dfrac{dy}{dx} = \tfrac{3}{4},$

when $x = 0$;

(x) $\dfrac{d^2y}{dx^2} - 8\dfrac{dy}{dx} + 25y = \sin 3x - \cos 3x,$ given that

$\dfrac{dy}{dx} = 15y$ when $x = 0,$ and $\dfrac{dy}{dx} = -\dfrac{3}{5}y$ when $x = \dfrac{\pi}{2}.$

289. Solve the differential equations :

(i) $x^2\dfrac{d^2y}{dx^2} - 4x\dfrac{dy}{dx} + 4y = 2x^2$;

(ii) $x^2\dfrac{d^2y}{dx^2} - 6y = x + 1$;

(iii) $x^2\dfrac{d^2y}{dx^2} + x\dfrac{dy}{dx} - \dfrac{9}{4}y = \dfrac{1}{x}$;

(iv) $4x^2\dfrac{d^2y}{dx^2} + 8x\dfrac{dy}{dx} + 5y = 5 \log x$;

(v) $(1 - x^2)\dfrac{d^2y}{dx^2} - x\dfrac{dy}{dx} + y = x,$ using the substitution

$x = \sin \theta.$

290. If m and k are real constants, find the solutions of the differential equation
$$\frac{d^2u}{d\theta^2} + mu = k,$$
when (i) $m > 0$, (ii) $m = 0$, (iii) $m < 0$.

291. Solve the differential equation
$$\frac{d^2y}{dx^2} + 2a\frac{dy}{dx} + by = 0,$$
when (i) $a^2 = b - 1$, (ii) when $a^2 = b$.

292. A point moves along the x-axis in accordance with the equation
$$\frac{d^2x}{dt^2} + \frac{dx}{dt} - 2x = -12e^{-t}.$$
If initially $x = -3$, and $\frac{dx}{dt} = 12$, show that the maximum value of x is 1.

293. Find the solution of the differential equation
$$\frac{d^2x}{dt^2} + 4x = 6a \sin t$$
which satisfies the conditions $x = 0$, $\frac{dx}{dt} = 0$, when $t = 0$. Show that for all values of t,
$$-3\sqrt{3a} \leqq 2x \leqq 3\sqrt{3a}.$$

294. Show that the solution of the equation
$y'' + 10y' + 9y = 3 \cos 3x$, where $y = 0$ and $\frac{dy}{dx} = -\frac{1}{2}$ when $x = 0$, may be expressed in the form
$$10y = \sin 3x - 2e^{-5x} \sinh 4x.$$

295. Find the complete solution of the equation
$$x^2\frac{d^2y}{dx^2} + 2x\frac{dy}{dx} - 2y = \frac{1}{x}.$$
Verify your result independently by first showing that the left-hand side of the equation may be expressed in the form
$$x^2\frac{d}{dx}\left(\frac{dy}{dx} + \frac{2}{x}y\right).$$

296. Show that the substitution $x = \sinh z$ transforms the equation

$$(1 + x^2)\frac{d^2y}{dx^2} + x\frac{dy}{dx} - y = x^2$$

into the equation $\dfrac{d^2y}{dz^2} - y = \sinh^2 z$,

and hence find the complete solution of the original equation.

297. Solve the simultaneous differential equations :

(i) $x + \dfrac{dy}{dt} = y + \dfrac{dx}{dt} = 1$;

(ii) $\dfrac{dx}{dt} + x - 2y = \dfrac{dy}{dt} + 2x + y = 0$, given that $x = 4$, $y = 3$, when $t = 0$;

(iii) $\dfrac{dx}{dt} = x + 2y, \dfrac{dy}{dt} = x + \dfrac{9}{2}e^{-t}$, given that $x = y = 0$ when $t = 0$;

(iv) $\dfrac{dx}{dt} - 7x + y = 0, \dfrac{dy}{dt} - x - 5y = 0$, given that $x = 4$, $y = 0$ when $t = 0$;

(v) $\dfrac{dx}{dt} - x + 2y - 2\cos t = 0, \dfrac{dy}{dt} + y - 5x + \sin t = 0$, given that $x = 0$, $y = \frac{5}{8}$, when $t = 0$;

(vi) $\dfrac{dx}{dt} + \dfrac{dy}{dt} + x + y = 0, \dfrac{dy}{dt} + x - y = 0$, given that $x = 3$, $y = 0$, when $t = 0$;

(vii) $\dfrac{dx}{dt} + y = te^t, 2\dfrac{dx}{dt} + \dfrac{dy}{dt} = x + 2te^t$, given that $x = y = 0$ when $t = 0$;

(viii) $\dfrac{d^2x}{dt^2} - y = \dfrac{d^2y}{dt^2} - x = 0$;

(ix) $t\dfrac{dx}{dt} = y + 3t^2, t\dfrac{dy}{dt} = x - 3t^2$, given that $x = 3$, $y = -1$, when $t = 1$;

(x) $t\dfrac{dx}{dt} = 4x - y - t\log t, t\dfrac{dy}{dt} = 6x - 3y + 2t\log t - 2t$, given that $x = 2$, $y = 6$, when $t = 1$.

298. The differential equation
$$x\frac{d^2y}{dx^2} + 2(1-x)\frac{dy}{dx} + yf(x) = 0$$
has two particular solutions y_1 and y_2 such that $y_2 = xy_1$; find $f(x)$.

299. If $u = \sqrt{(1+x^2)}\sin(m\tan^{-1}x)$, show that
$$\frac{d^2u}{dx^2} = \frac{(1-m^2)u}{(1+x^2)^2}.$$
If $y = uz$, show that
$$\frac{d^2y}{dx^2} = \frac{(1-m^2)y}{(1+x^2)^2},$$
provided that
$$u\frac{d^2z}{dx^2} + 2\frac{du}{dx}\cdot\frac{dz}{dx} = 0,$$
and hence find the most general value of y.

300. Prove that, if $Q - \frac{1}{2}P' - \frac{1}{4}P^2$ is constant, the second order differential equation
$$\frac{d^2y}{dx^2} + P\frac{dy}{dx} + Qy = 0,$$
where P and Q are functions of x, can be reduced to an equation with constant coefficients by the substitution $y = ve^u$, where
$u = -\frac{1}{2}\int P\,dx$. Apply this method to solve the equation
$$\frac{d^2y}{dx^2} + \left(\frac{2}{x} - 3\right)\frac{dy}{dx} - \left(\frac{3}{x} - 2\right)y = x^2e^x.$$

PART II.

ANSWERS.

§ 25. 7. $\frac{4}{9}$.

8. (i) $-\dfrac{1}{x^2}$, (ii) $\dfrac{1}{2\sqrt{x}}$, (iii) $\cos x$, (iv) $-\sin x$.

9. (i) 4. (ii) 3. (iii) $\frac{3}{4}$.
   (iv) $\frac{1}{2}$. (v) -6. (vi) 0.
   (vii) 1. (viii) 0. (ix) 3.
   (x) $\dfrac{a}{2}$.

10. (i) 2. (ii) $\frac{2}{3}$. (iii) 0.
   (iv) -1. (v) 2. (vi) $\frac{1}{2}$.
   (vii) $\frac{1}{2}$. (viii) 0. (ix) 0.
   (x) $\frac{1}{2}$.

11. $\frac{1}{3}\pi r^2 h$.

12. $\frac{4}{3}\pi r^3$.

14. $\frac{7}{3}$.

§ 27. 12. (i) $8(2x-5)^3$. (ii) $-15(3-5x)^2$.

(iii) $\dfrac{-1}{2\sqrt{(3-x)}}$. (iv) $\dfrac{-4x}{\sqrt{(3-4x^2)}}$.

(v) $16x(2x^2-3)^3$. (vi) $\dfrac{2x-1}{2\sqrt{(x^2-x+1)}}$.

(vii) $3\cos 3x$. (viii) $-2\sin 2x$.

(ix) $\frac{1}{2}\sec^2\dfrac{x}{2}$. (x) $2\cos(2x-1)$.

(xi) $4\sin(3-4x)$. (xii) $\frac{1}{3}\sec^2\left(\dfrac{x-2}{3}\right)$.

(xiii) $\dfrac{2}{1+2x}$. (xiv) $\dfrac{6x}{3x^2-1}$.

(xv) $3e^{3x}$. (xvi) $-2e^{-2x}$.

(xvii) $- xe^{-\frac{1}{2}x^2}$.

(xviii) $- 6 \sin 3x \cos 3x$.

(xix) $6 \sin^2 2x \cos 2x$.

(xx) $2a \tan (ax + b) . \sec^2 (ax + b)$.

(xxi) $\cot x$.

(xxii) $e^{\sin x} \cos x$.

(xxiii) $\dfrac{-1}{\sqrt{(2x - x^2)}}$,

(xxiv) $\dfrac{1}{2 + 2x + x^2}$.

(xxv) $\dfrac{- \sin x}{1 + \cos x}$.

(xxvi) $\cos x \cos (\sin x)$.

(xxvii) $- \dfrac{1}{2\sqrt{x}} e^{-\ell x}$.

(xxviii) $\dfrac{e^x}{1 + e^x}$.

(xxix) $\dfrac{1}{x \log x}$.

(xxx) $- 1$.

13.　　(i) $24x - 25$.

(ii) $x (2 - 5x)(1 - x)^2$.

(iii) $2 (3x + 5)(6x^2 + 5x + 3)$.

(iv) $\dfrac{3x + 5}{2\sqrt{(x + 1)}}$.

(v) $\dfrac{1 - 6x}{\sqrt{(3 + 4x)}}$.

(vi) $\dfrac{1 + x^{\frac{1}{6}} + 2x^{\frac{1}{2}}}{6x^{\frac{2}{3}} (1 + x^{\frac{1}{2}})^{\frac{2}{3}} (1 + x^{\frac{1}{4}})^{\frac{1}{2}}}$.

(vii) $3x^2 + 4x - 5$.

(viii) $\sin^2 x \cos x (3 - 10 \sin^2 x)$.

(ix) $m \cos mx \cos nx - n \sin mx \sin nx$.

(x) $3 \sin^2 x \cos 4x$.

(xi) $6 \cos^2 2x \sin 3x \cos 5x$.

(xii) $\sin^2 \dfrac{x}{3} \cos \dfrac{x}{2} \cos \dfrac{5x}{6}$.

(xiii) $2x \tan 2x + 2 (x^2 + 1) \sec^2 2x$.

(xiv) $e^x (\cos x - \sin x)$.

(xv) $e^{ax} (a \cos bx - b \sin bx)$.

(xvi) $xe^{3x} (3x + 2)$.

(xvii) $e^{-x^2} (1 - 2x^2)$.

(xviii) $- 2e^{-x} \sin x$.

(xix) $x^{n-1} (n \log x + 1)$

(xx) $\dfrac{\sin^{-1}x}{2\sqrt{x}} + \sqrt{\left(\dfrac{x}{1 - x^2}\right)}$.

14.

(i) $\dfrac{x(x-2)}{(x-1)^2}$.

(ii) $\dfrac{-x^2+6x-7}{(x-3)^2}$.

(iii) $\dfrac{2x(x^2+3x+3)}{(x+1)^2}$.

(iv) $\dfrac{2(x-1)}{(x+1)^3}$.

(v) $\dfrac{3x+1}{(2x+1)^{3/2}}$.

(vi) $\dfrac{4x-7}{(3-2x)^{3/2}}$.

(vii) $\dfrac{3(6x-13)}{2(3x-2)^{3/2}}$.

(viii) $\dfrac{2}{(x+1)^3}$.

(ix) $\dfrac{8}{(x-2)^3}$.

(x) $\dfrac{-2(3x^2-3x+1)}{x^3(x-1)^3}$.

(xi) $\dfrac{-x(2x^2+17)}{(2x^2-1)^2\sqrt{(x^2+4)}}$.

(xii) $\dfrac{-1}{(1+x)^{3/2}(1-x)^{1/2}}$.

(xiii) $\dfrac{7}{(2x^2-2x-3)^{3/2}}$.

(xiv) $\dfrac{-6\sqrt{(4x-x^2)}}{x^3}$.

(xv) $\dfrac{-11}{2(3-x+x^2)^{3/2}}$.

(xvi) $\dfrac{-3a(2ax-x^2)^{1/2}}{x^3}$.

(xvii) $\dfrac{-(3x^2+2x+11)}{(x^2+2x-3)^{1/2}(x^2-4x-5)^{3/2}}$.

(xviii) $\dfrac{\cos x + x \sin x}{\cos^2 x}$.

(xix) $\dfrac{2\cos x}{(1-\sin x)^2}$.

(xx) $\dfrac{\cos^3 x - \sin^3 x}{(\cos x + \sin x)^2}$.

15.

(i) $12\sec^2 4x \tan^2 4x$.

(ii) $\dfrac{\sec^2 2x}{\sqrt{(\tan 2x)}}$.

(iii) $-2e^{-\sin^2 x}\sin x \cos x$.

(iv) $\dfrac{2e^x}{(e^x+1)^2}$.

(v) $\dfrac{-2}{(1-x)(1+x)}$.

(vi) $\dfrac{-\sin x \cos x}{\sqrt{(3\sin^2 x + 4\cos^2 x)}}$.

(vii) $\dfrac{2e^x \sin x}{(\sin x + \cos x)^2}$.

(viii) $\dfrac{-1}{x\sqrt{(x^2-1)}}$.

(ix) $\cos^{-1}\left(\dfrac{x-1}{x}\right) - \dfrac{x+1}{x\sqrt{(2x-1)}}$.

(x) $\dfrac{1}{2\sqrt{x}}\sin^{-1}\sqrt{x} + \dfrac{1}{2\sqrt{(1-x)}}$.

(xi) $\dfrac{3\sqrt{x}}{x^3+1}$.

(xii) $\left(x-\dfrac{1}{x^2}\right) \cdot \dfrac{\cos\left(x^2+\dfrac{2}{x}\right)}{\sqrt{\left\{\sin\left(x^2+\dfrac{2}{x}\right)\right\}}}$.

(xiii) $\dfrac{1}{(2x-3)\sqrt{(x^2-3x+2)}}$.

(xiv) $\dfrac{1-2\sin x}{\cos x\,(2-\sin x)}$. (xv) $\dfrac{1}{x^2+1}$.

(xvi) $\dfrac{-6\,(1+\cos x)}{5+4\cos x}$. (xvii) $2e^{\sin^{-1}x}$.

(xviii) $\dfrac{-\sqrt{(x^2-a^2)}}{x^2}$. (xix) $\sin^{-1}(x-1)$.

(xx) $\dfrac{x^2}{(x-x^2)^{3/2}}$.

16. (i) $2^{x+1}\log 2$.

(ii) $2x\,(x^2+1)^{x^2-1} \cdot \{(x^2+1)\log(x^2+1)+x^2\}$.

(iii) $\dfrac{9-10x}{6x^{\frac{1}{2}}(3-x)^{\frac{5}{6}}(2x+1)^{\frac{5}{3}}}$.

(iv) $(\sin x)^{x-1}\{\sin x\log(\sin x)+x\cos x\}$.

(v) $2e^{\cos 2x}\sin^2 x\,\sin x\cos 3x$.

(vi) $\dfrac{-3\,(12x+11)}{(2x+1)^{\frac{1}{2}}(4x+5)^{\frac{3}{4}}(4x-3)^{\frac{1}{4}}}$.

(vii) $\dfrac{-3x^{\frac{1}{2}}(2-x)(2x^3+17x^2-x-10)}{2\,(5+2x)^4}$.

(viii) e^{e^x+x}.

17.

(i) $-\dfrac{y^{\frac{1}{3}}}{x^{\frac{1}{3}}}$.

(ii) $\dfrac{y-2x}{8y-x}$.

(iii) $\dfrac{2\,(y+3x)}{3y-2x}$.

(iv) $\dfrac{3-4x-2y}{2\,(x+y)}$.

(v) $-\dfrac{ax+hy}{hx+by}$.

(vi) $-\dfrac{ax+hy+g}{hx+by+f}$.

(vii) $\dfrac{3x^2-6xy+y^2}{x\,(3x-2y)}$.

(viii) $\dfrac{x+y-1}{x+y+1}$.

(ix) $\dfrac{y\,(\log y+2\sin 2x)}{2y\cos 2y-x}$.

(x) $\dfrac{x}{y\,(2\log y+1\,)}$.

18.

(i) $n\,!$.

(ii) $\dfrac{(2n)\,!}{n\,!}\,x^n$.

(iii) $\dfrac{(-1)^n\,n!}{x^{n+1}}$.

(iv) e^x.

(v) $(-1)^n\,e^{-x}$.

(vi) $(-3)^n\,e^{-3x}$.

(vii) $2^{n-1}\cos\left(2x+\dfrac{n\pi}{2}\right)$.

(viii) $\dfrac{(-1)^{n-1}\,2\,(n-3)!}{x^{n-2}}$.

19. $\dfrac{2\,(-1)^{n-1}\,n!}{(3+x)^{n+1}}+\dfrac{2^n\,n!}{(1-2x)^{n+1}}$.

20. $2^{\frac{n}{2}}\,e^x\sin\left(x+\dfrac{n\pi}{4}\right)$.

21.

(i) $y''+n^2y=0$.

(ii) $y''+4y'+13y=0$.

(iii) $y''+2ny'+n^2y=0$.

(iv) $xyy''+2y'\,(y-xy')=0$.

(v) $4x^2y''+4xy'-y=0$.

(vi) $y''+2y'+5y=10+20x+25x^2$.

(vii) $xy''+(2x+1)y'+(x+1)\,y=0$.

(viii) $xy''+y'\,(xy'+2)=0$.

(ix) $y''\,(x^2+1)+xy'-y=0$.

(x) $x^2y''-xy'+y=x$.

(xi) $xy''-2\,(x-1)\,y'+(x-2)\,y=0$.

(xii) $xyy''+y'\,(2y-xy')+4xy^2\log y=0$.

24. $\dfrac{dy}{dx} = \dfrac{1}{6\,(1+x)^{1/2}\,\{1+(1+x)^{1/2}\}^{2/3}}$; $x = y^6 - 2y^3$;

$\dfrac{dx}{dy} = 6y^2\,(y^3 - 1)$.

26. $3y = 4x - 1$; $(-\tfrac{2}{3},\ -\tfrac{11}{9})$.

28. $\dfrac{-(x+18)}{6\,(12-x)^{3/2}\,(2-x)^{2/3}}$; $x + 108\sqrt{2}\,.\,y = 66$.

   (i) $x = -18$;   (ii) $x = 2$.

29. $\dfrac{a^2}{(x+a)^2}$; $\dfrac{1-x}{(1-2x)^{3/2}}$; $\dfrac{2\,(x^2-4x+2)}{(2-x)^2}$.

30. $\dfrac{dy}{dx} = (3x + 4\sin x)^2$.

31. $\dfrac{dy}{d\theta} = \cos\theta\,(\theta - \sin\theta)$.

32. $\dfrac{dy}{dx} = \dfrac{x^3}{1+x}$; positive.

33. $(\pm 1,\ \pm 1)$; $\left(\pm\sqrt{5},\ \pm\dfrac{1}{\sqrt{5}}\right)$.

35. $\dfrac{4}{5\pi^2}\,(2\pi - 3\sqrt{3})$.

36.   (i) $y' = \dfrac{4t^2 - 1}{4t}$; $y'' = \dfrac{4t^2 + 1}{48t^3}$.

   (ii) $y' = \dfrac{t^2 + 1}{t^2 - 1}$; $y'' = -\dfrac{4t^3}{(t^2 - 1)^3}$.

   (iii) $y' = \dfrac{2\cos 2t + \sin 2t}{\cos 2t - 2\sin 2t}$; $y'' = \dfrac{10}{e^t\,(\cos 2t - 2\sin 2t)^3}$.

   (iv) $y' = \dfrac{\sin\theta}{1 - \cos\theta}$; $y'' = \dfrac{-1}{a\,(1-\cos\theta)^2}$.

   (v) $y' = \tan\dfrac{3\theta}{2}$; $y'' = \dfrac{3}{8\cos^3\dfrac{3\theta}{2}\sin\dfrac{\theta}{2}}$.

   (vi) $y' = \dfrac{2t\,(1-t^2)}{1 - 3t^2}$; $y'' = \dfrac{(1+3t^4)(1+t^2)^3}{2a\,(1-3t^2)^3}$.

38. $\dfrac{dy}{dx} = 2 \cos \theta$; $\dfrac{d^2y}{dx^2} = -\dfrac{2}{a} \tan \theta = \dfrac{2}{a} \cdot \dfrac{a - x}{\sqrt{(2ax - x^2)}}$.

§ 28. 12. (i) Concave down always.

(ii) (a) $x > 1$; (b) $x < 1$. P.I. (1, 0), $y' = 1$.

(iii) Concave up always.

(iv) (a) $x > 1$; (b) $x < 1$. P.I. (1, 0), $y' = 0$.

(v) (a) $x > 0$; (b) $x < 0$. No P.I.

(vi) (a) $x < -2$, $x > 1$; (b) $-2 < x < 1$. No. P.I.

(vii) (a) $x < \dfrac{-\sqrt{2}}{2}$, $x > \dfrac{\sqrt{2}}{2}$; (b) $\dfrac{-\sqrt{2}}{2} < x < \dfrac{\sqrt{2}}{2}$.

P.I. $\left(\pm \dfrac{\sqrt{2}}{2}, \dfrac{1}{\sqrt{e}} \right)$, $y' = \mp \sqrt{\dfrac{2}{e}}$.

(viii) (a) $x < -2$, $0 < x < 2$; (b) $x > 2$, $-2 < x < 0$.

P.I. (± 2, $\mp \frac{5}{2}$), $y' = \frac{3}{4}$.

13. (i) $x = 3$; $y = -2$.   (ii) $x = 1, -2$; $y = 1$.

(iii) $x = -2, -1$; $y = 4$.

(iv) $y = 0$.   (v) $x = 2$; $y = 4$.

(vi) $x = \pm\sqrt{3}$; $y = x$.   (vii) $x = 0$; $y = x - 5$

(viii) $x = 0$; $y = x - 3$.   (ix) $x = -2$.

(x) $x = 2$.   (xi) $x = 2$, $y = \pm 1$.

(xii) $x = -2$.

14. (i) $\dfrac{2\pi}{3}$.   (ii) 4π.   (iii) 3π.   (iv) 8.

(v) $\dfrac{2\pi}{5}$.   (vi) 6.   (vii) $\dfrac{8\pi}{3}$.   (viii) $\dfrac{1}{b}$.

(ix) π^2.   (x) π.   (xi) 4.   (xii) 60.

(xiii) π.   (xiv) $\dfrac{\pi}{2}$.   (xv) π.

15. (i) $x \geqq 0$.   (ii) $x \leqq 1$, $x = 2$.

(iii) $-1 \leqq x \leqq 1$.

(iv) $x \leqq -2$, $x = 0$, $x \geqq 2$.

(v) All values of x.   (vi) $0 \leqq x \leqq 2$.

(vii) $-\sqrt{2} \leqq x \leqq \sqrt{2}$.   (viii) $x \leqq 0$, $x \geqq \frac{3}{2}$.

(ix) $x \leqq a,\ (a > 0)$ (x) $-a \leqq x \leqq a.$

(xi) $0 \leqq x \leqq 2a.$

(xii) $-4\sqrt{2}a \leqq x \leqq 4\sqrt{2}a.$

16.   (i) Min. value $-\dfrac{1}{e}$, when $x = \dfrac{1}{e}\,$·

(ii) Max. value $\dfrac{1}{2e}$, when $t = \dfrac{1}{\sqrt{e}}\,$·

(iii) Min. value $-\dfrac{3\sqrt{6}}{4}\,e^{-\frac{3}{2}}$, when $x = -\dfrac{\sqrt{6}}{2}$;

Max. value $\dfrac{3\sqrt{6}}{4}\,e^{-\frac{3}{2}}$, when $x = \dfrac{\sqrt{6}}{2}\,$·

(iv) Period 2π.   Max. value 1, when $x = \dfrac{5\pi}{6}$;

Min. value -1, when $x = \dfrac{7\pi}{6}\,$·

(v) Period 2π.   Max. values $2\sqrt{2}$, when $\theta = \dfrac{\pi}{4},\ \dfrac{3\pi}{4}$,

and -2, when $\theta = \dfrac{3\pi}{2}$;

Min. values $-2\sqrt{2}$, when $\theta = \dfrac{5\pi}{4},\ \dfrac{7\pi}{4}$, and 2,

when $\theta = \dfrac{\pi}{2}\,$·

(vi) Period π.   Max. value $2\frac{1}{4}$, when $x = \dfrac{\pi}{6},\ \dfrac{5\pi}{6}$;

Min. values 2, when $x = 0,\ \pi$, and 0, when $x = \dfrac{\pi}{2}\,$·

(vii) Period π.   Min. value 16, when $\theta = \dfrac{\pi}{6},\ \dfrac{5\pi}{6}\,$·

(viii) Min. value $\dfrac{-\sqrt{2}}{2}$, when $x = 1$;

Max. value $\dfrac{4\sqrt{5}}{5}$, when $x = \dfrac{5}{2}\,$·

17.   (i) No T.Ps. P.I. $(\pm\sqrt{2},\ \pm 8\sqrt{2})$, $y' = 0$; $(0,\ 0)$, $y' = 15.$

(ii) Min. T.P. $\left(-\frac{5}{2},\ -\frac{27}{16}\right)$. P.I. $(-1,\ -1)$, $y' = \frac{2}{3}$;

$(2,\ 0)$, $y' = 0.$

(iii) Max. T.P. $(0, 2)$; min. T.P. $(2, -2)$.

P.I. $(1, 0), y' = 0$; $\left(1 \pm \dfrac{\sqrt{2}}{2}, \mp \dfrac{7\sqrt{2}}{8}\right), y' = -\dfrac{15}{4}$.

(iv) Max. T.P. $(0, 1)$. P.I. $\left(\pm \dfrac{\sqrt{3}}{3}, \tfrac{3}{4}\right), y' = \mp \dfrac{3\sqrt{3}}{8}$.

(v) No T.Ps. P.I. $(0, 0), y' = 0$; $\left(\pm \sqrt{3}, \pm \dfrac{3\sqrt{3}}{4}\right)$,

$y' = \tfrac{9}{8}$.

(vi) Max. T.P. $(0, 1)$.

P.I. $\left(\pm \dfrac{\sqrt{2}}{2}, e^{-\frac{1}{2}}\right), y' = - \sqrt{\left(\dfrac{2}{e}\right)}$.

(vii) Min. T.P. $\left(-\dfrac{\sqrt{2}}{2}, -\dfrac{\sqrt{2}}{2} e^{-\frac{1}{2}}\right)$; max. T.P.

$\left(\dfrac{\sqrt{2}}{2}, \dfrac{\sqrt{2}}{2} e^{-\frac{1}{2}}\right)$. P.I. $(0, 0), y' = 1$;

$\left(\pm \dfrac{\sqrt{6}}{2}, \pm \dfrac{\sqrt{6}}{2} e^{-\frac{3}{2}}\right), y' = -2e^{-\frac{3}{2}}$.

(viii) The range $0 \leqq x \leqq 2\pi$ covers a period.

Min. T.P. $(1{\cdot}95, -4{\cdot}41)$; max. T.P. $(4{\cdot}34, 4{\cdot}41)$.

P.I. $(0, 0), y' = -2$; $\left(\dfrac{\pi}{3}, \dfrac{-3\sqrt{3}}{2}\right), y' = -3$;

$(\pi, 0), y' = 6$; $\left(\dfrac{5\pi}{3}, \dfrac{3\sqrt{3}}{2}\right), y' = -3$;

$(2\pi, 0), y' = -2$.

18.

(i) As. $x = \tfrac{2}{3}, y = \tfrac{2}{3}$. No T.Ps. or P.I.

(ii) As. $x = 1, y = x + 1$. Max. T.P. $(0, 0)$. Min. T.P. $(2, 4)$. No P.I.

(iii) As. $x = 0, y = 0$. Min. T.P. $(\tfrac{3}{2}, -4)$. P.I. $(2, -\tfrac{27}{8}), y' = \tfrac{27}{16}$.

(iv) As. $x = 0$. No T.Ps. P.I. $(\pm 1, \mp 2), y' = 6$.

(v) As. $x = 1, y = 1$. Min. T.P. $(0, 0)$. P.I. $(-\tfrac{1}{2}, \tfrac{1}{9})$, $y' = -\tfrac{8}{27}$.

(vi) As. $x = \pm 1, y = 2$. Max. T.P. $(0, 0)$. No P.I.

(vii) As. $y = 0$. Min. T.P. $(-2, -\tfrac{1}{4})$. Max. T.P.

(2, $\frac{1}{4}$). P.I. (0, 0), $y' = \frac{1}{4}$; $\left(\pm 2\sqrt{3}, \pm \dfrac{\sqrt{3}}{8}\right)$, $y' = -\frac{1}{32}$.

(viii) As. $x = 0$, $y = x$. Max. T.P. $(-2, -3)$. Min. T.P. (2, 3). No P.I.

(ix) As. $x = 3$, $y = 0$. Min. T.P. $(-3, -\frac{3}{4})$. P.I. $(-6, -\frac{2}{3})$, $y' = -\frac{1}{27}$.

(x) As. $y = x$. No T.Ps. P.I. (0, 0), $y' = 0$; $(\pm 3, \pm \frac{9}{4})$, $y' = \frac{9}{8}$.

(xi) As. $x = 2$. Max. T.P. $(3, -27)$. P.I. (0, 0), $y' = 0$.

(xii) As. $x = \pm 2$. Max. T.P. (0, 0). Min. T.Ps. $(\pm 2\sqrt{2}, 16)$. No P.I.

19.

(i) Max. T.P. $(\frac{4}{3}, \frac{8}{9})$, min. T.P. $(\frac{4}{3}, -\frac{8}{9})$. No P.I. Node at (4, 0).

(ii) Max. T.Ps. $(\pm 1, \frac{1}{4})$, min. T.Ps. $(\pm 1, -\frac{1}{4})$. P.I. (0, 0), $y' = \pm \dfrac{\sqrt{2}}{4}$. Node at (0, 0).

(iii) Max. T.P. (0, 2), min. T.P. $(0, -2)$. No P.I. Node at (2, 0).

(iv) No T.Ps. No P.I. At the point (3, 0), the two branches of the curve meet and have a common tangent but neither branch passes beyond this point. Such a point is called a **cusp**.

(v) Max. T.P. $(3, 3\sqrt{3})$, min. T.P. $(3, -3\sqrt{3})$. P.I. $(3 - \sqrt{3}, \pm 2\cdot 4)$, $y' \doteqdot \pm 2\cdot 4$. Cusp at (0, 0).

(vi) Max. T.P. $(0, \frac{2}{3})$, min. T.P. $(0, -\frac{2}{3})$. P.I. $\left(\pm \dfrac{\sqrt{2}}{2}, \dfrac{\sqrt{2}}{6}\right)$, $y' = \mp 1$; $\left(\pm \dfrac{\sqrt{2}}{2}, -\dfrac{\sqrt{2}}{6}\right)$, $y' = \pm 1$. Cusps at $(\pm 1, 0)$.

(vii) No T.Ps. P.I. $(\pm \sqrt{6}, \pm 2\sqrt{3})$, $y' = 4\sqrt{2}$; $(\pm \sqrt{6}, \mp 2\sqrt{3})$, $y' = -4\sqrt{2}$. The point (0, 0) is an **isolated point** of the curve.

(viii) As. $x = 2$. No T.P. P.I. $\left(\frac{1}{2}, \pm \dfrac{\sqrt{3}}{3}\right)$, $y' = \pm \dfrac{4\sqrt{3}}{9}$.

(ix) As. $x = 2$, $y = \pm 1$. No T.P. No P.I.

(x) As. $x = 2$. Max. T.P. $(1 - \sqrt{5}, 0\cdot 6)$, min. T.P. $(1 - \sqrt{5}, -0\cdot 6)$. No P.I. Node at (0, 0).

20.   (i) Max. T.P. (3, 2), min. T.P. (3, − 2). No P.I. Node at (9, 0).

(ii) As. $y = \pm x$. Max. T.P. (0, − 2), min. T.P. (0, 2). No P.I.

(iii) Max. T.Ps. $(\pm 1, \frac{1}{4})$, min. T.Ps. $(\pm 1, -\frac{1}{4})$. P.I. (0, 0), $y' = \pm \dfrac{\sqrt{2}}{4}$. Node at (0, 0).

(iv) No T.Ps. No P.I. Cusps at $(0, \pm 1)$, $(\pm 1, 0)$.

(v) Max. T.Ps. $(\pm 1, 1)$, min. T.P. (0, 0). No P.I. The point (0, 0) is a **triple point,** made up of a cusp and a minimum T.P.

21.   (i) Period π. Max. T.P. $\left(\dfrac{\pi}{6}, \dfrac{3\sqrt{3}}{2}\right)$, min. T.P. $\left(\dfrac{5\pi}{6}, \dfrac{-3\sqrt{3}}{2}\right)$. P.I. occur where $x = 0$, $0\cdot91$, $\dfrac{\pi}{2}$, $2\cdot23$, π.

(ii) Period π. Max. T.Ps. $(0\cdot47, 0\cdot9)$, $(1\cdot85, 0\cdot19)$; min. T.Ps. $(1\cdot29, -0\cdot19)$, $(2\cdot67, -0\cdot9)$. P.I. occur where $x = 0$, $0\cdot85$, $\dfrac{\pi}{2}$, $2\cdot29$, π.

(iii) Period 2π. Symmetrical about $x = \pi$. Max. T.Ps. $\left(\dfrac{\pi}{4}, 2\sqrt{2}\right)$, $(\pi, -2)$, min. T.Ps. (0, 2), $\left(\dfrac{3\pi}{4}, -2\sqrt{2}\right)$. P.I. occur where $x = 0\cdot42$, $\dfrac{\pi}{2}$, $2\cdot72$.

(iv) Period 2π. Symmetrical about $x = \pi$. Max. T.Ps. $(0\cdot96, 0\cdot77)$, $(\pi, 0)$, min. T.Ps. (0, 0), $(2\cdot18, -0\cdot77)$. P.I. occur where $x = 0\cdot49$, $\dfrac{\pi}{2}$, $2\cdot65$.

(v) Period 2π. As. $x = \dfrac{3\pi}{4}$, $x = \dfrac{7\pi}{4}$. Max. T.P. $\left(\dfrac{\pi}{4}, \frac{1}{2} \log 2\right)$. No P.I.

No part of the curve lies in the range $\dfrac{3\pi}{4} \leqq x \leqq \dfrac{7\pi}{4}$.

22.   (i) As. $y = 0$. No T.V. or inflexional values.

      (ii) As. $y = 0$. No T.V. or inflexional values.

      (iii) As. $y = 0$. Min. T.V., $-1/e$, where $x = -1$; inflexional value, $-2/e^2$, where $x = -2$.

      (iv) As. $y = 0$. Min. T.V., 0, where $x = 0$, max. T.V., $4/e^2$, where $x = 2$; inflexional values where $x = 2 \pm \sqrt{2}$.

      (v) As. $y = 0$. Min. T.V., -1, where $x = 0$, max. T.V., $9/e^{5/2}$, where $x = \frac{5}{2}$; inflexional values where $x = \frac{1}{4}(9 \pm \sqrt{41})$.

      (vi) As. $x = 0$, $y = 1$. No T.Vs. Inflexional value, $1/e^2$, where $x = -\frac{1}{2}$.

      (vii) Min. T.V., $-1/e$, where $x = 1/e$.

      (viii) As. $y = 0$. Max. T.V., $1/e$, where $x = e$; inflexional value, $3/2e^{3/2}$, where $x = e^{3/2}$.

23. Stationary values occur when $t = \dfrac{1}{a}\left(n\pi + \tan^{-1}\dfrac{a}{k} - b\right)$.

    Max. T.V. when $t = n\pi - 0\cdot09$; min. T.V. when $t = n\pi + \left(\dfrac{\pi}{2} - 0\cdot09\right)$.

25. Max. T.Ps. $(\pi a, 2a)$, $(3\pi a, 2a)$, $(5\pi a, 2a)$, etc. **No P.I.** Cusps at $(0, 0)$, $(2\pi a, 0)$, $(4\pi a, 0)$, etc.

27. Each side is 4 inches long.

29. Height $= \dfrac{\sqrt{2}}{2}\, a$ feet.

§ 29. 11.   (i) $x + \dfrac{x^3}{6} + \dfrac{3x^5}{40} + \dfrac{5x^7}{112} + \cdots$.

      (ii) $1 + x + \dfrac{x^2}{2} - \dfrac{x^4}{8} + \cdots$.

      (iii) $x - \dfrac{x^2}{2} + \dfrac{x^3}{6} - \dfrac{x^4}{12} + \cdots$.

      (iv) $x + x^2 + \dfrac{x^3}{3} - \dfrac{x^5}{30} + \cdots$.

      (v) $\log 2 + \dfrac{x}{2} + \dfrac{x^2}{8} - \dfrac{x^4}{192} + \cdots$.

(vi) $1 + x + \dfrac{x^2}{2} - \dfrac{x^3}{6} + \dots$.

(vii) $1 + 2x + \dfrac{5x^2}{2} + \dfrac{5x^3}{2} + \dots$.

(viii) $\dfrac{x^2}{2} + \dfrac{x^4}{12} + \dfrac{x^6}{45} + \dfrac{17x^8}{2520} + \dots$.

(ix) $x + \dfrac{x^3}{3} + \dfrac{2x^5}{15} + \dfrac{17x^7}{315} + \dots$.

(x) $x - x^2 + \dfrac{5x^3}{6} - \dfrac{5x^4}{6} + \dots$.

12.   (i) $0 \cdot 5543$.   (ii) $0 \cdot 9962$.
(iii) $0 \cdot 5150$.   (iv) $1 \cdot 2214$.
(v) $0 \cdot 0212$.

13. $1 \cdot 9420$.

14. $3 \cdot 141593$.

15. $\cosh x = 1 + \dfrac{x^2}{2!} + \dfrac{x^4}{4!} + \dfrac{x^6}{6!} + \dots$;

$\sinh x = x + \dfrac{x^3}{3!} + \dfrac{x^5}{5!} + \dfrac{x^7}{7!} + \dots$;

$\tanh x = x - \dfrac{x^3}{3} + \dfrac{2x^5}{15} - \dfrac{17x^7}{315} + \dots$.

22.   (i) $\tan^{-1}(1 + x) = \dfrac{\pi}{4} + \dfrac{x}{2} - \dfrac{x^2}{4} + \dfrac{x^3}{12} + \dots$.

(ii) $y = \dfrac{\pi}{4} + \dfrac{p}{2}x + \dfrac{(2q - p^2)}{4}x^2$.

26. $y = -x + x^2 - x^3 + \dots$.

27.   (i) $\frac{1}{2}$.   (ii) $-\frac{1}{6}$.   (iii) $\frac{1}{12}$.
(iv) 1.   (v) 1.

28.   (i) 1.   (ii) na^{n-1}.   (iii) $\frac{3}{2}$.
(iv) $\sin a - a \cos a$.   (v) $\log a - \frac{1}{2}$

0. **13.**   (i) $\frac{4}{5}x^{5/4}$,   (ii) $18x^{1/3}$,

(iii) $\sqrt{\dfrac{6}{x}}$,   (iv) $x + \dfrac{3}{2}e^{-\frac{3}{2}x}$

(v) $-\dfrac{2}{9}(1-3x)^{3/2}$,   (vi) $\dfrac{-1}{(2x-5)^{1/2}}$,

(vii) $\dfrac{2}{5}\sqrt{x}\cdot(2x^2-5)$,   (viii) $\dfrac{9}{4}e^{-\frac{1}{3}(1-x)}$,

(ix) $-\log(1-x)$,   (x) $x-\log(x+1)$,

(xi) $-x-\dfrac{x^2}{2}-2\log(1-x)$,

(xii) $\dfrac{3x^2}{2}-2x+\dfrac{9}{2}\log(2x+1)$,

(xiii) $-\dfrac{x^2}{4}-\dfrac{x}{4}-\dfrac{1}{8}\log(1-2x)$,

(xiv) $\dfrac{2x^2}{3}+\dfrac{8x}{9}-\dfrac{11}{27}\log(2-3x)$,

(xv) $(x+1)(2x+1)^{1/2}$.

14.   (i) $-\tfrac{2}{3}\sin\left(\dfrac{2\pi}{3}-\dfrac{3x}{2}\right)$,   (ii) $\tfrac{4}{3}\cos\tfrac{3}{4}(\pi-x)$,

(iii) $\dfrac{x}{2}+\dfrac{1}{4}\sin 2x$,   (iv) $-\dfrac{x}{2}-\dfrac{5}{4}\sin 2x$,

(v) $\tfrac{1}{2}(\sin x+\tfrac{1}{3}\sin 3x)$,   (vi) $\tfrac{1}{4}(\cos 2x-\tfrac{1}{4}\cos 8x)$

(vii) $-\tfrac{1}{2}(\cos x+\tfrac{1}{4}\cos 4x)$,

(viii) $-\tfrac{3}{4}(\cos 2x+\tfrac{1}{4}\cos 4x)$,

(ix) $\tfrac{1}{4}(3\sin x+\tfrac{1}{3}\sin 3x)$,

(x) $\tfrac{1}{4}\{3\cos(1-x)-\tfrac{1}{3}\cos 3(1-x)\}$.

15.   (i) $\tfrac{1}{6}(9\sqrt{3}-1)$,   (ii) $\tfrac{17}{5}$,

(iii) $4\sqrt{a}(\sqrt{3}-1)$,   (iv) $-\dfrac{12a}{5\pi}$,

(v) l,   (vi) $\tfrac{1}{8}(5\pi-14)$,

(vii) $\dfrac{\pi}{16}$,   (viii) $\pi+6$,

(ix) $24+3\log 3$,   (x) $\tfrac{64}{3}$.

16.   (i) $\tfrac{1}{2}\tan^{-1}2x$,
(ii) $\tfrac{1}{2}\log\{2x+\sqrt{(4x^2+1)}\}$,
(iii) $\tfrac{1}{2}\log\{2x+\sqrt{(4x^2-1)}\}$,
(iv) $\tfrac{1}{2}\sin^{-1}2x$,

(v) $\dfrac{2}{\sqrt{3}} \ \tan^{-1} \dfrac{2x+1}{\sqrt{3}}$,

(vi) $\log\{(x+\tfrac{1}{2}) + \sqrt{(x^2+x+1)}\}$,

(vii) $\dfrac{1}{6} \log \dfrac{5+x}{1-x}$,   (viii) $\sin^{-1} \dfrac{x+2}{3}$,

(ix) $\dfrac{2\sqrt{23}}{23} \tan^{-1} \dfrac{4x-3}{\sqrt{23}}$,   (x) $\tfrac{1}{2} \sin^{-1} \dfrac{8x+3}{\sqrt{41}}$.

17.   (i) $\log \dfrac{x+5}{\sqrt{(x^2+4)}} + \dfrac{5}{2} \tan^{-1} \dfrac{x}{2}$,

(ii) $\log \dfrac{x-1}{\sqrt{(3x^2+2)}} - \dfrac{\sqrt{6}}{2} \tan^{-1} \dfrac{\sqrt{6}}{2} x$,

(iii) $x + \dfrac{1}{2} \log (x^2+4x+13) + \dfrac{1}{3} \tan^{-1} \dfrac{x+2}{3}$,

(iv) $\dfrac{1}{16} \log \dfrac{2x-1}{\sqrt{(4x^2+9)}} + \dfrac{1}{48} \tan^{-1} \dfrac{2x}{3}$,

(v) $\dfrac{3}{2} \log \dfrac{x^2}{x^2+x+1} - \dfrac{1}{\sqrt{3}} \tan^{-1} \dfrac{2x+1}{\sqrt{3}}$,

(vi) $\log \dfrac{\sqrt{(1-x+x^2)}}{1+x} - \sqrt{3} \tan^{-1} \dfrac{1-2x}{\sqrt{3}}$.

18.   (i) $\tfrac{3}{2} + \tfrac{3}{2} \log \tfrac{5}{3} - 2 \log 2$,

(ii) $\tfrac{1}{32}$,   (iii) $\log 2 - \dfrac{\pi}{4}$,

(iv) $1 - \tfrac{1}{2} \log 3 + \dfrac{\sqrt{3}}{18} \pi$,

(v) $2 + \log 3 + \dfrac{\sqrt{3}}{3} \pi$.

19. $A = 3$, $B = 2$.   Integral $= \dfrac{3\pi}{4} + 3 \log 2$.

20. π.

24. $y = \tfrac{1}{3}(3x - 1 + 4e^{-3x})$.

25. $y = x - 6x^2 - \cos 2x$.

26.   (i) 0·37,   (ii) 0·55,

(iii) 3·78.   (iv) 0·97.

§ 31. 21. $x - 4\sqrt{x} + 8 \log (2 + \sqrt{x})$. [Let $\sqrt{x} = u$.]

22. $-\sqrt{(1 - x^2)}$. [Let $1 - x^2 = u^2$.]

23. $\frac{1}{6} (2x^2 + 3)^{3/2}$. [Let $2x^2 + 3 = u^2$.]

24. $-\log (1 + \cos x)$. [Let $1 + \cos x = u$.]

25. $\log (x + 2 \cos x)$. [Let $x + 2 \cos x = u$.]

26. $\log (\sin x)$. [Let $\sin x = u$.]

27. $-\frac{1}{5} \cos^5 x$. [Let $\cos x = u$.]

28. $-\frac{1}{15} (15 \cos x - 10 \cos^3 x + 3 \cos^5 x)$. [Let $\cos x = u$.]

29. $\frac{1}{15} \cos^3 x (3 \cos^2 x - 5)$. [Let $\cos x = u$.]

30. $\frac{1}{3} \tan^{-1} (e^{3x})$. [Let $e^{3x} = u$.]

31. $\log (\tan x) - \frac{1}{2} \cot^2 x$. [Let $\tan x = u$.]

32. $-\frac{1}{3} \sqrt{(2 + 3 \cos^2 x)}$. [Let $2 + 3 \cos^2 x = u$.]

33. $\frac{1}{3} \sec^3 x$. [Let $\cos x = u$.]

34. $-\dfrac{1}{b} \log (a + b \cos^2 x)$. [Let $a + b \cos^2 x = u$.]

35. $-\frac{1}{105} (1 - x^2)^{3/2}(8 + 12x^2 + 15x^4)$. [Let $1 - x^2 = u^2$.]

36. $\sqrt{(x^2 - 1)} + \tan^{-1} \sqrt{(x^2 - 1)}$. [Let $x^2 - 1 = u^2$.]

37. $\frac{1}{35} (5x^2 - 6x + 6)(2x + 3)^{3/2}$. [Let $2x + 3 = u^2$.]

38. $\sec x + \log (\tan \frac{1}{2}x)$. [Let $\cos x = u$.]

39. $\log (\tan \frac{1}{2}x)$. [Let $\tan \dfrac{x}{2} = u$.)

40. $\frac{1}{13} \log \tan (\frac{1}{2}x + \tan^{-1} \frac{2}{3})$. [Let $\tan \dfrac{x}{2} = u$.]

41. $\frac{1}{2} \tan \dfrac{x}{2} + \log \sqrt{\left(\dfrac{1 + \sin x}{\sin x}\right)}$. [Let $\tan \dfrac{x}{2} = u$.]

42. $\dfrac{2}{\sqrt{5}} \tan^{-1} \left(\dfrac{1}{\sqrt{5}} \tan \dfrac{x}{2}\right) - \log (3 + 2 \cos x)$. [Let $\tan \dfrac{x}{2} = u$.]

43. $\frac{1}{2}x \sqrt{(4 - x^2)} + 2 \sin^{-1} \dfrac{x}{2}$. [Let $x = 2 \sin \theta$.]

44. $\frac{9}{2} \sin^{-1} \dfrac{x}{3} - \frac{1}{2}x\sqrt{(9 - x^2)}$. [Let $x = 3 \sin \theta$.]

45. $\dfrac{2x - 1}{(1 + x^2)^{\frac{1}{2}}}$. [Let $x = \tan \theta$.]

46. $\sin^{-1} \sqrt{\dfrac{x}{2}} - \dfrac{1 - x}{2}\sqrt{(2x - x^2)}$. [Let $x = 2 \sin^2 \theta$.]

47. $\sin^{-1}\sqrt{x} - \sqrt{(x - x^2)}$. [Let $x = \sin^2 \theta$.]

48. $\dfrac{x}{a^2 \sqrt{(x^2 + a^2)}}$. [Let $x = a \tan \theta$.]

49. $2 \sin^{-1} \sqrt{\dfrac{x}{2a}}$, or $\cos^{-1} \left(1 - \dfrac{x}{a}\right)$. [Let $x = 2a \sin^2 \theta$.]

50. $\frac{1}{4} \log (x^4 + 1) + \frac{1}{2} \tan^{-1} (x^2)$. [Let $x^2 = u$.]

51. $2 + 2 \log \frac{5}{3}$. [Let $x + 4 = u^2$.]

52. $\dfrac{\pi}{4}$. [Let $x - 1 = u^2$.]

53. $11 - 12 \log 2$. [Let $x + 1 = u^2$.]

54. $\dfrac{\pi^2}{8}$. [Let $\sin^{-1} x = u$.]

55. $\log \frac{3}{2}$. [Let $1 + x^2 = u^2$.]

56. $\frac{1}{3}$. [Let $4 + x^2 = u^2$.]

57. $\dfrac{a^2}{24} (8\pi + 3\sqrt{3})$. [Let $x = 2a \sin^2 \theta$.]

58. $\dfrac{\pi}{2} + 1$. [Let $x = \sin \theta$.]

59. $\dfrac{1}{12a^2} (4 - \sqrt{2})$. [Let $x = a \tan \theta$.]

60. $\dfrac{a^4}{192} (16\pi - 3\sqrt{3})$. [Let $x = a \sin \theta$

61. $2 - \dfrac{\pi}{2}$. [Let $x = a \sin^2 \theta$.]

62. $\dfrac{27\pi}{8}$. [Let $x = 3 \sin^2 \theta$.]

63. $\pi - \sqrt{3}$. [Let $x = 2 \sin \theta$.]

64. $\dfrac{\pi}{2a\sqrt{(a^2 + b^2)}}$. [Let $\tan x = u$.]

65. $\frac{1}{6} \tan^{-1} \frac{2}{3}$. [Let $\tan \dfrac{x}{2} = u$.]

66. $\dfrac{\pi}{4}$. [Let $\tan \dfrac{x}{2} = u$.]

67. $\dfrac{\pi}{4}$. [Let $\tan \dfrac{x}{2} = u$.]

68. $\dfrac{\pi}{12}$. [Let $\tan \dfrac{x}{2} = u$.]

69. $\dfrac{\sqrt{5} \cdot \pi}{5}$. [Let $\tan \dfrac{x}{2} = u$.]

70. $\frac{1}{4}\log 3$.   [Let $\sin x = u$.]

71. $\sin^{-1}\left(\dfrac{x-2}{x\sqrt{5}}\right)$.

72. $\dfrac{\sqrt{(2x^2-3)}}{3x}$.

73. $-\dfrac{1}{2a^2}\sin^{-1}\left(\dfrac{a^2}{x^2}\right)$.

74. $\dfrac{\pi}{3} + \dfrac{3\sqrt{3}}{2} - \dfrac{8}{3}$.

75. $\dfrac{\pi}{8}(b-a)^2$.

76. $\dfrac{\pi\sqrt{3}}{9}$.

77. $2\log\{\sqrt{x} + \sqrt{(x-a)}\} - 2\sqrt{\left(\dfrac{x-a}{x}\right)}$.

78. $\frac{1}{2}\log 3$.

§ 32. 10. $x\tan x + \log\cos x$.

11. $\frac{1}{5}e^x(\sin 2x - 2\cos 2x)$.

12. $\frac{1}{2}(x^2-1)\log(1+x) - \frac{1}{4}x(x-2)$.

13. $\frac{1}{2}(x^2+4x)\log x - \frac{1}{4}x(x+8)$.

14. $\frac{1}{2}(x^2\tan^{-1}x - x + \tan^{-1}x)$.

15. $\frac{1}{10}e^{-x}(\cos 2x - 2\sin 2x - 5)$.

16. $\cos x(1 - \log\cos x)$.

17. $-x - \frac{1}{3}(4-3x)\log(4-3x)$.

18. $\frac{1}{4}(2x^2-1)\sin 2x + \frac{1}{2}x\cos 2x$.

19. $-e^{-x}(x^2+4x+5)$.

20. $-\dfrac{1}{4x^2}(1 + 2\log x)$.

21. $(x^3+x^2)e^{-3x}$.

22. $\dfrac{x^{n+1}}{(n+1)^2}\{(n+1)\log x - 1\}$.

23. $x(\log x)^2 - 2x\log x + 2x$.

24. $\dfrac{x}{x+1}\log x - \log(x+1)$.

25. $\dfrac{e^x}{1+x}$.

26. $\dfrac{x}{9}(3-x^2) - \frac{1}{3}(1-x^2)^{3/2}\cdot\sin^{-1}x$.

27. $4\log 2 - \frac{15}{16}$.

28. $-\frac{2}{3}$.

29. $\dfrac{\pi^2}{4}$.

30. $\dfrac{\pi}{8} - \dfrac{1}{4}$.

31. $\dfrac{\pi^3}{48} - \dfrac{\pi}{8}$.

32. $\frac{1}{6} + \frac{1}{2}\log 2 - \frac{1}{3}\log 3$.

33. $\dfrac{\pi}{\sqrt{3}} - \log 2$.

34. $\frac{1}{8}(3 - 19e^{-2})$.

35. $2\sqrt{3}\log 2 - 2\sqrt{3} + \dfrac{2\pi}{3}$.

36. $\frac{18}{37}$.

37. $-\frac{2}{13} e^{-2\pi}$.

38. $\frac{3}{8}$.

39. $\dfrac{\pi}{32}$.

40. $\dfrac{5\pi}{64}$.

41. $\dfrac{32}{105}$

42. $\dfrac{3\pi}{16}$.

43. $\frac{1}{3}$.

44. $\dfrac{3\pi}{16} + \dfrac{16}{15}$.

45. $\dfrac{7\pi}{2048}$.

46. $\{\sqrt{3} + \frac{1}{2}\log(2 + \sqrt{3})\}a^2$.

47. $\dfrac{\pi}{4} - \dfrac{2}{3}$.

48. $\dfrac{\pi^4}{16} - 3\pi^2 + 24$.

50. $\dfrac{a^4}{8}\{22\sqrt{3} + 3\log(2 + \sqrt{3})\}$.

51. $\dfrac{2}{15}(3\sin 5x + 5\sin 3x + 15\sin x)$.

33. 13. $y^2 = x^2 + C$.

14. $\sin y \cos x = C$.

15. $xy = Ce^x$.

16. $y^2 + 2xy - x^2 = C$.

17. $y^2 + 2xy - 2x^2 = C$.

18. $3y + 2\sqrt{x} = Cx^2$.

19. $y \cos x = \cos^2 x + C$.

20. $y = \sin x - x \cos x + C \cos x$.

21. $y = Ce^{-y/x}$.

22. $(y - 3)(3x + 1) = Cx$.

23. $x(x + y) = Ce^{y/x}$.

24. $x^2y = C(y + 2x)$.

25. $(x + 3)^2(3 - y) = Cy$.

26. $x^2(x - y) = C(x + y)$.

27. $(1 + x^2)(1 + y^2) = Cx^2$.

28. $y + \sqrt{(x^2 + y^2)} = Cx^2$.

29. $(y + \beta)^p(x + \alpha)^q = C$.

30. $y^3 = Cx^2e^{-x/y}$.

31. $y + 1 - \tan x = Ce^{-\tan x}$.

32. $x(x - y) = 3y$.   33. $xy^3 = -27e^{3x+y}$.

34. $x^2 + y^2 = 4e^{-2\tan^{-1}y/x}$.

35. $y = x - 2\sqrt{(1 + x^2)}$.   36. $4x^2 + y^2 = 4e^{-2\tan^{-1}y/2x}$.

37. $y = x^4 e^x (x - 1) - x^4$.   38. $27y^2 = 2(3y + x)$.

39. $y = (x + 1) xe^x$.   40. $xy = (1 + x^2) \tan^{-1} x$.

41. $y = x + 5x\sqrt{(1 - x^2)}$.   42. $y^2 + 1 = Cy^2 (1 - x^2)$.

43. $x^3 = y^3 (3 \sin x + C)$.   44. $2 = e^x y^{3/2} (Ce^x - 1)$.

45. $x + y = \tan(x + C)$.   46. $(1 - x - y)^2 = Ce^{-(3x+2y)}$.

47. $\sqrt{(x^2 + y^2)} = 2e^{\left(\frac{\pi}{3} - \tan^{-1}\frac{y}{x}\right)}$

48. $y^2 = 4x^2 + 1$.   49. $y^2 = 2Cx + C^2$.

50. $y^2 = 4(y - x)$.   51. $I = I_0 e^{-kx}$.

54. $16\frac{1}{3}°$.   55. $1\frac{1}{4}$ atmospheres.

59. $4 \cdot 482 \times 10^7$ units.

60. $y - \sqrt{(C^2 - x^2)} = C \log \dfrac{C - \sqrt{(C^2 - x^2)}}{x}$.

63. $y = Ae^{-x} + Be^{-3x}$.   64. $y = Ae^{-x} + Be^{3x}$.

65. $y = Ae^x + Be^{4x}$.   66. $y = Ae^x + Be^{-2x}$.

67. $y = A \sin 2x + B \cos 2x$.

68. $y = (A + Bx) e^{5x}$.

69. $y = e^{-2x} (A \sin x + B \cos x)$.

70. $y = e^{-x} (A \sin x + B \cos x)$.

71. $y = (A + Bx) e^{\frac{1}{2}x}$.   72. $y = Ae^{3x} + Be^{-\frac{3}{2}x}$.

73. $y = Ae^{2x} + Be^{-\frac{1}{3}x}$.   74. $y = A + Be^{-\frac{1}{3}x}$.

75. $y = xe^{3x}$.   76. $y = e^{-3x} (\cos x + 3 \sin x)$.

77. $y = 2(1 - e^{-\frac{1}{2}x})$.   78. $y = e^{-3x} - 3e^x$.

79. $y = \frac{1}{2}e^{-\frac{3}{2}x} \left(8 \sin \dfrac{5x}{2} + 5 \cos \dfrac{5x}{2} \right)$.

80. $y = Ae^{2x} + Be^{-x} - \frac{1}{3}xe^{-x}$.

81. $y = e^{-4x} (A \sin 3x + B \cos 3x) + \frac{1}{2} \cos 3x + \frac{3}{4} \sin 3x$.

82. $y = e^{-2x} (A \sin x + B \cos x) + 5x^2 - 8x + 5$.

83. $y = (A + Bx) e^{2x} + \frac{1}{2}x^2 e^{2x} - \frac{1}{8} \sin 2x$.

84. $y = e^{-3x} (A \sin x + B \cos x) - 2 \cos 2x + \sin 2x$.

85. $y = Ae^x + Be^{-3x} - \frac{1}{3}x - \frac{2}{9} + \frac{1}{10} (2 \sin x + \cos x)$.

xli   16

86. $y = Ae^{-x} + Be^{-\frac{1}{2}x} - 7e^{-2x}$.

87. $y = Ae^{-x} + Be^{-4x} + 8x^2 - 20x + 21$.

88. $y = A \sin 2x + B \cos 2x + \frac{1}{4}x \sin 2x$.

89. $y = A + Be^{-\frac{1}{2}x} + x^2 - 4x - xe^{-\frac{1}{2}x}$.

90. $y = e^x - e^{2x} + xe^{2x}$.

91. $y = \frac{3}{10}e^{-x}(3 \sin x + \cos x) + \frac{1}{2}e^{-2x} + \frac{1}{5}(\cos x + 2 \sin x)$.

92. $y = 8e^{3x} - 11e^x + 3x + 4 - \cos 2x - 8 \sin 2x$.

93. $y = \pi \sin \frac{1}{2}x + \frac{8}{3} \cos \frac{1}{2}x - \frac{4}{3} \sin x$.

94. $y = e^{-\frac{1}{2}x}\left(2 \sin \frac{3}{2}x - \cos \frac{3}{2}x\right) + \frac{1}{25}(25x^2 - 70x + 33)$.

95.   (i) $y = Ax^2 + \dfrac{B}{x^2} - \frac{1}{4}\log x$;

    (ii) $y = Ax^2 + \dfrac{B}{x^5} + \dfrac{x^2}{7}\log x$;

    (iii) $y = \dfrac{1}{x^3}(1 + x + 2 \log x)$.

96. $y = Ax + \dfrac{B}{x} + \dfrac{x}{2}\log x$.

97. $m = \pm n$, $y = Ax^n + \dfrac{B}{x^n}$.

98. $y = \dfrac{A(x + a)^3 + B(x + b)^3}{(x + a)(x + b)}$.

99. $y = A \cos\left(\dfrac{a}{x}\right) + B \sin\left(\dfrac{a}{x}\right) + 1$.

100. $x = e^{3t} + e^t$, $y = e^{3t} - e^t$.

101. $x = e^{3t}(A + Bt)$, $y = 3e^{3t}(A - B + Bt)$.

102. $x = e^t(A \cos t + B \sin t)$, $y = e^t(A \sin t - B \cos t)$.

103. $x = \frac{1}{3}e^{2t} + \frac{2}{3}te^{-t}$, $y = \frac{2}{3}e^{2t} - \frac{1}{3}e^{-t} - \frac{2}{3}te^{-t}$.

104. $x = \frac{3}{2}e^{2t} - e^{-t} + \frac{1}{2}e^{-2t}$, $y = \frac{3}{4}e^{2t} + e^{-t} - \frac{3}{4}e^{-2t}$.

105. $x = 10e^{-t} - 5e^t + 5$, $y = 5e^{-t} + 10e^t - 5$.

106. $x = \frac{1}{4}(3e^{2t} + te^{-2t})$, $y = \frac{3}{4}(e^{2t} - e^{-2t} - te^{-2t})$.

107. $x = Ae^{-2t} + Be^{3t} - \frac{1}{3}e^t + \frac{1}{25}(7 \sin t - \cos t)$,

    $y = 2Ae^{-2t} - \frac{1}{2}Be^{3t} + \frac{1}{3}e^t + \frac{1}{50}(13 \sin t - 9 \cos t)$.

108. $x = 2 + 3e^{-t} - e^{2t}$, $y = \frac{3}{2} + \frac{3}{2}e^{2t}$.

109. $x = At + \dfrac{B}{t^6} + 2t \log t$, $y = 3At - \dfrac{4B}{t^6} + 6t \log t - t$.

110. $x = \tfrac{1}{2}t + 2t \log t, \quad y = -2t \log t.$

111. $x = At^2 + \dfrac{B}{t^4} + \tfrac{1}{2}t^2 \log t + \tfrac{12}{7}t^3,$

$y = At^2 - \dfrac{5B}{t^4} + \tfrac{1}{2}t^2 \log t + \tfrac{10}{7}t^3 + \tfrac{1}{2}t^2.$

§ 34. 7. $\dfrac{61a}{216}.$　　　　　　　　8. $\dfrac{a\,(e^2 - 1)}{2e}.$

9. $2 \log (\sqrt{2} + 1).$　　　　10. $2 - \sqrt{2} + \log (\sqrt{6} - \sqrt{3}).$

11. $a\,[\sqrt{2} + \log (1 + \sqrt{2})].$　　12. $\sqrt{2}\,.\,e.$

13. $C.$　　　　　　　　　　14. $6\pi.$

15. $6a.$　　　　　　　　　16. $2\pi.$

17. $3\pi.$　　　　　　　　　18. $8a.$

19. $\dfrac{17}{12}, \ \dfrac{47\pi}{16}.$　　　　20. $\dfrac{779}{240}, \ \dfrac{87\pi}{8}.$

21. $\dfrac{2\sqrt{3}}{3}, \ \dfrac{\pi}{3}.$　　　　　22. $\dfrac{\pi}{2}, \ \dfrac{\pi}{2}.$

23. $4\sqrt{3}, \ \dfrac{56\sqrt{3}\,.\,\pi}{5}.$　　24. $\dfrac{\pi^2}{8}, \ 6\pi - \dfrac{\pi^3}{2}.$

25. $\dfrac{3\sqrt{2}\,.\,a}{4}, \ \tfrac{3}{5}\pi a^2\,(2\sqrt{2} - 1).$

26. $4\sqrt{3}, \ 3\pi.$　　　　　27. $\dfrac{16\sqrt{3}}{3}, \ \dfrac{16\pi}{3}.$

28. $\dfrac{8\sqrt{3}}{3}, \ \dfrac{4\pi}{3}.$　　　29. $12\sqrt{3}, \ 27\pi.$

30. $6a, \ \tfrac{12}{5}\pi a^2.$

31. $2\sqrt{2} - \tfrac{1}{2}\sqrt{5} + 2 \log \{ \tfrac{1}{2}\,(\sqrt{2} + 1)(\sqrt{5} - 1)\}.$

34. $8a, \ \dfrac{32}{5}\pi a^2.$　　　　35. $\tfrac{42}{36}\pi r^2.$

36. $\dfrac{(1 + x^4)^{3/2}}{2x}.$　　　　37. $\dfrac{2\,(a + x)^{3/2}}{\sqrt{a}}.$

38. $2.$　　　　　　　　　39. $a.$

40. $\tfrac{1}{2}.$　　　　　　　　41. $\tfrac{3}{2}a \sin 2\theta.$

42. $9.$　　　　　　　　　43. $\dfrac{1}{4ab}\,(a^2 + 12b^2)^{3/2}.$

44. $\dfrac{4ab}{a+b} \sin\left(\dfrac{a-b}{b}\,\theta\right).$

45. $\dfrac{1}{ab}\,(a^2 \tan^2 \Phi + b^2 \sec^2 \Phi)^{3/2}.$

46. $\left(-\tfrac{1}{2}\log 2,\ \dfrac{1}{\sqrt{2}}\right).$

49. $\xi = a\,(\theta + \sin\theta),\ \eta = -a\,(1 - \cos\theta).$

§ 35.   13. 7.   14. $\dfrac{38}{15}.$

15. $2\log 2 - 1.$ 16. $\dfrac{2}{\pi}\log 2.$

17. $\dfrac{1}{3}\left(\log\dfrac{3}{4} + \dfrac{\pi}{\sqrt{3}}\right).$ 18. $\tfrac{3}{8}.$

19. $\dfrac{\pi}{2}.$ 20. $\dfrac{\pi a^5}{32}.$

21. $\tfrac{1}{2}I_1 I_2 \cos(\alpha_1 - \alpha_2).$ 22. $8\tfrac{1}{15}$ inches per second.

23. $7\tfrac{9}{13}$ pounds per square inch.

24. $\dfrac{\pi b}{4}.$ 25. $p\,;\ \ \sqrt{\left(p^2 + \dfrac{q^2}{2}\right)}.$

26. $\sqrt{\left(\dfrac{I_1{}^2 + I_2{}^2}{2}\right)}.$

27. On the axis of symmetry, distant $\tfrac{3}{4}h$ from the vertex.

28. $\bar{x} = 0,\quad \bar{y} = \tfrac{1}{4}.$ 29. $\bar{x} = \tfrac{3}{5}a,\quad \bar{y} = 0.$

30. On the radius of symmetry, distant $\dfrac{4r}{3\pi}$ from the centre.

31. $\bar{x} = \tfrac{12}{7},\quad \bar{y} = 0.$ 32. $\bar{x} = \tfrac{5}{9},\quad \bar{y} = 0.$

33. On the axis of symmetry, distant $\dfrac{3(r+c)^2}{4(2r+c)}$ from the centre of the sphere.

34. $\bar{x} = \dfrac{4a}{3\pi},\quad \bar{y} = \dfrac{4b}{3\pi}.$ 35. $\bar{x} = \pi a,\quad \bar{y} = \tfrac{5}{6}a.$

36. On the radius of symmetry, distant $\dfrac{2}{3}\cdot\dfrac{r\sin\alpha}{\alpha}$ and $\dfrac{r\sin\alpha}{\alpha}$, respectively, from the centre.

37. On the radius of symmetry, distant $\frac{1}{3}r$ from the centre.

38. On the radius of symmetry, distant (i) $\dfrac{4r}{3\pi}$, (ii) $\dfrac{2r}{\pi}$ from the centre.

39. $2\pi^2 ab^2$, $4\pi^2 ab$.

40. (i) 4π, (ii) $4\pi^2$; $\bar{x} = \frac{1}{2}$, $\bar{y} = 0$.

41. $\frac{4}{3}Ma^2$, $\frac{1}{3}Ma^2$, $\frac{1}{3}M(a^2 + b^2)$.

42. $\frac{1}{12}M(a^2 + b^2)$, $\frac{1}{12}M(a^2 + 4b^2)$.

43. Mr^2, $\frac{1}{2}Mr^2$.   44. $\frac{2}{5}Mr^2$, $\frac{7}{5}Mr^2$; $\frac{2}{5}Mr^2$.

45. $\frac{1}{6}Mh^2$, $\frac{1}{2}Mh^2$, $\frac{1}{24}Mb^2$, $\frac{1}{24}M(12h^2 + b^2)$.

46. $\frac{1}{6}M\dfrac{a^2 b^2}{a^2 + b^2}$.

47. $\frac{1}{2}Mr^2$, $\frac{1}{12}M(l^2 + 3r^2)$, $\frac{1}{12}M(4l^2 + 3r^2)$.

48. $\frac{1}{2}M(R^2 + r^2)$, $\frac{1}{2}M(R^2 + r^2)$.

49. $\dfrac{6d^2 + 8dh + 3h^2}{2(3d + 2h)}$, $\frac{3}{4}h$.

50. On the median through A, at a depth $h/2$.

51. $\frac{5}{6}\rho ah^2$, where ρ is the density of the liquid ; $\frac{7}{10}h$.

52. $\frac{5}{7}h$.

53. On the axis at a depth $\frac{4}{7}h$.

54. At a depth $\dfrac{5r}{4}$, distant $\dfrac{4r}{3\pi}$ from the diameter.

55. 7 feet.   56. $833\frac{1}{3}$ lb.

57. Greater than $0 \cdot 87$ pound per square inch.

ANSWERS TO FURTHER
MISCELLANEOUS EXAMPLES.

1.   (i) $2\sqrt{2}$;   (ii) $2/5$;   (iii) 0 ;
     (iv) $3/2$;   (v) 2 ;   (vi) 2.

2.   (i) $1/2$;   (ii) $10/9$;   (iii) x ;
     (iv) $1/3$;   (v) $2a^3$;   (vi) $1/3$.

3.   (i) $-2a$;   (ii) $\sqrt{2}$;   (iii) 0 ;
     (iv) 0 ;   (v) $1/2$;   (vi) $\dfrac{1}{\sqrt{(2a)}}$.

4.   (i) $\dfrac{\pi^2}{2e}$;   (ii) $1/6$;   (iii) $-\tfrac{1}{2}e^2$;
     (iv) 1 ;   (v) $\log\left(\dfrac{m}{n}\right)$;   (vi) $\tfrac{4}{9}\log 2$.

5.   (i) 2 ;   (ii) 1 ;   (iii) $-\tfrac{5}{54}$;
     (iv) $\tfrac{10}{3}$;   (v) $\tfrac{1}{2}(\log 2)^2$;   (vi) -1 ;
     (vii) -2 ;   (viii) $\tfrac{1}{18}$;   (ix) $-\tfrac{7}{30}$;
     (x) $\tfrac{38}{15}$.

6.   (i) $\log 2$;   (ii) $\dfrac{1-\cos a}{a}$;   (iii) $\dfrac{1}{k+1}$;
     (iv) $\dfrac{\pi}{4}$;   (v) $2(\sqrt{2}-1)$;
     (vi) $\dfrac{2}{\pi}\left(1-\dfrac{2}{\pi}\right)$.

7. 1.   **9.** a^3.

10. $\tfrac{1}{6}abc$.   **11.** $\dfrac{5}{24}\pi r^3$.

12. $\dfrac{x^2(15-11x^2)}{(5-3x^2)^{2/3}}$.   **13.** $\dfrac{2x(x^2-1)(x^2+3)}{(x^2+1)^2}$.

14. $\dfrac{2a^2x}{(x^2-a^2)(x^2+a^2)}$.   **15.** $-2\sec 2x$.

16. $2e^{-x^2}(\cos 2x - x\sin 2x)$.

17. $-2e^{-x} x \sin x.$

18. $e^{\frac{1}{2}x^2} (\cos x - x \sin x - x^2 \cos x).$

19. $\dfrac{n\{x + b + \sqrt{(x^2 + 2bx + c)}\}^n}{\sqrt{(x^2 + 2bx + c)}}.$

20. $\dfrac{16 - 4x - x^2}{(4 - x)^{1/2} (4 + x)^{3/2}}.$ 21. $\dfrac{x^4 + 2a^2x^2 - a^4}{(x^2 - a^2)^{1/2} (x^2 + a^2)^{3/2}}.$

22. $\dfrac{2}{a^2} \cdot \dfrac{\{\sqrt{(x^2 + a^2)} + x\}^2}{\sqrt{(x^2 + a^2)}}.$

23. $\dfrac{39 - 16x^2}{(1 - 2x)^2 (x + 3)^{1/2} (3 - x)^{3/2}}.$

24. $\dfrac{(a - x)(2x^2 - 5ax + a^2)}{x^{1/2} (2a - x)^{3/2}}.$

25. $\dfrac{4}{3x^{1/3} (x^{2/3} - 1)(x^{2/3} + 1)}.$ 26. $\dfrac{6 (a + b) \sin^5 x \cos x}{(a + b \cos^2 x)^4}.$

27. $\dfrac{a \cos x}{(a \cos^2 x + b \sin^2 x)^{3/2}}.$ 28. $\dfrac{\sqrt{3}}{2 + \cos x}.$

29. $\dfrac{3}{5 + 4 \cos x}.$ 30. $\dfrac{\sin^{-1}x + x\sqrt{(1 - x^2)}}{(1 - x^2)^{3/2}}.$

31. $-\dfrac{1}{\sqrt{(1 - x^2)}}.$ 32. $\dfrac{x^2}{(x^2 - 1)(x^2 + 2)}.$

33. $\dfrac{x \tan^{-1} x}{\sqrt{(1 + x^2)}}.$ 34. $-\dfrac{\sqrt{2} \sin x}{\cos 2x \cos^2 x}.$

35. $\dfrac{1}{x^3 + 1}.$ 47. $\dfrac{1 - \sin x + \sin^2 x}{(2 \sin x - \sin^2 x)^{3/2}}.$

48. $\dfrac{d^2y}{dx^2} = \dfrac{2x}{(1 + x^2)^2}$; $\dfrac{d^2x}{dy^2} = \dfrac{-2x (1 + x^2)}{(2 + 3x^2)^3}.$

50. $\dfrac{-3}{4 (2 - 3u)^{3/2}}.$

54.   (i) $\dfrac{-(n - 1)!}{(1 - x)^n}$;   (ii) $\dfrac{2n!}{(1 - x)^{n+1}}$;

   (iii) $\dfrac{(-1)^{n-1}n!}{(1 + x)^{n+1}}$;

(iv) $\frac{1}{2}(-1)^n n! \frac{(x+1)^{n+1} + (x-1)^{n+1}}{(x^2-1)^{n+1}}$;

(v) $\frac{(-1)^{n-1} 2(n-3)!}{x^{n-2}}$;

(vi) $\frac{(n-1)!}{x}$;

(vii) $2(-1)^{n-1}(n-1)! \left\{ \frac{2^{n-1}}{(2x+3)^n} - \frac{1}{x^n} \right\}$;

(viii) $2^n e^{\sqrt{3}x} \cos \left(x + \frac{n\pi}{6} \right)$;

(ix) $e^{-\frac{1}{2}x} \sin \left(\frac{\sqrt{3}x}{2} + \frac{2n\pi}{3} \right)$;

(x) $5^n e^{4x} \sin (3x + n\alpha)$, where $\alpha = \tan^{-1} \frac{3}{4}$.

57. $a^n \cos \left(ax + \frac{n\pi}{2} \right)$.

58. (i) $x^2 \frac{d^2y}{dx^2} - x \frac{dy}{dx} + y = 0$;

(ii) $x \frac{d^2y}{dx^2} + 2 \frac{dy}{dx} + xy = 0$;

(iii) $x \frac{d^2y}{dx^2} + (1-2x) \frac{dy}{dx} + (x-1) y = 0$;

(iv) $4x \frac{d^2y}{dx^2} + 2 \frac{dy}{dx} + y = 0$;

(v) $x^4 \frac{d^2y}{dx^2} + 2x^3 \frac{dy}{dx} + a^2 y = 0$;

(vi) $\frac{d^2y}{dx^2} + 6 \frac{dy}{dx} + 13y = 0$;

(vii) $4x \frac{d^2y}{dx^2} + 6 \frac{dy}{dx} + m^2 y = 0$;

(viii) $x^2 \frac{d^2y}{dx^2} - x \frac{dy}{dx} + 2y = x \log x$;

(ix) $x \frac{d^2y}{dx^2} + 2(3x+1) \frac{dy}{dx} + (13x+6) y = 0$;

(x) $2x^2 \frac{d^2y}{dx^2} + y = 0$.

61.　(i) $(\pm 3, \pm 6)$,　　　　(ii) $(\pm 6, \pm 3)$,
　　(iii) $(\pm 3, \mp 3)$, $(\pm 3\sqrt{3}, \pm 3\sqrt{3})$.

66. $\left(\dfrac{3a}{4}, -\dfrac{a}{8}\right)$.　　　　　67. $2y = x + 2$.

72. $\dfrac{dy}{dx} = -\dfrac{n(n-1)(n-2)\,x^2}{2(1+x)^{n+1}}$.

76. $\delta s = \left\{ \dfrac{\sqrt{(a^2+4v^2)}}{v} - \dfrac{a^2}{2v^2}\log\dfrac{2v+\sqrt{(a^2+4v^2)}}{a} \right\}\delta v$.

78. $\dfrac{\sqrt{3}}{18}\pi l$ inches per second.

79. Decreases by $\dfrac{\pi}{18}\,e^{-\frac{\pi}{12}}$.

80. 18π seconds.

81.　(i) $\frac{75}{64}$ inches per second ;
　　(ii) -150 square inches per second.

82. $10\sqrt{2}$ feet per second.

83. $\dfrac{\sqrt{6}}{2}$ feet per second.

84. $\dfrac{\sqrt{3}}{6}$ radian per second ; $\dfrac{\sqrt{3}}{72}$ radian per second per second.

85. $\dfrac{40}{9}$ inches per second.

86. -72 inches per second per second.

87. $\dfrac{4vr^2}{9a^2-4r^2}$ cubic feet per minute.

88. $13\frac{1}{2}$ feet per second ; $2\frac{1}{40}$ feet per second per second.

89.　(i) 3 feet per second ; $\frac{16}{25}$ foot per second per second.

　　(ii) $\dfrac{5\sqrt{5}}{3}$ feet per second ; $\frac{10}{27}$ foot per second per second.

90.　(i) $-\frac{5}{2}$ inches per second ;
　　(ii) $-\frac{45}{64}$ inch per second per second ;
　　(iii) $\frac{9}{8}$ inches per second.

91. $-\frac{48}{5}$ feet per second ; $2\frac{76}{25}$ feet per second per second ;
　　towards the y-axis.

92. (i) $\frac{24}{169}$ radian per second ;

(ii) $\frac{480}{134}$ radian per second per second.

93. (i) $\frac{4}{25}$ radian per second ;

(ii) $\frac{24}{625}$ radian per second per second ;

1 unit per second at an angle $\frac{\pi}{2} + \tan^{-1} 7/24$ with OX.

94. (i) As. $x = \frac{5}{3}$, $y = 1$. No T.Ps. No P.I.

(ii) As. $x = \frac{1}{2}$, $y = 2x + 3$. Max. T.P. $(-\frac{1}{2}, 0)$; min. T.P. $(\frac{3}{2}, 8)$. No. P.I.

(iii) As. $x = 0$, $y = 1$. Min. T.P. $(-1, 0)$. P.I. $(-\frac{3}{2}, \frac{1}{9})$.

(iv) As. $x = 1$, $x = 3$, $y = 1$. No T.Ps. P.I. between $x = 2$, $x = 3$.

(v) As. $y = 0$. Min. T.P. $\left(-\sqrt{3}, -\dfrac{\sqrt{3}}{6}\right)$; max. T.P. $\left(\sqrt{3}, \dfrac{\sqrt{3}}{6}\right)$. P.Is. $(0, 0)$, $(\pm 3, \pm \frac{1}{4})$.

(vi) As. $x = 0$, $x = 2$, $y = -1$. Max. T.P. $(-1, 0)$; min. T.P. $(\frac{1}{2}, 3)$. P.I. between $x = -2$, $x = -1$.

(vii) As. $y = 1$. Min. T.P. $(-1, 0)$; max. T.P. $(1, 2)$. P.Is. $(0, 1)$, $\left(\pm \sqrt{3}, 1 \pm \dfrac{\sqrt{3}}{2}\right)$.

(viii) As $y + x = 0$. Min. T.P. $(-0{\cdot}68, -1{\cdot}18)$; max. T.P. $(0{\cdot}68, 1{\cdot}18)$. P.Is. $(0, 0)$, $(\pm\sqrt{3}, 0)$.

(ix) As. $x = 0$, $y = 0$. Min. T.P. $(1, 0)$; max. T.P. $(3, 4)$. P.Is. when $x = 3 \pm \sqrt{3}$.

(x) As. $x = -1$, $y = 0$. Min. T.P. $(2, 0)$; max. T.P. $(8, \frac{4}{81})$. P.Is. when $x = 8 \pm 3\sqrt{3}$.

(xi) As. $x = 2$, $y = 1$. Min. T.P. $(0, -\frac{1}{4})$; max. T.P. $(1, 0)$. P.Is. when $x = \frac{1}{4}(-1 \pm \sqrt{17})$.

(xii) As. $y = 0$. Max. T.Ps. $(\pm 2, 1)$; min. T.P. $(0, -1)$. Four P.Is.

95. (i) Period 2π. Max. T.Ps. $\left(\dfrac{\pi}{4}, \dfrac{2\sqrt{2}}{3}\right)$, $\left(\dfrac{3\pi}{4}, \dfrac{2\sqrt{2}}{3}\right)$, $\left(\dfrac{3\pi}{2}, -\dfrac{2}{3}\right)$. Min. T.Ps. $\left(\dfrac{\pi}{2}, \dfrac{2}{3}\right)$, $\left(\dfrac{5\pi}{4}, -\dfrac{2\sqrt{2}}{3}\right)$,

1

$$\left(\frac{7\pi}{4}, \ -\frac{2\sqrt{2}}{3}\right).$$

(ii) Period 2π. Max. T.Ps. $\left(0{\cdot}96, \ \frac{4\sqrt{3}}{9}\right)$, $(\pi, \ 0)$,

$\left(5{\cdot}32, \ \frac{4\sqrt{3}}{9}\right)$.   Min. T.Ps. $(0, \ 0)$, $\left(2{\cdot}18, \ -\frac{4\sqrt{3}}{9}\right)$,

$\left(4{\cdot}10, \ -\frac{4\sqrt{3}}{9}\right).$

(iii) Period π. Max. T.Ps. $\left(\frac{\pi}{3}, \ 0\right)$, $\left(\frac{17\pi}{18}, \ 0{\cdot}83\right)$. Min.

T.Ps. $\left(\frac{5\pi}{18}, \ -0{\cdot}01\right)$, $\left(\frac{11\pi}{18}, \ -0{\cdot}45\right).$

(iv) Period 2π. As. $x = \frac{n\pi}{2}$.   Max. T.P. $\left(\frac{5\pi}{4}, \ -2\sqrt{2}\right).$

Min. T.P. $\left(\frac{\pi}{4}, \ 2\sqrt{2}\right).$

(v) Period π. As. $x = \frac{\pi}{3}, x = \frac{2\pi}{3}$.   Max. T.P. $\left(\frac{\pi}{2}, \ -1\right).$
Min. T.Ps. $(0, \ 0)$, $(\pi, \ 0)$.

(vi) Non-periodic. No T.Ps. P.Is. $(0, \ 0)$, $(\pi, \ \pi)$.

(vii) Non-periodic. Max. T.Ps. $(0, \ 1)$. $(2\pi, \ e^{-2\pi})$. Min.

T.P. $(\pi, \ -e^{-\pi})$. P.Is. $\left(\frac{\pi}{4}, \ \sqrt{2}e^{-\pi/4}\right)$, $\left(\frac{5\pi}{4}, \ -\sqrt{2}e^{-5\pi/4}\right).$

(viii) As. $y = x$. No. T.Ps. P.Is. $(0, \ 0)$, $(\pm 2, \ \pm 2e^{-1/2})$.

96.　(i) Max. T.P. $(1, \ \frac{2}{3})$. Min. T.P. $(1, \ -\frac{2}{3})$. No P.I. Node at $(3, \ 0)$.

(ii) Max. T.P. $(\frac{3}{2}, 3)$. Min. T.P. $(\frac{3}{2}, \ -3)$. No P.I. Node at $(\frac{9}{2}, \ 0)$.

(iii) Max. T.Ps. $(\pm\sqrt{3}, \ 3)$. Min. T.Ps. $(\pm\sqrt{3}, \ -3)$. P.I. $(0, \ 0)$. Node at $(0, \ 0)$.

(iv) Max. T.P. $\left(\frac{3}{2}, \ \frac{3\sqrt{3}}{4}\right).$ Min. T.P. $\left(\frac{3}{2}, \ -\frac{3\sqrt{3}}{4}\right).$
P.I. when $x = \frac{1}{2}(3 - \sqrt{3})$. Cusp at $(0, \ 0)$.

(v) Max. T.P. $(0,\ 1)$. Min. T.P. $(0,\ -1)$. P.Is.
$\left(\pm\dfrac{\sqrt{2}}{2},\dfrac{\sqrt{2}}{4}\right)$, $\left(\pm\dfrac{\sqrt{2}}{2},-\dfrac{\sqrt{2}}{4}\right)$. Cusps at $(\pm 1,\ 0)$.

(vi) Max. T.P. $\left(\dfrac{5}{2},\ \dfrac{25\sqrt{5}}{8}\right)$. Min. T.P. $\left(\dfrac{5}{2},\ -\dfrac{25\sqrt{5}}{8}\right)$.
P.I. when $x=\frac{1}{4}(10-\sqrt{10})$. Cusp at $(0,\ 0)$.

(vii) Max. T.P. $(0,\ 2)$. Min. T.P. $(0,\ -2)$. No P.I.

(viii) Max. T.P. $\left(\dfrac{4}{5},\ \dfrac{4}{5^{5/4}}\right)$. Min. T.P. $\left(\dfrac{4}{5},\ -\dfrac{4}{5^{5/4}}\right)$. No P.I.
Node at $(0,\ 0)$.

(ix) As. $x=-1$. No T.Ps. P.Is. $\left(\dfrac{1}{2},\ \pm\dfrac{\sqrt{3}}{3}\right)$.

(x) As. $x=-1$, $y=\pm(x-1)$. T.Ps. when
$x=-\frac{1}{2}(1+\sqrt{5})$. P.Is. $\left(2,\ \pm\dfrac{2\sqrt{3}}{3}\right)$. Origin is
an isolated point.

97. (i) As. $y=2$. Min. T.P. $(0,\ 0)$. P.Is. $\left(\pm\dfrac{2\sqrt{3}}{3},\dfrac{1}{2}\right)$.

(ii) For given range, $0\leqq x\leqq\sqrt{2}$, $0\leqq y\leqq\frac{1}{4}$. Max.
T.P. $(1,\ \frac{1}{4})$. P.I. $(0,\ 0)$.

(iii) Closed curve within range $-3\leqq x\leqq\frac{3}{2}$. Max. T.P.
$\left(-\dfrac{1}{2},\dfrac{3\sqrt{3}}{2}\right)$. Min. T.P. $\left(-\dfrac{1}{2},-\dfrac{3\sqrt{3}}{2}\right)$. Cusp at $(1,0)$.

(iv) Closed curve within range $-\frac{1}{4}\leqq x\leqq 2$. Max. T.P.
$\left(\dfrac{3}{4},\ \dfrac{3\sqrt{3}}{4}\right)$. Min. T.P. $\left(\dfrac{3}{4},\ -\dfrac{3\sqrt{3}}{4}\right)$. Cusp at $(0,\ 0)$.

(v) Closed curve within ranges $-1\leqq x\leqq 1$, $-1\leqq y\leqq 1$.
Max. T.P. $\left(0,\ -\dfrac{\sqrt{2}}{2}\right)$. Min. T.P. $\left(0,\ \dfrac{\sqrt{2}}{2}\right)$. Cusps
at $(\pm 1,\ 1)$, $(\pm 1,\ -1)$.

(vi) Closed curve within ranges $-2\sqrt{2}\leqq x+1\leqq 2\sqrt{2}$,
$-2\sqrt{2}\leqq y-1\leqq 2\sqrt{2}$. Max. T.P. $(-1,\ -1)$. Min.

T.P. $(-1, 3)$. Cusps at $(-1 \pm 2\sqrt{2}, 1 + 2\sqrt{2})$, $(-1 \pm 2\sqrt{2}, 1 - 2\sqrt{2})$.

98. (i) Min. T.V. $= \frac{1}{2}$, when $x = 2$.

(ii) Max. T.V. $= \frac{39}{7}$, when $x = -\frac{6}{5}$; min. T.V. $= 1$, when $x = 2$.

(iii) Max. T.V. $= \frac{4\sqrt{5}}{5}$, when $x = \frac{5}{2}$; min. T.V. $= -\frac{\sqrt{2}}{2}$, when $x = 1$.

(iv) Max. T.V. $= \frac{5\sqrt{5}}{8}$, when $x = \frac{5}{3}$.

99. P.I. $\left(\frac{3\pi}{2}, 0\right)$. Concave down for $x = \frac{3\pi}{2} -$; concave up for $x = \frac{3\pi}{2} +$.

100. P.I. $(0, 0)$, $y' = 2$. Concave down for $x < 0$; concave up for $x > 0$.

104. Common T.P. $(0, 1)$.

108. (i) Approximately 1·5 radians ;
(ii) 6 seconds.

109. ωL.

110. $\sqrt{\dfrac{nR}{r}}$.

111. $2\sqrt{2}$ square units.

112. $\dfrac{14\sqrt{3}}{27} \pi l^3$, when $r = \dfrac{\sqrt{6}}{3} l$.

115. $2ab$.

116. No ; the greatest possible length is 12·7 feet.

117. $(a^{2/3} + b^{2/3})^{3/2}$ feet.

118. Base-radius $= \dfrac{\sqrt{6}}{3} R$; height $= \dfrac{\sqrt{3}}{3} R$.

121. $\dfrac{\sqrt{2}}{16} a$.

122. (i) 2 ; (ii) $\frac{1}{2}$; (iii) c.

124. 8.

125. $4a \cos 3\theta$; curvature $= \dfrac{1}{4a}$, in each case.

127. $\dfrac{16a}{15}$.

129.   (i) $27ay^2 = 4(x - 2a)^3$;
    (ii) $(ax)^{2/3} + (by)^{2/3} = (a^2 - b^2)^{2/3}$;
    (iii) $(x + y)^{2/3} - (x - y)^{2/3} = (4c)^{2/3}$.

131.   (i) $0 \cdot 0872$;   (ii) $0 \cdot 9781$;
   (iii) $0 \cdot 0953$;   (iv) $1 \cdot 0176$;
    (v) $0 \cdot 6009$;   (vi) $0 \cdot 5075$;
  (vii) $0 \cdot 7193$;   (viii) $11°$.

132. $0 \cdot 6931$.

134. $\dfrac{\pi}{4} + \dfrac{x}{2} - \dfrac{x^2}{4} + \dfrac{x^3}{12} - \dots$.

135.   (i) $\dfrac{(n+1)^2 x^n}{n!}$;   (ii) $\dfrac{4n\, x^{2n+1}}{(2n+1)!}$.

136.   (i) $x + \tfrac{1}{6}x^3 + \tfrac{1}{24}x^5 + \dots$;
    (ii) $\tfrac{1}{2}x^2 + \tfrac{1}{12}x^4 + \dots$.

138. $\cosh x = 1 + \dfrac{x^2}{2!} + \dfrac{x^4}{4!} + \dots$;

    $\sinh x = x + \dfrac{x^3}{3!} + \dfrac{x^5}{5!} + \dots$.

139. $0 \cdot 55065$.

141. $x + \tfrac{1}{2}x^2 - \tfrac{2}{3}x^3 + \tfrac{1}{4}x^4 + \tfrac{1}{5}x^5 - \tfrac{1}{3}x^6 + \dots$.

142. $0 \cdot 9887$.

143. Let $\theta = \dfrac{\pi}{6}$; $\pi = 3 \cdot 142$.

145. $y = \dfrac{2x^2}{2!} - \dfrac{8x^6}{6!} + \dfrac{32x^{10}}{10!} - \dots$;

    $T_n = \dfrac{(-1)^{n-1}\, 2^{2n-1}\, x^{4n-2}}{(4n-2)!}$.

146. $3 \cdot 141593$.

147. $\tfrac{2}{15}(3x + 13)(x + 1)^{3/2}$.

148. $\tfrac{9}{2}$.

149. $\tfrac{2}{5}(5 - \sin^2 x)\sqrt{(\sin x)}$.

150. 5π.

151. $\frac{1}{2}\log(4+x^2)+2\tan^{-1}\frac{x}{2}$.

152. $\frac{3}{2}$.

153. $-2\cot 2x$.

154. $\frac{3\pi}{32}$.

155. 0.

156. $\frac{\pi}{4}$.

157. $-\frac{1}{x(x-1)}$.

158. $\frac{1}{2}\log 2-\frac{3}{20}$.

159. $\frac{1}{6}\log\frac{(x-1)^2}{x^2+x+1}-\frac{1}{\sqrt3}\tan^{-1}\frac{2x+1}{\sqrt3}$.

160. $\frac{3}{8}\log 3+\frac{7\sqrt3}{72}\pi$.

161. $\frac{3}{2}\log\frac{(x-2)^2}{x^2-4x+5}+2\tan^{-1}(x-2)$.

162. $\frac{1}{3}-\frac{\sqrt2}{18}\tan^{-1}\frac{1}{\sqrt2}-\frac{1}{9}\log 6$.

163. $x+\log\frac{(x+1)^3}{2x-1}$.

164. $2+\log 2-\frac{\pi}{2}$.

165. $\frac{1}{\sqrt2}\log\{x-\frac{3}{2}+\sqrt{(x^2-3x-\frac{9}{2})}\}$.

166. $2\sqrt3+\frac{\pi}{6}-4$.

167. $9\sin^{-1}\frac{x-4}{5}-\sqrt{(9+8x-x^2)}$.

168. $\frac{3}{8}\pi a^2$.

169. $\sqrt{(x^2+2x+4)}-\log\{x+1+\sqrt{(x^2+2x+4)}\}$.

170. $1-\log 2$.

171. $\frac{1}{3}(x^2 + a^2)^{\frac{1}{2}}(x^2 - 2a^2)$.

172. $\frac{3}{10a^4}(5\sqrt{2} - 3\sqrt{5})$.

173. $\frac{1}{60}$.

174. $\frac{\pi}{2} - 1$.

175. $\frac{9\pi}{8}$.

176. $\sin^{-1}\dfrac{x-2}{3x}$.

177. $\dfrac{\pi a^3}{16}$.

178. $\dfrac{\pi\sqrt{2}}{4}$.

179. $\dfrac{\sqrt{5}}{12}(2\sqrt{3} - 3)$.

180. $2\sqrt{(\tan x)}$.

181. $\frac{\pi}{2} - 1$.

182. $x - \log(\cos x + \sin x)$.

183. $\dfrac{\pi\sqrt{6}}{24}$.

184. $\frac{1}{5}\tan^5 x + \frac{1}{3}\tan^3 x$.

185. $\frac{2}{3}$.

186. $-\frac{1}{3}\log(1 + \cot^3 \theta)$.

187. $\log 3 - \dfrac{\pi}{3}(2\sqrt{3} - 3)$.

188. $\dfrac{2}{\sqrt{5}}\tan^{-1}\left(\dfrac{2 + 3\tan^{x/2}}{\sqrt{5}}\right)$.

189. $\frac{1}{2}\log 3$.

190. $\frac{1}{2}\tan^2 x + \log\tan x$.

191. $\frac{1}{4}(1 - 5e^{-2})$.

192. $\frac{1}{4}x\sin 2x + \frac{1}{8}\cos 2x\,(1 - 2x^2)$.

193. $\frac{5}{9}(12\log 2 - 5)$.

194. $(x - x^3) \sin^{-1} x + \frac{1}{3} (1 - x^2)^{\frac{3}{2}}$.

195. $\frac{3}{13}$.

196. $x \tan^{-1} (\frac{1}{2}x) - \log (x^2 + 4)$.

197. $\frac{1}{4} \log 2$.

198. $x \log (1 - x^2) - 2x + \log \dfrac{1 + x}{1 - x}$.

199. $\frac{26}{225}$.

200. $\log (\log x)$.

201. $- \dfrac{1}{(n - 1)(\log x)^{n-1}}$.

202. $\frac{32}{105}$.

203. $\dfrac{\pi}{4}$.

204. $\dfrac{x}{9} (3 - x^2) - \frac{1}{3} (1 - x^2)^{\frac{3}{2}} \sin^{-1} x$.

205. $\frac{1}{8}x (2x^2 + 5a^2)\sqrt{(x^2 + a^2)} + \frac{3}{8}a^4 \log \{ x + \sqrt{(x^2 + a^2)} \}$.

206. $\frac{1}{8}x (2x^2 - a^2) \sqrt{(x^2 - a^2)} - \frac{1}{8}a^4 \log \{ x + \sqrt{(x^2 - a^2)} \}$.

207. $\tan^{-1} \sqrt{\left(\dfrac{x - 2}{3x + 2}\right)}$.

208. $\dfrac{2\sqrt{3}}{3} \tan^{-1} [\sqrt{3} \{ x + \sqrt{(x^2 - 1)} \}]$.

209. $\dfrac{2}{a^2 - b^2} \tan^{-1} \dfrac{a - b}{a + b}$.

213. $\dfrac{\pi}{2}$.

214. $\dfrac{5}{24} + \dfrac{35\pi}{512}$.

215. $\dfrac{8}{15} a^5, \dfrac{5\pi a^6}{32}$.

216. $\dfrac{x^3}{3}\{ (\log x)^2 - \frac{2}{3} \log x + \frac{2}{9} \}$.

217. 0.

218. $2 \cdot 7183$.

220. $0 \cdot 583$.

221. $102 - 64 \log 2 = 57 \cdot 64$.

224. $y = 2 \log (x + 2) + \frac{1}{4} (2x - 1) \log (2x - 1) + \frac{1}{2} (1 - x)$.

225. $\dfrac{x^2}{9} + \dfrac{y^2}{4} = 1$.

227. (i) $\frac{3}{4}\pi$;   (ii) $\dfrac{\pi}{8}$;

 (iii) $\frac{4}{3}ab$;   (iv) $\frac{1}{4}a^2 (4 - \pi)$;

 (v) $\frac{8}{15}a^2$;   (vi) $4 \sin \left(\dfrac{\pi}{4} + \dfrac{\alpha}{2} \right)$;

 (vii) $3\sqrt{e} - 5$;   (viii) 2π.

229. $\frac{1}{6}\pi a^3 (10 - 3\pi)$.

230. $\frac{1}{2}\pi c^3 (2 + \sinh 2)$.

232. (i) $\frac{4}{3}\pi a^2 b$;   (ii) $2\pi^2 a^2 b$.

233. $\frac{1}{3}\pi b^2 (3\pi a - 4b)$.

234. (i) $\dfrac{8\sqrt{3}}{5}, \frac{3}{4}\pi$;   (ii) $\pi, \frac{8}{5}\pi$;

 (iii) $\dfrac{\pi}{2} - 1, \dfrac{\pi^2}{48} (\pi^2 - 6)$;   (iv) $\frac{4}{3}a^2, \dfrac{4\pi}{15}a^3$;

 (v) $\dfrac{9\pi}{2}, \dfrac{456}{35} \pi$;   (vi) $1 - \dfrac{\pi}{4}, \dfrac{\pi^2}{12}$.

235. $h = \frac{144}{49}$.

236. $\dfrac{3^6}{35} \pi a^7$.

237. $8\pi, \frac{256}{5} \pi$.

238. $\dfrac{\pi a^3}{6\sqrt{2}} (10 - 3\pi), \dfrac{\pi a^2}{\sqrt{2}} (4 - \pi)$.

239. $\dfrac{243\pi}{10}$.

240. $\frac{1}{16}\pi c^2 (15 + 16 \log 2)$.

241. (i) $\frac{1}{2}a (e^{\frac{x}{a}} - e^{-\frac{x}{a}})$;

 (ii) $\dfrac{1}{2a}\left\{ x\sqrt{(a^2 + x^2)} + a^2 \log \dfrac{x + \sqrt{(a^2 + x^2)}}{a} \right\}$.

For the catenary, $s = 10 \cdot 02$; for the parabola, $s = 10 \cdot 01$.

243. $\dfrac{16\sqrt{3}}{3}, \dfrac{16\pi}{3}$.

244. $8\pi a,\ \dfrac{160\sqrt{2}}{3}\pi a^2$.

245. Arc $AP = \frac{7\,7\,9}{2\,4\,0}$ units ; surface area $= \dfrac{87\pi}{8}$ square units.

246. $\dfrac{\sqrt{3}}{2}\log(2+\sqrt{3})$.

248. $8a,\ \frac{3\,2}{5}\pi a^2$.

249. (i) $\dfrac{18\sqrt{3}}{5}$, (ii) $6\sqrt{3}$, (iii) $\dfrac{27\pi}{4}$.

251. $\dfrac{\pi}{256}(92 - 20\pi - \pi^2)$.

252. $3y^2 = x\,(x-1)^2$.

254. $\dfrac{4r}{\pi}$.

255. (i) $\dfrac{32}{3\pi} = 3\cdot40$; (ii) $\sqrt{13} = 3\cdot61$.

256. $1,\ 1\cdot18$.

257. $(\frac{7}{6} + \frac{1}{2}\log 2,\ \frac{2\,1}{3\,2} + \frac{1}{2}\log 2)$.

259. $\left(\dfrac{3\pi a}{16}, \dfrac{b}{5}\right)$.

260. (i) $(\frac{2}{5}a, \frac{2}{5}a)$, (ii) $\left(\dfrac{256a}{315\pi}, \dfrac{256a}{315\pi}\right)$.

261. $\left(\dfrac{3e^4+1}{2(e^4-1)}, 0\right)$.

262. On the axis of symmetry, distant $\frac{2}{3}h$ from the vertex.

263. On the axis of symmetry, distant $\dfrac{19r}{15}$ from the point of contact.

264. On the axis of symmetry, distant $\dfrac{r}{\pi-2}$ from the apex of the surface.

265. $\frac{1}{3}M(3d^2 + 6dl + 4l^2)$.

266. $\frac{1}{36}ah^3$.

267. $\dfrac{3M}{16 \log 2}$.

268. $\dfrac{\sqrt{6}}{4}$.

269. (i) $F_0[l + (a - 1)\tan^{-1} l]$,

  (ii) $\frac{1}{2}F_0\left[(a + 1)\tan^{-1} l + \dfrac{(a - 1)l}{1 + l^2}\right]$.

270. $17\frac{1}{7}$ feet.

271. (i) $e^{-2y} = 2 \log \dfrac{C}{1 + e^x}$;

  (ii) $4x^2 - y^2 = Cx$;

  (iii) $y \cos^2 x = \sin x + x + C$;

  (iv) $x^2 + y^2 = Cy$;

  (v) $e^y = e^x + x^3 + C$;

  (vi) $(3x + y)(x - 3y) = C$;

  (vii) $xy = Ce^{x-y}$;

  (viii) $y + x^2 + 1 = C(x^2 + 1)^{3/2}$;

  (ix) $x^2 y = 1 + Ce^{-x}$;

  (x) $2y = x^2 - 1 + Ce^{-x^2}$.

272. (i) $1 + y = (1 - x)e^{x+y}$;

  (ii) $x^2 - xy + 2y = 0$;

  (iii) $4(x - 1)^2 y + e^{-2x}(2x - 1) = 0$;

  (iv) $y + 1 = (x + 1)e^{x-y}$;

  (v) $y = x^2 - 1$;

  (vi) $y = x - \sqrt{(1 - x^2)}$;

  (vii) $2y^2 = x^2$;

  (viii) $(x^2 + y^2)\, e^{2 \tan^{-1}\frac{y}{x}} = 1$;

  (ix) $xy + 4e^{-\frac{x + y}{xy}} = 0$;

  (x) $y(1 + x)^2 = x(1 - x)$.

273. (i) $y = \dfrac{\sin x}{\cos x + C}$;

  (ii) $x^3 = Ce^{-\frac{x}{y^2}}$;

(iii) $\sqrt{y} = C (x^2 + 1)^{\frac{1}{4}} + 4$;

(iv) $xy^{\frac{1}{2}} (C - x) = x + 1$.

274. (i) $e^{-y} = 1 + \cos x$;   (ii) $y = 2 - \sqrt{(1 - x^2)}$;

(iii) $y = \sin^{-1} x$;   (iv) $3y = (1 + x^2)^{\frac{3}{2}}$.

275. $1 + \sqrt{5}$.

276. $y = Cx^2$.

277. $y^2 = 4C (x + C)$.

278. $x^2 + y^2 = k^2 (x + 1)^2$.

279. $v = v_0 e^{-kt}$.

280. $\omega = \dfrac{\omega_0}{\omega_0 kt + 1}$ radians per second, where k is a positive

constant ; $\theta = \dfrac{1}{k} \log (\omega_0 kt + 1)$ radians.

284. $4y = x$, $2xy = x^2 - 8$.

286. $V = \sqrt{\dfrac{a}{b}}$.

287. (i) $y = Ae^{-x} + Be^{-3x} + \frac{1}{5}e^{4x}$;

(ii) $y = Ae^{-x} + Be^{3x} - e^{2x} + 4$;

(iii) $y = (A + Bx) e^{3x} + \frac{1}{9} \cos 3x$;

(iv) $y = e^{-2x} (A \sin x + B \cos x + 1)$;

(v) $y = e^x (A \sin x + B \cos x + 1) + \frac{1}{5}e^{-x}$;

(vi) $y = (A + Bx) e^{\frac{1}{2}x} + x + 6 - 2 \sin x + \frac{3}{2} \cos x$;

(vii) $y = Ae^{2x} + Be^{-\frac{3}{2}x} + xe^{2x} + \frac{1}{10} \sin 2x + \frac{7}{10} \cos 2x$;

(viii) $y = Ae^x + Be^{-x} + \frac{1}{2}axe^x - \frac{1}{2}bxe^{-x}$;

(ix) $y = e^{-2x} (A \sin 4x + B \cos 4x) + xe^x - \frac{6}{25}e^x$;

(x) $y = Ae^x + (Bx + C)e^{-x}$.

288. (i) $y = \frac{1}{2}x (a \sin x - b \cos x)$;

(ii) $y = x (1 + x) e^{-x} + \frac{1}{2} \sin x + \cos x$;

(iii) $y = \frac{5}{6} (e^x - e^{9x}) + 3x^2 + \frac{20}{3}x - \frac{7}{27} + \frac{1}{3} \cos 3x$;

(iv) $y = \frac{1}{108} (16e^{\frac{3}{2}x} + 33e^{-\frac{2}{3}x} - 18x^2 - 6x - 49)$;

(v) $y = 2 (e^{-2x} - 2)(\cos x - \sin x) + \sin 2x - 8 \cos 2x$;

(vi) $y = x - 2 - \cos x$;

(vii) $y = \dfrac{e^x}{56}(8x - 7 + 7e^x)$;

(viii) $y = e^{2x}(1 + x) - 3\sin x + \cos x$;

(ix) $y = \frac{1}{16}(e^{2x} - e^{-2x}) + \frac{1}{2}xe^{-2x}(1 + x)$;

(x) $y = \frac{1}{104}(5\sin 3x + \cos 3x)$.

289. (i) $y = Ax + Bx^4 - x^2$;

(ii) $y = Ax^3 + \dfrac{B}{x^2} - \frac{1}{6}(x + 1)$;

(iii) $y = Ax^{\frac{3}{2}} + \dfrac{B}{x^{\frac{3}{2}}} - \dfrac{4}{5x}$;

(iv) $y = \dfrac{1}{\sqrt{x}}(A\cos\log x + B\sin\log x) + \log x - \frac{4}{3}$;

(v) $y = Ax + B\sqrt{(1 - x^2)} - \frac{1}{2}\sin^{-1}x\sqrt{(1 - x^2)}$.

290. (i) $u = A\cos\sqrt{m}\theta + B\sin\sqrt{m}\theta + \dfrac{k}{m}$;

(ii) $y = A + B\theta + \frac{1}{2}k\theta^2$;

(iii) $u = Ae^{x\sqrt{(-m)}} + Be^{-x\sqrt{(-m)}} + \dfrac{k}{m}$.

291. (i) $y = e^{-ax}(A\sin x + B\cos x)$;

(ii) $y = (A + Bx)e^{-ax}$.

293. $x = 2a\sin t(1 - \cos t)$.

295. $y = \dfrac{A}{x^2} - \dfrac{1}{2x} + Bx$.

296. $y = Ax + B\sqrt{(1 + x^2)} + \frac{1}{3}(x^2 + 2)$.

297. (i) $x = 1 + Ae^t + Be^{-t}$, $y = 1 - Ae^t + Be^{-t}$;

(ii) $x = e^{-t}(4\cos 2t + 3\sin 2t)$,
$y = e^{-t}(3\cos 2t - 4\sin 2t)$;

(iii) $x = e^{2t} - e^{-t} - 3te^{-t}$, $y = \frac{1}{2}e^{2t} - \frac{1}{2}e^{-t} + 3te^{-t}$;

(iv) $x = 4e^{6t}(1 + t)$, $y = 4te^{6t}$;

(v) $x = \frac{1}{4}(\sin 3t - \cos 3t + \cos t)$,
$y = \frac{1}{8}(\sin t + 9\cos t - 2\sin 3t - 4\cos 3t)$;

(vi) $x = 2e^{-t} + e^{2t}$, $y = e^{-t} - e^{2t}$;

(vii) $x = \frac{1}{6}t^2e^t(3 - t)$, $y = \frac{1}{6}t^3e^t$;

(viii) $x = Ae^t + Be^{-t} + C \sin t + D \cos t,$
$\quad\quad y = Ae^t + Be^{-t} - C \sin t - D \cos t$;

(ix) $x = t + \dfrac{1}{t} + t^2, \quad y = t - \dfrac{1}{t} - t^2$;

(x) $x = t^3 + \dfrac{1}{t^2} + t \log t, \quad y = t^3 + \dfrac{6}{t^2} - t + 2t \log t.$

298. $f(x) = x - 2.$

299. $y = \surd(1 + x^2)\{ A \sin (m \tan^{-1} x) + B \cos (m \tan^{-1} x)\}.$

300. $xy = Ae^{2x} + Be^x - e^x (\tfrac{1}{4}x^4 + x^3 + 3x^2 + 6x).$

INDEX

INDEX

The numbers refer to pages